SUNKEN CITIES

Frontispiece

Part of the manuscript of the so-called ' Ancient Survey of Pen Maen Mawr '

Containing the passage describing the changes caused by the inundation and, references to the ' Traeth Ell soe called from the ryver Ell' (lines 6 and 7).

SUNKEN CITIES

Some legends of the coast
and lakes of Wales

by

F. J. NORTH

CARDIFF
UNIVERSITY OF WALES PRESS
1957

Printed by
J. D. Lewis and Sons Ltd., Gomerian Press, Llandysul

PREFACE

THE purpose of this book and the circumstances in which it came to be written are indicated in the introductory chapter, but a preface provides an opportunity to return thanks for information and advice graciously given whenever and wherever it was sought.

The number and variety of the works that are either e-numerated in the bibliography on pages 246-52 or referred to in the text are sufficient to indicate the extent of my indebtedness to the Librarians in the National Library at Aberystwyth, the Central Library, Cardiff, and the National Museum of Wales. In particular I must mention Mr. E. D. Jones, B.A., of Aberystwyth and my colleague, Miss E. H. Edwards, F.L.A., who, being nearest at hand, has been most frequently consulted on the bibliographical problems that are inseparable from a work of this kind.

Others to whom I am indebted include Sir Ifor Williams, F.B.A., Mr. R. J. Thomas, M.A., and Professor D. J. Davies for information regarding the significance and spellings of certain place names, Professor Henry Lewis for constructive comments after reading the typescript, Dr. Elwyn Davies of the University Press Board whose sustained interest has made publication possible, and the following for permission to reproduce certain illustrations : the Llandudno, Colwyn Bay, and District Field Club—photographs that appeared in my account of a visit to Llys Helig organized by the Club in 1939, the National Library of Wales—part of the manuscript re-counting the story of Llys Helig, Mr. G. C. Dunning and the Council of the Cambrian Archaeological Association—the photographs on pl. 10, Miss L. M. North and Messrs. J.

Challinor, M.A., F.G.S., and A. L. Leach, M.A., F.G.S.,—the photographs to which their names are attached, and Mr. Eric Ashton—Figs. 2, 4 and 17a. Finally it is a pleasure to mention the advantages of service in the National Museum of Wales which has so greatly facilitated access not only to literature and maps, but also to those who work in fields that, having common boundaries with one's own, had to be entered during the course of an inquiry that became ever wider in scope as it proceeded.

Cardiff, 1956.   F. J. NORTH.

CONTENTS

CONTENTS—*Continued*

LIST OF ILLUSTRATIONS

I

LLYS HELIG IN CONWAY BAY

THE legend of Llys Helig relates to a stony patch on the floor of
Conway Bay, traditionally regarded as the site of the palace of
the sixth century kinglet, Helig ap Glannawg, whose territory is
supposed to have been overwhelmed by a sudden inundation.
An expedition to see the ' ruins.'

(a) Introduction

THIS book originated in a lecture delivered at Llandudno
many years ago. The topic was ' The Scenery of the Welsh
Coast ' and whilst discussing local changes involving encroachment of the sea it became necessary to mention the legend of
Llys Helig.

According to what are described as ' ancient documents ' the
territory of an old-time kinglet, Helig ap Glannawg (or
Glannog) lies beneath the waters of Conway Bay, and some
stones seen occasionally at the lowest of tides, a couple of miles
out in the sea, are the ruins of his palace—Llys Helig.

The legend is widely regarded as a record of historical fact,
but, in discussing the probable origin of the submerged reef
with which it has for long been associated, I suggested that an
originally simple tale has been obscured by an accumulation of
irrelevant detail, just as the ruins of an old building may be
obscured by ivy. It is true that the foliage contributes to the
picturesqueness of the scene in the same way that literary
embellishments may contribute to the interest of a story, but it
more or less effectively conceals the masonry beneath and
makes it difficult to study the stones that the builders used.

In developing the theme I did no more than try to strip away
the ' ivy,' so to speak, so that attention could be focussed upon
the origin of the story instead of upon the fantasy that modern
popular opinion had made of it, but a newspaper report of the
occasion gleefully credited me with having 'debunked' an old
Welsh legend.

Nothing had been farther from my mind, for destructive
criticism, as unprofitable as it is easy, serves no useful purpose ;

critical examination is quite another thing. It is, indeed, a necessary preliminary to progress, for, as Francis Bacon put it in his *Advancement of Learning*, ' as water will not ascend higher than the level of the springhead from which it descendeth, so knowledge derived from Aristotle and exempted from liberty of examination will not rise again higher than the knowledge of Aristotle.'

I had not set out to destroy a legend but to discover when and how it came into being. In doing so it had transpired that whilst the literary evidence shows that the story, as now told, is a modern compilation conflicting with the evidence provided by the rocks and the physical features of the region to which it was supposed to relate, in the simple form in which it was first committed to writing it may have grown out of the personal experiences of folk who lived in Wales in pre-historic days.

Legends about lands beneath the sea do not fully reveal themselves when attention is confined to manuscripts and the printed page, for, unlikely as it may seem to those who take it for granted that literature and science have nothing in common, there *is* a scientific background against which such stories can be set. It is an illuminating background, for it draws attention to details that are not apparent without it and thus helps to differentiate between original framework and subsequent elaboration. It is a background compounded partly of the geography of today, but principally of what we can discover about the geography of past ages—and many of the inconsistencies in the legends only appear as such when we try to equate them with the conditions which obtain today.

Legends like those with which we are here concerned belong to the realm of folklore. ' Give any legends of sunken cities, etc.', is, indeed, one of the items in the ' Questionary ' for the guidance of collectors in *The Handbook of Folklore*, published by the Folklore Society [50*]. Many people are inclined to regard such studies as too trivial for serious attention, but in the words of Sir John Rhŷs, ' as a reality to those who believed in them, the superstitions of our ancestors form an integral part of

*Numbers in brackets refer to books, papers, and manuscripts which are the authorities for statements made, or to which those desirous of obtaining fuller information are referred. The list begins on page 246.

their history, [and] it is a mark of an uncultured people not to know, or care to know about the history of the race,' [145]

Our subject is a complicated one, for Wales has several stories of sunken cities—or towns, or palaces, or fertile plains—and each has several versions. They are so intermingled in their modern forms that it is not possible to deal once and for all with each of them in turn : it might have been, if we were merely re-telling the tales, but that has often been done and to do so again would merely increase and help to perpetuate the confusion.

The time has almost if not completely gone when fresh material of indubitable authenticity relating to our subject can be collected, but there is still a long way to go before we can claim to have made full use of what is already at our disposal. Anyone who reads the books in which they are recorded soon realizes that, with much re-telling, folk-tales and legends tend to become less and less like the corresponding stories of even a single generation ago, and the best tribute we can pay to those who, like Sir John Rhŷs, laboured so hard to collect and pre-serve these interesting survivals from the past, is to classify and evaluate the material they have placed at our disposal—to regard their work as a means to an end, and not the end itself.

The more obvious and usual approaches to a subject like this are by way of literature and history, and as my own special knowledge relates to geology the inquiry involved excursions into unfamiliar fields. On that account I have followed the advice of Francis Bacon in presenting the results. ' But know-ledge ' he wrote, in his *Novum Organum*, ' ought to be delivered . . . in the same methods wherein it was invented,' and these pages are a record of research in progress rather than an impersonal report upon its results : that is why much of it is written in the first person.

The expert will probably find that part of what is here written has already been stated (or hinted at) before—not, perhaps, with the same object in view and usually as something taken for granted—but the chosen mode of approach will, it is hoped, be helpful to the general reader who may like to know how the results were arrived at, as well as what they are.

The impression created by a comparative study of our 'ancient' legends is that in their present forms many of them owe more to educated authors than to simple country folk— more to journalism than to tradition. This is no new discovery, but, as far as I know, few attempts have been made to continue the study in the light of its implications. My own efforts to do so, are, of necessity, limited by the choice of geographical and geological lines of approach, and I have confined my attention to stories that seem to have originated in records of inundations, or that purport to explain the presence of water where, in certain circumstances, there might have been land.

Much of the evidence needed in an inquiry like this relates to matters that may appear trivial, but since the subject is one in which fact and fiction, history and legend, have been so commingled that it is by no means easy to decide which is which, the apparently trivial often proves to be important ; and if some chapters seem detailed to the point of tediousness it is because I have tried to put the reader in a position to be able to draw his own conclusions in cases where my own may prove unacceptable. It is for this reason that so many references to sources of information are given.

It now only remains to be seen to what extent the conclusions here arrived at may be supported or undermined by evidence that has been overlooked ; if any such is brought to mind by the perusal of these pages one of the objects in writing them will have been achieved. They are intended to arouse and stimulate interest in the matter, not to say the last word upon it.

(b) An early morning expedition

At 3 o'clock in the morning of August 17th, 1939, a small party of early risers, myself amongst them, made its way along the sea-front at Degannwy on the Conway estuary. It was not really dark, but fog obscured the distant view and things near at hand seemed out of focus as we peered into the damp clinging mist, looking for the boat in which we were to commence our search for the origin of an old Welsh legend.

It was necessary to get to the seaward of certain banks of sand and stones before the falling tide left us stranded upon them, and, setting out across the estuary as rapidly as the limited visibility allowed, we reached the open water with no more than some ominous bumps and grindings on bouldery patches like those which the Admiralty Charts call the ' Bwrlingau Rocks.'

By this time the fog had almost cleared, but an attenuated mist still softened the outlines of the 'mountains huge emergent' —to borrow from Milton—and made the massive headland of Penmaen-mawr seem greater and more distant than it really was.

Our objective was a reef of stones, but when we reached what we believed to be our destination there was nothing but water of oily smoothness all around and nothing to do but wait. Eventually, as the tide continued to fall, a few dark specks broke the surface a hundred yards or so away and we knew that our course had been set aright.

As the dark specks increased in number and in size they merged into what appeared to be three long straight lines at right angles to one another, looking, at the distance from which we viewed them, and as the photograph on Pl. 4 shows, remarkably like the tops of blackened rectilinear walls.

This was the traditional site of *Llys Helig*, the palace of an old-time kinglet named Helig ap Glannawg, whose territory, or at least the most desirable part of it, is supposed to have been overwhelmed by the sea sometime during the sixth century A.D. —or the fourth, the fifth, the seventh, or the ninth, according to various ' ancient documents ' which popular opinion rather vaguely cites as its authorities.

We were by no means the first to visit the so-called Llys (court or palace). There are references to expeditions made as early as the 17th century, but the first adequately recorded attempt to see the ' sunken ruin' was made in 1864 by Charlton R. Hall of Liverpool and the Rev. Richard Parry (better known by his bardic name, Gwalchmai) of Llandudno. [63]

Mr. Hall saw lines of seaweed growing upon the top of what appeared to him to be walls and came back convinced that he had seen the ruins of ' a grand old Hall of magnificent dimensions, of whose shape and proportions there still remain distinguishable traces.' Subsequently others went to see (and were satisfied that they saw) the ruins of *Llys Helig*, although there was a tendency to discount the idea that the stones represent a ' grand old hall ' and to interpret them as the remains of a walled enclosure—a much more appropriate description, for the area involved is about five and a half acres.

Before proceeding farther it is necessary to amplify these allusions to Helig, for whilst his story may be well-known in the area to which it relates and to students of the folk-tales of Wales, there are many to whom it may not be familiar ; and in any case it is desirable to indicate why it was considered necessary to make another expedition to the site which tradition assigned to his palace.

For reasons that will appear later, no two modern writers have told quite the same story, but the version in *The Falls, Lakes, and Mountains of North Wales* by L. F. Costello (1845) is a typical nineteenth century one :

' A spot in the neighbourhood of Penmaenmawr is called Trwyn yr Wylva—The Point of the Place of Wailing—from having been the scene of a frightful inundation which overwhelmed part of the beautiful Vale of Conway. This event was prophesied for generations previously to its occurrence ; a great threat had gone forth, that vengeance should overtake the family of Helig ab Glanawg for the crimes of his ancestors.

Night after night, on the wild rocks and shores, amidst the hills and in the valleys, was heard the fearful cry of "Dial a ddaw ! Dial a ddaw !" (i.e. vengeance is coming) but the wailer was invisible to all. At length it came, and suddenly, as mighty calamities generally do ; there was a great feast in the house of Helig, and the guests forgot in their jovial carousal that fate was only pausing to overtake them. They called for more wine, and a servant was despatched into the cellar to procure some while the old harper sat leaning on his harp, and the tears ran down upon the strings for his spirit foresaw some coming evil. They reproached him for his silence, and he put forth his hand to awaken the chords, when a cry struck his ear, and the next moment the servant who had gone for wine rushed wildly into the hall, shrieking "The tide ! The tide !"

Pl. 1A.   A map-reference to Llys Helig

Part of the map of Wales, by W. Owen (1788) prepared to illustrate Warrington's
History of Wales. It places Llys Helig at the extremity of the Lavan Sands.

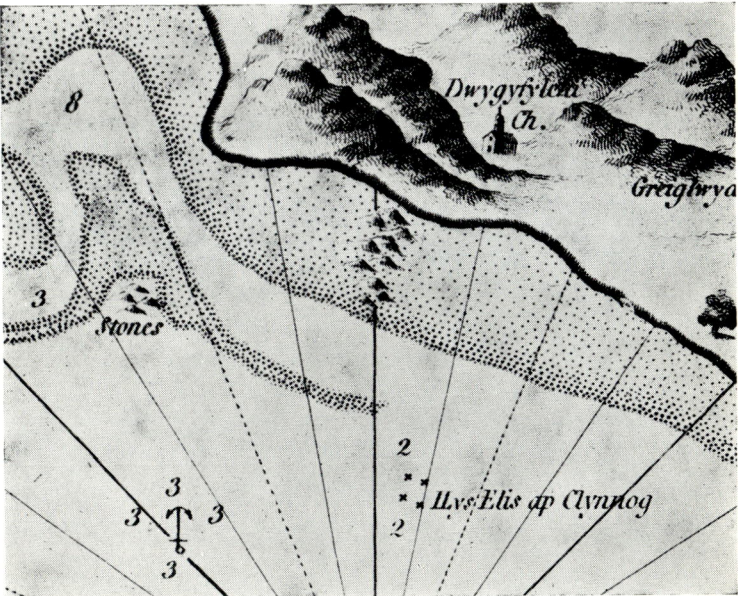

Pl. 1B.   Llys Helig on a Sea Chart

Part of the Chart of Conway Bay by Lewis Morris (1801). Llys Helig is misnamed
but placed in the position assigned to it by the 'Ancient Survey of Pen Maen Mawr.'

Pl. 2A.   The Meini Hirion, Penmaen-mawr

from J. O. Halliwell's *Notes on family excursions in North Wales* (1860).

Pl. 2B.   The road around Penmaen-mawr in 1750

from an engraving by J. Boydell.

Those two alone had time to quit the house of Helig and found safety in the mountains ; all besides were swallowed— lands, flocks and villages—by the impetuous torrent ; and the fertile vale of Conway for miles was all one sheet of foaming waters, as it remains to this day.'

It has from time to time been suggested that such a story owes more to imagination than to events that actually occurred, but many who heard it, enthusiastically supported by local popular opinion, regarded it as history and cited as their principal authority an ' old document ' described as *An Ancient Survey of Pen Maen Mawr, by Sir John Gwynn of Gwedyr.* [64, 94]

Several years before the visit described at the beginning of this chapter, when discussing the story of Helig in its relation to the geological history of North Wales, I had suggested, to members of the Llandudno, Colwyn Bay and District Field Club, that not only was much of the so-called evidence associat- ing the legend with the submerged stones called Llys Helig inadmissible, but that there was, on the other hand, a good deal of valid evidence to show that the site where the stones occur could not have been occupied by man at any of the periods to which the legend is supposed to relate.

Such views were, not unnaturally perhaps, challenged by those who accepted the story at its face value, and especially by those who had actually visited Llys Helig and could speak from first-hand knowledge of the ' ruined walls '—which at that time I could not—and the discussion that followed resulted in a proposal for another expedition.

Various circumstances conspired to delay the execution of the plan. The stones are only exposed at the time of equinoctial tides when the fall of the water is greatest, and the visit is only worth while when the lowest tide of all comes in daylight ; this usually rules out the equinox in spring. The sea must, more- over, be perfectly calm, for even small waves are sufficient to prevent the proper examination of the stones. All this means that whilst plans have to be made well in advance, notice that they can be put into operation is apt to be embarrassingly short.

The approach of the autumn equinox in 1939 gave promise that the necessary conditions were going to be fulfilled, and I

B

was summoned to Degannwy by the Field Club Committee which had arranged the expedition and whose hospitality I am glad to have this opportunity to acknowledge. The party included Councillors L. S. Underwood and R. J. Gresley Jones, the late Mr. F. Talfourd Jones and Dr. Willoughby Gardner, other officers and members of the Field Club, with Mr. W. F. Grimes to study the archaeological aspects of the site, and Mr. L. Munroe, of H.M. Office of Works, its architectural features, if any.

The first stage of the expedition has already been described ; what we saw and what some of us thought of it will appear later. In the meantime it is sufficient to say that as we compared notes after our return and discussed the matter with others who had not been able to journey with us, appeal was made to documents, to maps, to local indications of coast erosion and submergence, and to every other kind of ' evidence ' that had been adduced to support the views of those who accepted the legend as history and associated it with the site called Llys Helig.

Opinion was divided ; some felt that many of the so-called ' facts ' were popular notions that had been accepted without examination and that theories based upon them were unsound, but all were agreed that a general examination of the whole matter was desirable—that a revaluation of the evidence, and a review of alternative explanations of the origin and distribution of the biannually exposed stones, would be informative even if they should also prove to be iconoclastic.

Having been primarily responsible for creating the circumstances in which the discussion originated, I could not decline to act upon the suggestion that I should undertake the investigation, and its results were, in due course, published in the Transactions of the Field Club [118] : but determining the significance of Llys Helig, the stones, gave added interest to the problem of Llys Helig, the legend, and called for an account of its relation to the inundation stories told of other parts of Wales. Hence this book.

II

AN ' ANCIENT SURVEY OF PEN MAEN MAWR '

THE ' authority ' for the story of Llys Helig is a so-called ' Survey of Pen Maen Mawr ' attributed to Sir John Wynn of Gwydir. The earliest known copy is not in his handwriting although there is evidence that it was written during his lifetime and that he may have compiled it or have had a hand in its compilation. It is not a survey but a series of notes relating to a manuscript by an author not as yet certainly identified. Contemporary books, and some manuscripts that still survive, provided the author of the ' Survey ' with most of his information.

(a) *A manuscript attributed to Sir John Wynn of Gwydir*

THE ' old document ' in which the story of Helig's lost land is supposed to have been recorded was the obvious starting point for an inquiry into the significance of the legend. The title *An Ancient Survey of Pen Maen Mawr* was given by J. O. Halliwell (better known as Halliwell Phillipps, biographer of Shakespeare), when, in 1859, he published a little volume which he described as being based upon a manuscript in the possession of Thomas Wright—a well-known antiquary of the time. [64]

A good deal of the manuscript, which ran to over 5,000 words, has nothing to do with the story of Helig, but it is necessary to give a brief summary of the whole because all parts of it must be considered when we come to discuss its origin and authorship. It was entitled ' *Notes to bee observed before you lett your Survay passe your handes*' and it comprised the following three distinct and unrelated parts of unequal length (the descriptive headings are introduced for present convenience and do not form part of the original) :

1. *Notes about the ancestry and descendants of Helig and an account of the calamity that befell his lands.*

This includes pedigrees connecting Helig ap Glannawg with Cunedda Wledig, claimed as one of the ' Dukes of Britain ' and sometime guardian of Hadrian's Wall, followed by an enumeration of Helig's estates and an account of an inundation which deprived him of a large part of his territory. Then follow pedigrees to show that most of the principal men then living [i.e., early in the 17th century] in Caernarvonshire were descended from Cunedda, and the section concludes with notes to the effect that Helig had three sons who became saints and a brother Seiriol, a holy priest, who built an embankment from Priestholm to Penmaen-mawr and cut a road on the mountainside from Dwygyfylchi to Llanfairfechan.

2. *An account of some of the antiquities in the vicinity of Penmaen-mawr.*

This section describes the ancient stronghold called Dinas on the summit of Penmaen-mawr (the Braich y Dinas or Penmaen Dinas of the Ordnance Survey maps, now entirely removed by quarrying), the stones called Y Meini Hirion, and some cairns (he called them Carneddi) near Dwygyfylchi. It speculates upon their significance and gives an account of a legend concerning some stones that formerly stood on ' Moelvre ' near the ' Carneddi ' : these were supposed to have originated in three women, who, for the sin of winnowing corn upon the Sabbath, were converted into pillars of stone.

3. *Critical notes about Degannwy Castle and Bangor.*

These are intended to show that Degannwy Castle was the chief seat of the ancient Kings in North Wales, and that it was not founded by an Earl of Chester although one of the Earls rebuilt it for King John. The concluding notes challenge a statement that ' Bangor Vawr was destroyed by Owen Glyndwr,' and assert that it was burnt by King John in 1202 whilst Owen fired only the Cathedral and its associated buildings.

The existence and significance of the manuscript seems to have been taken for granted, but an exhaustive search for it led to the conclusion that although there is, indeed, a 17th century manuscript that could have been the basis of Halliwell's little book, it was not written by Sir John Wynn although he almost certainly had something to do with its preparation. It is, as the foregoing summary indicates, rather inaptly described as a

Survey of Penmaenmawr, and, as far as the parts relating to Helig and the lost lands are concerned, it owes less to knowledge than it does to imagination.

This being the case, it might be thought sufficient, as Sir J. E. Lloyd put it, to leave it to students of folk-lore to say whether the stories embody genuine tradition or history, or are local specimens of a class of story known in all parts of the world. [91] But this would not solve the problems relating to the authorship and authenticity of the 17th century manuscript or the origin of the submerged stones that are supposed to be the ruins of Helig's palace, and it would leave those who regard the story as history free to assert that it has never been disproved.

A rolling stone (to shift from our former comparison with an ivy-covered ruin) is said to gather no moss, but an oft-told story acquires much extra detail by reason of which the original nucleus may be effectively concealed. The nucleus is, however, rarely destroyed, and it seemed worth while to strip the Llys Helig story of its embellishments in the hope of being able to discover how and in what circumstances it originated. Thus examined it provides an excellent example of the way in which legends tend to acquire the status of history, and ' airy nothing-ness ' is given ' a local habitation and a name.'

In order to show that legend does indeed tend to pass for ' history ' we can take the following passage from Rice Rees' *Essay on the Welsh Saints :* ' the inundation which formed the Lavan Sands appears to have occurred in this generation [i.e., between A.D. 634 and 664] while Helig was still living ; his sons, upon the loss of their patrimony embraced a monastic life in the colleges of Bangor Deiniol and Bangor Enlli.' Even more positive assertions occur in the Flintshire volume of the *Cambridge County Geographies* (1914) : ' In the fifth century there was a great inundation along the whole of the North Wales Coast, and the sea once more regained a large tract of land. . . . When the present coastline is compared with that of the fifth century, it is seen that the ancient Flintshire must have been nearly twice as large as it is at present.'

These, and the reference in an eighteenth century map reproduced as Pl. 1A, are objective statements, but whilst there is a *legend* relating to an inundation there is no *evidence* that such a catastrophe actually occurred, neither is there any evidence whatever upon which we can institute (with the certainty that the foregoing passage implies) comparisons between the coastline of the fifth century and that of the present day.

We can picture in a general way the changes that have taken place within the area, but the ' reconstructions ' of the fifth century coastline that have been drawn to illustrate the supposed relation between land and sea at that time (e.g., Figs. 1 and 4) are not proof that the story is history : they are merely an indication that it has been accepted as such—that the cart has been put before the horse, so to speak ; besides, the territorial sub-divisions of which Flintshire is one had not been recognized in the 5th century.

The chronological differences between the passages quoted above are indicative of the vagueness that pervades the whole of the relevant literature. In the one case the inundation is assigned to the 7th century on account of the author's view concerning the period during which Helig is supposed to have lived, but its association with the 5th century arose because an author forgot that a three-figure date beginning with 5 is not in the fifth century ! As we shall see, he and others who have referred to the fifth century were really thinking of the year 520.

Since our object is to show how evidence accumulated as the inquiry progressed and not merely to enumerate the conclusions that can be based upon it, we must now start with the simple fact that in 1859 a book called *An Ancient Survey of Pen Maen Mawr, North Wales, from the original manuscript of the time of Charles I* was published by J. O. Halliwell, who stated that it was copied from a manuscript in the possession of Thomas Wright.

In the following year Halliwell included extensive extracts from the ' Survey ' in his *Notes of Family Excursions in North Wales,* whilst in 1861 the manuscript was printed in *Archaeologia Cambrensis,* under the title, *Caernarvonshire Antiquities, from a MS communicated by Thomas Wright.* Wright did not mention Halliwell's little volume and it is difficult to see why it should have been thought necessary to reprint the ' Survey ' after so short an interval unless it was because the original small edition failed to satisfy the demand, or because it was realized that Halliwell was unfortunate in his guesses concerning what he could not readily decipher and so made numerous mistakes.

The nature of the errors will be discussed when we come to consider the problem of the authorship of the so-called ' Survey ' ; in the meantime it is sufficient to say that, until 1940, exhaustive inquiries in all likely directions failed to locate the manuscript that had been in Thomas Wright's possession.

Although Halliwell deserves most of the credit for stimulating popular interest in the story, either through his original volume or its reprint by W. Bezant Lowe in 1906 as *An Ancient Survey of Pen Maen Mawr, by Sir John Gwynn of Gwedyr*, the *Notes to bee observed* had already appeared in print once before. Miss Angharad Llwyd of Caerwys had published them in *The Cambrian Quarterly Magazine* in 1831. The title she chose was *History of Helig ap Glanawg* and she described the story as being based upon ' A copy made by Mr. David Lloyd, a clergyman, from the original which is lost.' This description raised a new problem—was the ' original ' rediscovered by Thomas Wright, or have we to think in terms of two early copies, one of which was used by Lloyd and the other by Wright ?

Fortunately, David Lloyd's manuscript, after passing into the possession of William Pamplin was bought by Sir John Williams and deposited in the National Library of Wales. [Addn. MS 27]. How Pamplin acquired it is not recorded. As he lived for some years at Llandderfel he may have come into contact with someone in North Wales who had no further use for it, or it may have come to his notice during the course of his business as a bookseller and publisher in London.

The manuscript occurs in a vellum-bound book of the shape and size that is usually indicated by the term ' exercise book ' ; on the outside cover is written *A Copy of Sir John Wynne of Gwiddir Baronet's Manuscript* and on the front page there are the signature and date, *David Lloyd, 1720*.

The book contains copies of three distinct manuscripts : the first is a series of biographical sketches of eminent men in North Wales, starting with an account of six who were Bishops in the first Queen Elizabeth's time. The internal evidence leaves little room for doubt but that these *Memoirs*, as they are now usually called, were originally compiled by Sir John Wynn, and they were first printed in 1827 in an edition of *The History of the Gwydir Family*, also prepared by Miss Angharad Llwyd.

The second and largest section of the manuscript is entitled *The True copy of a manuscript written by Sir John Wynne of Gwyddir Kt. and Bart. 1607*. This is the *History of the Gwydir Family*, of which the first printed edition was prepared by the Hon. Daines Barrington in 1770, with subsequent editions by Miss Llwyd in 1827, Askew Roberts with the assistance of W. W. E. Wynne of Peniarth in 1878 [148], and [Sir] John Ballinger in 1927.

The third part, headed, *Notes to bee observed before you lett your Survay passe your handes*, is what has since come to be known as the *Ancient Survey of Pen Maen Mawr*.

Some of the manuscript is in the writing of David Lloyd himself, and the remainder, including the whole of the third part—*the Notes to bee observed*—is the work of some other person who was a neat writer but had little comprehension of what he copied.

At least one item (*The History of the Gwydir Family*) in this series of copies, made in part by and in part for David Lloyd, was taken from a manuscript that had been in the possession of Humphrey Humphreys, Bishop of Bangor, shortly before 1700. This is indicated by the fact that at the end of the part relating to Wynn's *History*, there is an additional note of about four pages, beginning, ' I find that this Meredeth Wynn ap Evan ap Robert made two journeys to Rome,' and ending with a reference to entries in a visitors' book attested by Owen Wynn of Cae'r Milwr and dated June 14, 1588 : after this additional note is written, *Signed, H. Bangor, 1700*.

Humphreys, described by Anthony Wood (seventeenth century antiquary and historian of Oxford) as being ' excellently well versed in the antiquities of Wales ' [180] wrote memoirs of several eminent Welshmen. He is known to have had a manuscript copy of Wynn's *History* because Thomas Mostyn of Gloddaeth wrote of having seen it when he made his own copy

[National Library of Wales MS 3075] of that work about the year 1674. In the circumstances it seemed not unreasonable to wonder whether the other two manuscripts might also have been in the Bishop's possession, but inquiries in all likely depositories for papers that once belonged to him failed to produce a copy of the *Notes to bee observed*—and another line of investigation seemed to have come to a dead end.

There is no essential difference between David Lloyd's manuscript and Miss Llwyd's printed version, apart from the omission from the latter of the first two paragraphs of pedigrees and some minor corrections necessitated by the fact that the 1720 copyist was not familiar with the subject. He made numerous mistakes, the nature and significance of which will appear in due course.

There are, however, several slight differences between Lloyd's manuscript and the printed version based upon Thomas Wright's. Most of them are obviously such as can be attributed to careless or inexpert copying, but there is one feature which shows beyond doubt that Lloyd's copy was not the one which subsequently came into the hands of Wright.

The *Notes to bee observed* refer to a submerged land surface on the site of the Lavan Sands—the strand exposed at low tide between Anglesey and the north Caernarvonshire coast—where the roots of trees were exposed when the water ebbed farthest ' upon Spring tides in March and August.' Wright, however, inserted a note to the effect that, in his manuscript, August had been written over an obliterated June ; but in the Lloyd manuscript there is no trace of any erasure or addition and it could not, therefore, have been the one which Wright used. At this stage of the inquiry the most that could be said was that Wright had either rediscovered the manuscript from which Lloyd's copy had been made, or else had acquired some other one very closely related to it. The former seemed the more likely because it would be quite understandable if, in making his copy, Lloyd did not consider it necessary to include something which the original author had crossed out.

At the time, this appeared to be as far as it would be possible to go in attempting to trace the ' ancient document,' but at the end of 1940, when the second part of the *Handlist of Manuscripts* in the National Library of Wales was being prepared, an obviously 17th century copy of the *Notes to bee observed* was discovered amongst papers that had formerly belonged to Edward Breese of Portmadoc and subsequently to Edward Humphrey Owen of Tŷ Coch, Caernarvon. Part of it is reproduced in our Frontispiece.

It did not take long to establish that the Breese manuscript (now MS 820D in the National Library of Wales) was indeed the one which had belonged to Wright and had been copied by Halliwell. That it had the alteration from June to August was sufficient to show that it was the original of Wright's *Caernarvonshire Antiquities*, and that it was also the original of Halliwell's *Ancient Survey of Pen Maen Mawr* is shown by the way it enables us to appreciate the significance of some of the mistakes which he made. These mistakes are worth mentioning because they illustrate the way in which errors arise and can be perpetuated when copies are accepted at their face value and the originals not consulted.

The text starts off with a flourish that makes it easy to understand why Halliwell transcribed the first word as Lyelig instead of Helig. If one looks at the appearance of the words as a whole and not at the individual letters (many of which have forms different from those we are familiar with today) his Trevyn yr Wylfa for Trwyn yr Wylfa is also understandable, so is his rendering of sainctes as Churches in a reference to the sons of Helig.

Anyone who has copied extensively from manuscript will know how easy it is for mistakes of this kind to be made and how likely it is that a mistake, once made, will escape detection, especially if it is trivial and does not introduce obvious nonsense.

The next point to be settled was whether it was really this manuscript (820D) which David Lloyd's amanuensis used, or whether we have to envisage two 17th century copies of the *Notes to bee observed*. There are many differences between the Lloyd manuscript and 820D, as for convenience we may now call it, but they, also, are mostly of the kind that would be expected to occur in such circumstances, e.g., minor omissions, the substitution of spellings characteristic of the period when the copy was made for those prevailing when the original was written, and the systematic use of *ye* for *the*. It is certain that Lloyd's amanuensis was copying from 820D, although, here and there, he only succeeded in misrepresenting it.

There are a few curious differences between the Lloyd manuscript and the printed version by Wright which a casual observer might regard as proof that they could not have been related, but they are, in fact, clear evidence that both were copies of the same original.

The Lloyd manuscript, for example, refers to a river *Dee* where the earlier manuscript has *ell*. (Frontispiece). In 820D the letter *e* frequently looks very much like a small *d*, as many would write it, and the *ll* has a strong resemblance to *ee*, so that if the writer of the Lloyd copy temporarily forgot, as obviously he often did, the peculiarities of the handwriting of the earlier manuscript, he could easily have read *ell* as *dee*. Then, making what he thought to be a necessary correction and writing *Dee*, he made it appear as if a river of that name separated Caernarvonshire from Anglesey.

We have, then, established that there *is* an early 17th century manuscript in which the story of Helig and his submerged land is told in a comparatively simple form ; we now have to consider who wrote it and what were the sources of his information.

It happens that there is sufficient material available in Sir John Wynn's handwriting to make it certain that he did not actually write the manuscript 820D. The question of authorship must therefore be settled by reference to internal evidence and as a basis for the necessary discussion the relevant parts of the document will be quoted in full later in this chapter.

It might be thought that the discovery of the manuscript 820D in 1940 renders the earlier part of this chapter unnecessary ; but the account of the search for it, of the conclusions arrived at in its absence, and of its unexpected re-appearance, provides an illustration of what often happens in such inquiries and demonstrates the danger of assuming that a document which cannot be found, does not, in fact, exist.

Indeed, as will be shown in the next chapter, there are features in 820D which point to the existence of another manuscript of which the present whereabouts, if it still exists, are not known.

(b) Who wrote the so-called ' Survey ' and why

The *Notes to bee observed* are too long to be copied here in full, but the necessity for quoting at least the part relating to Helig has already been indicated. It is as follows, and it has been broken into paragraphs (not in the original) in order that it might be easier to read :

' Helig ap Glannog was lord of Abergele, Rhos, Arllech-wedd, Llyn, Cantre gwaylod, and Earle of Herefford.

' In his tyme happened the greate inundacōn which surrounded Cantred Gwayloi and the most delicate fruytfulle and pleasant vale leynge from Bangor vawr yn gwynedd to Gogarth and soe to Tyganwy or Gannog Castle, in leangth and breadth from Dwygyfylchi to the poynte of Flyntshire, which came upp from Ruthlan to Priestholme, and in the upper end thereof did extend in breadth from Aber and Llanvair unto the ryver ell, which did devide Carnarvonshire from Anglesey, and did liekwiese devide Anglesey from Flyntshire, rynnynge betweene Penmon and Priestholme, and soe dischardgyinge ytself into the sea a greate way beyond Priestholme, and did surround many other riche and fruytfulle bottomes and vales, within the countyes of Car-narvon, Flynt, Anglesey, and Merionudd,

' Most of them beynge the land of Helig ap Glannog, whose chieffest palace stood in this vale muche about the mydle way from Penmen Mawer to Gogarth (in Englishe Armes Head) the ruynes whereof is nowe to bee seene uppon a grownd ebbe some two myles within the sea directly over against Trwyn yr Wylva, which is a hill leynge in the myddst of the parishe of Dwygyfylchi within the landes of Sir John Bodnel [i.e. Bodvel] knight, unto which hyll Helyg ap Glannog and his people did runn upp to save themsealves, beynge endaungered with the sudden breakynge in of the sea upon them, and there saved their lyves.

' And beynge come upp to the poynte of that hill, and

lookynge backe and behouldynge that dreadfull and ruthfull spectacle which they hadd to survay and looke upon, insteade of there incomparable vale which did abound in fruytfullnes and excell all other vales in this part of England in all fertility and plentifullnes, Helig ap Glannog and all his people, wryngynge there handes togeyther, made a greate outcry bewaylinge there misfortune and callynge unto God for mercy, the poynt of which hill to this day is called Trwyn (r) Wylfa, that is to say the point of the dolefull hill or the mowrnynge hill . . .

' And sithence this inundacõn, the commotte of . . . Llechweth Ucha doth meare north west uppon the mayne sea that surrounded the delicate vale aforesaid, and in the upper end of the sayd commotte, vidzt from Penmen Mawr to Bangor, doth meare North and West uppon the greate washe called Traeth ell, soe called from the ryver ell (formerly the meare betweene Carnarvonshire and Anglesey) as Traeth Mawr hath his denomination from the ryver Mawr which dischardgeth ytt sealf through that washe into the mayne sea.

' And ytt is allsoe called Traeth yr laven, as much to say as Traeth aflawen, that is an unpleasant wharffe, because ytt is an unpleasant sight unto the spectators, and a fearefull and dismal objecte unto the eyes of thinhabitantes, bryngynge them dayly in mynde how unhappy they weare to loose soe fayre soe fruytfull and soe feartill a countrey, beynge beaten backe with unpleasant overwhelmynge waves to inhabytt and dwell in higher growndds uppon the edges and skyrtes of the hills and mountaynes . . .'

It will be noted that there is nothing about retribution for a mis-spent life, or a harper, or a servant, or a wine-cellar ! The essential features are that the inundation was sudden and unexpected, and that Helig and his people survived to survey the damage and bewail their misfortune.

We have already seen that the title *Ancient Survey of Pen Maen Mawr* was not part of the manuscript itself. It was given by Halliwell in 1859, and the story just quoted, considered in relation to its context (given on page 20) shows that the title is not a good one. Barely a third of the manuscript relates to

Penmaen-mawr and even that small part is in no sense a
'survey.' Miss Llwyd called it the *History of Helig ap Glanawg*,
but that also is unsatisfactory because only about one eighth of
the whole is really about Helig.

Wright's title, *Caernarvonshire Antiquities*, is the most appropriate of the three that have been used in association with
printed copies of the manuscript but the original compiler
called it *Notes to bee observed before you lett your survay passe your
handes*, and this, in association with the notes themselves, makes
it clear that the manuscript was not, in itself, either a survey or a
history. It is a collection of critical and supplementary notes
relating to something that had already been written—it was a
means to an end, not the end itself.

The only thing about which we can be sure is that the *Notes*
were written early in the 17th century. This is apparent from
the handwriting and from the general nature of the spelling ;
but there is one piece of evidence that fixes the date within
narrow limits. There are (in the genealogical portions of the
manuscript, not copied here because they have no bearing upon
an inundation) two references to ' John, Bishop of Lincoln and
Lord Keeper of the Great Seal ' in terms that suggest that they
relate to a person then living, and John Williams held those
two offices from 1621—1625.

As Sir John Wynn died in 1626 the *Notes* were compiled
during his life-time : are they, we may ask, a copy of something
he wrote, or were they prepared at his behest, or under his
supervision ?

The manuscript contains many alterations and corrections of
such a nature as to suggest that it is an original document.
Many of the emendations were obviously made whilst the work
was in progress, and others are of the kind one would expect
to find in a manuscript corrected by an author himself. There
are many similarities in spelling between this manuscript and
Wynn's *History of the Gwydir Family*—a double *f* in words like
ffyrst and *ffind*, and contractions like *p'don* for *pardon* and
poss'ions for *possessions* ; but they are not conclusive evidence, for
many of them can be matched in other writings of the time.
They are met with, for example, in the early seventeenth

century works of George Owen, the historian of Pembrokeshire.

It is, at this stage, desirable to digress a little in order to consider the circumstances in which Wynn's name came to be associated with the *Notes to bee observed*. The first printed reference to the manuscript occurs in the 1695 edition of Camden's *Britannia*, edited by Bishop Gibson [10]. Here, in the additional notes about Caernarvonshire contributed by Edward Lhuyd, are extracts from what is stated to have been a manuscript written by ' a person of quality of the reign of Charles I,' and communicated to Lhuyd by his ' worthy friend Mr. Griffith Jones, school master of Lhan Rwst.' The extracts relate only to the ancient fort and the standing stones near Penmaen-mawr, but it is clear from their wording that they were derived from the same source as the manuscript which eventually came into the hand of Thomas Wright, if not from that manuscript itself.

In Gibson's second edition (1722) of *Camden*, there are similar extracts and a similar reference to a person of quality, but the latter is amplified by a marginal note, ' Sir John Wyn of Guydyr.' In the preface, the editor stated that ' although Mr. Lhuyd is since dead, . . . yet it fell out Providentially for this Work that before his death, he had Revised the work of the Principality in order to this new Impression,' but since the information about the person of quality was given in a marginal note and not in the text, it does not necessarily follow that Lhuyd was responsible for it. It may well have been added by the editor, but in any case it is the first direct connexion between the manuscript and Sir John Wynn and it was printed nearly a century after his death.

The internal evidence that Wynn may himself have compiled the *Notes* (he did not, as we have seen, actually write the copy with which we are concerned) is not altogether conclusive ; it lies mainly in the spelling peculiarities already mentioned, in similarities of style between the *Notes* and the *History of the Gwydir Family*, and in the facts that the *Notes* were written during his lifetime and were (as will appear later) inspired by a book that he is likely to have possessed.

As *The History of the Gwydir Family* (written in 1607) begins quite abruptly with a reference to Gruffudd ap Cynan who died in 1137, several centuries after Helig is supposed to have lost his lands, and also ends abruptly, it might be suggested that the *Notes to bee observed* (written after 1620) relate to additions to the *History* that have not survived, were it not that the latter is concerned almost entirely with the activities and motives of men, and not with natural phenomena like inundations or objects like stones on the top of a mountain.

The phrase ' before you lett your survay passe your handes ' suggests that the *Notes* related to something written by another person. It is somewhat unusual, in criticizing one's own work, to write in the second person, and other phrases, such as ' Whereas you say . . .', and ' Soe that I can fynd none ells that houldeth landes . . .', also support the view that the author of the *Notes* was not annotating his own work.

We can, I think, safely say that the *Notes to bee observed* have nothing to do with the *History of the Gwydir Family*, nor, indeed, with any book or manuscript by Wynn or his contemporaries that has yet come to light.

An attractive possibility, for which, however, there is no supporting evidence, is that the *Notes* relate to a manuscript prepared by Sir Thomas ap William—Thomas Williams, physician and distinguished Welsh lexicographer. He was related to Wynn, who helped him financially and mentioned having made use of a Chronicle belonging to him when preparing the *History of the Gwydir Family*. Thomas Pennant, in a reference to the fort at Penmaen-mawr, stated that before it was described by ' that sensible old baronet Sir John Wynn of Gwedir,' it had previously been described by ' Sir Thomas ap William, medicus M.A., whose account has never appeared in print ' [131]. Pennant, however, gives Camden's *Britannia*, Vol. ii, 804, as his authority, so that he was using the second Gibson edition (1722), and his reference to ' the sensible old baronet ' has no real value. If Thomas Williams' manuscript could be discovered it might throw light upon this part of our problem, but his handwriting is known and he did not write the copy of the *Notes* with which we are concerned.

To summarize this survey of circumstantial evidence—which is supported by other evidence that will appear later on—for the present we can do no more than say that Sir John Wynn almost certainly had something to do with the preparation of the *Notes*. As the manuscript appears to be an original document and is not in Wynn's handwriting it could have been written to his dictation as a commentary upon something written by another, or it could be a commentary by another on something written by Wynn. In either case, the two persons most likely to have been concerned are Sir John and Thomas Williams.

(c) The authorities for the information incorporated into the 'Survey'

Almost all the references to Degannwy in what we have called Section 3 of the *Notes* (on page 20) have been taken from *The Historie of Cambria, now called Wales* which David Powel of Ruabon published in 1584. The book seems to have been the first attempt to compile a consecutive history of Wales, and Powel stated that learned men considered Caradoc of Llancarfan to have been its original author, but for the early medieval period it was based upon a translation by Humphrey Llwyd of *Brut y Tywysogion* (Chronicle of the Princes). [174] Llwyd, a native of Denbigh, was one of the foremost of the literary antiquarians of his time and after his death the manuscript of the *Brut* was entrusted to Powel who published it with numerous additions.

Some passages in the *Notes* were quotations from the *Historie*, but even when the wording is different the source of the information is apparent, e.g., ' Prince Llewelyn ap Gruffydd rased the castells of Tyganwy and Dyserth and destroyed the earldome of Chester ' in the *Notes to bee observed*, is obviously derived from ' Prince Llewellyn, being confederate with the Barons against the King, destroyed the Earldome of Chester, and rased two of Edward's castells, Tyganwy and Diserth,' in the *Historie*.

The account (in the *Notes*) of the ancient fortress and the standing stones and cairns near Penmaen-mawr is not a criticism of something already written, but is based upon the compiler's own observations, with suggestions concerning the significance of the structures and records of traditions associated with them. Of the Dinas, which ' when ytt stood was ympregnable,'

C

he said that according to tradition it was ' the ultimum refugium the strongest, surest, and safest refuge and place of defence that the ancient Britaynes had in all Snowdon, to defende themsealves from the incursions and inrodes of there enemyes.'

With its ten-feet-thick mortar-less walls enclosing in all some twelve acres, the Dinas must have been an impressive sight and the tradition would seem to have been well founded. When they were in use the reputation of the British hill-forts had penetrated as far as Rome, and Juvenal, writing in the time of Nero makes a father urge his son to prove his courage by destroying the forts of the Brigantes, i.e., a British tribe living in the north of England. [83].

Of Y Meini Hirion (subsequently popularly called the Druids' Circle, Pl. 2A) the writer of the *Notes* suggested that, ' ytt shoulde seeme that this was a place wherunto the ancient Britaynes came from the Dinas aforesayd to encampe themsealves and trayne ther souldiers.' It stood about a mile and a half away (ESE) from the Dinas and not far from Graig Lwyd, the site of one of the best known of the British stone-axe ' factories ' of prehistoric times. [170]. He thought that the nearby ' Carneddi ' marked the site of a great battle between the Romans and the ' Britaynes,' and that ' such as were slayne weare buried in heapes one uppon one another, and these stones caste uppon them lest the wilde bores and swyne should digge upp there bodyes, and withall for a memorial unto future ages that the bodyes of men lay buried there.'

The mountain slopes hereabouts are rich in mounds and piles of stones of varying origins and dates, and the writer of the *Notes* expressed the opinion that ' ytt is great pitty that our Brittishe histories are so ymbeseled [meaning ' ill-treated '] that we have noe certeynty for these thinges, but must onely rely uppon tradicõn,' and, as we have already seen, he recounted a tradition relating to three stones, ' one redd as blood, the other white, and the thyrd a little bluer than the white stone,' that formerly stood ' in triangel wiese,' upon the hill called Moelfre, near the Carneddau. They were stated to be the result of a miracle ' wrought in this place for the increasynge of our fayth.' Three women who insisted on winnowing corn upon the

Sabbath day, in spite of the protests of their neighbours, were instantly turned into pillars of stone, ' of the same collour as the women's clothes weare, one redd, the other white, and the thyrd bluishe.'

This section of the *Notes* shows that in addition to being familiar with the district, the writer was well acquainted with local tradition and saw nothing wrong in associating facts that could be verified with traditions for which there were no apparent foundations. He could not, of course, have been expected to know, in his day, that whereas the Dinas may have been occupied in the opening centuries of the present era, the Meini Hirion and the Carneddau were erections of an earlier prehistoric age.

The notes relating to Helig open with what is obviously an extract from an old genealogy : ' Helig ap Glannog ap Gwgan gledde Hyfryd ap Caradog Vreichvras earle of Hereford ap Llŷr Mereini ap Einion yrth ap Cunedda wyledig, &c.' Except for the inclusion of ' earle of Hereford,' this string of names corresponds with one given in the *Genealogies of Families of the Saints of the Island of Britain* which Iolo Morganwg claimed to have copied from ' The Long Book of Thomas Truman of Pantlliwydd in the parish of Llansanor, in Glamorgan.' [179]

Iolo Morganwg, it may be noted, was the bardic name of Edward Williams who was born at Pennon in Glamorgan. He was keenly interested in certain aspects of literature, collected and copied old Welsh manuscripts, and, as we shall frequently have occasion to note, added to their apparent number by the exercise of his fertile imagination. In this case, however, the similarity between the two lists suggest that Iolo's is not likely to have been one of his own inventions. It was, no doubt, derived from one of the late 16th century copies of what purported to be genealogies of the saints (*Bonedd y Saint*) and shows that we cannot ignore Iolo's work, although it is believed to be in so large a measure unreliable. It is not likely that he got his information relating to Helig's ancestry from the *Notes to bee observed* because the manuscript had not been printed at the time of his death in 1826, and, having regard to what we now know about him, it is inconceivable that he could have seen either the original manuscript or David Lloyd's copy of it without making use of some of the stories it contained.

'Gledde Hyfryd' was an unskilful copyist's rendering of Gleddehyf-ryd, and the person indicated is Gwgon Gleddyfrudd (Gwgon of the Bloody Sword) who figures in the *Triads* as one of the three 'obstructors of slaughter of the Island of Prydain' [154c] and one of the three sentinels at the apochryphal battle of 'Bangor Orchard' (Bangor Iscoed). The latter seems to have been a sequel to the battle and massacre of Chester, assigned by the *Anglo-Saxon Chronicle* to A.D. 607, and by other authorities to a few years later, e.g., circa 615. [91a].

The *Triad* is a form of expression in which objects or persons are grouped together in threes with a heading indicating the point of likeness, and the so-called Historical Triads or ' Triads of the Isle of Britain ' have to do with the personages of early British History, about whom they give information that often is not derivable from other sources. Early Welsh manuscripts preserve two series of Triads that are believed to embody genuine old allusions and may, therefore, have historical value, but there is also a third series, differing in certain respects from the others, and now believed to have been for the most part fabricated by Iolo Morganwg. [176]

Gwgon is mentioned as *gugaun cletyfrut* in the *Verses of the Graves* in the *Black Book of Carmarthen*, and also in a *Triad* relating to the celebrated horses (*a Bucheslum seri march gugaun cletywrut*). [154a]

The Black Book of Carmarthen, *Llyvyr Du Kaer Vyrddin* (*Llyfr du Caerfyrddin*), to which we shall frequently have occasion to refer, is one of the oldest known extant Welsh manuscripts. It is a collection of poems, and is now believed to have been written in the mid-thirteenth century. It was reproduced in facsimile in 1888 [31], and in modern print in 1906 [32] ; the latter volume contains an interesting account of its contents. The poems preserve relics of a literature that cannot be more recent than the 13th century though its maximum age is never likely to be determined with certainty—and some of them confirm the traditional status of a person cited as Helig's grandfather.

The second paragraph of the *Notes to bee observed* contains a list of the sons of Cunedda and their inheritances in North Wales. It was copied almost word for word from Price's *Description of Cambria, now called Wales* [134], from which also was derived the information in the next paragraph. In this, Cunedda is traced back to a sister of ' Elen Lueddog ' concerning whom the author repeats the erroneous notion (to be found, for example, in Geoffrey of Monmouth's *History*), that she was the Helena who was the mother of Constantine the Great. [57]

The descent of Helig is amplified as follows : ' Einion ap Cunedda who was lord of Caereinion hadd issue Llŷr Mereini, who had issue Caradog surnamed Vreichfras Earle of Hereford, called by the Saxons Caradog the kinge of North Wales, who hadd many greate conflicts with the Romans. Caradog hadd issue Gwgan Gleddehyfryd, who had issue Glannog, father to this same Helig ap Glannog.'

This paragraph provides a good illustration of the author's uncritical use of his material. He makes Helig to be the great-grandson of Caradog whom the Saxons called King of North Wales—*Caratauc rex Guenedote* in the so-called *Annales Cambriae* [173], where he is said to have died in A.D. 789. If this were the case an inundation which destroyed the lands of his great-grandson could not have taken place much earlier than the beginning of the 9th century. This does not agree with the more usual statements that indicate the 5th or 6th century as the one during which Helig lived, and it makes the acceptance of an inundation story even more difficult because a sudden subsidence of such magnitude in the 9th century would have left more tangible evidence, both physical and documentary, than Helig's Llys and the vague and contradictory allusions to his loss.

There is not, however, really a chronological problem here, because it transpires that the Caradog mentioned in the paragraph was compounded of three separate persons. The Caradog who had many fights with the Romans must have been Caratâcus, who was defeated by Ostorius in A.D. 51.

Caradog Vreichvras (Freichfras, Stout Arm) the son of Llŷr Mereini, figures in the Arthurian legends and is associated with the 5th century or the 6th ; the *Triads* speak of him as the chief elder when Arthur was the chief lord at Kelliwic (Celliwig) in Cornwall [154b]. Caradog, called King of Gwynedd, was descended from Owain Danwyn ap Cunedda Wledig, and was, as already indicated, killed by the Saxons towards the close of the eighth century.

The author completed his ' comedy of errors ' when he wrote of Caradog as the Earl of Hereford, for that earldom was not created until 1067 (for William Fitzosbern, who came with William the Conqueror), and Helig is supposed to have lost his lands in the 6th century.

Most of the early genealogies agree in citing Helig as the great grandson of Caradog Freichfras, but they do not put him in the direct line of descent from Cunedda Wledig ; they refer to Llŷr Mereini, Caradog's father, as Cunedda's great-nephew, not his son.

A further complication of the chronological aspect of the story is introduced by the manuscripts that cite Gwgon Gleddyf-rudd as the son of Caradog Freichfras, because if, as the *Triads* suggest, Gwgon was present at the battle of Bangor Orchard (which, whatever its precise location and date, must have taken place early in the 7th century), then his grandson Helig cannot have lived in the early part of the 6th century !

It is no part of our present purpose to attempt to reconcile these contradictory statements and inferences ; they are only introduced in order to illustrate the lack of agreement amongst the early writers concerning the period at which Helig may have flourished, and to indicate the danger of assigning a date to a physical occurrence that is supposed to have occurred during the lifetime of any one of these shadowy personages.

The ancient pedigrees, which are the principal and in many cases the only sources of relevant information, are notoriously inconsistent ; they contain mistakes due to the difficulty which copyists experienced in deciphering earlier manuscripts, and others, more serious, resulting from the elimination (by accident or design) of one or more names in a series, or from the combin-

ing of two persons bearing the same name. There are considerable divergencies in the periods assigned to persons like Cunedda
Wledig and Maelgwn Gwynedd, so that it is not a matter for
surprise if Helig, known only from references in genealogies,
appears to be equally at home in any one of three or four
centuries.

The paragraphs in 820D that deal with the descendants of
Helig give a clue to the object of the researches upon which the
Notes were based. The pedigrees were compiled with a view to
showing that ' most of the pryme men within the county of
Carnarvon ' were descended from Helig, and therefore (according to the author's erroneous notion) directly from Cunedda,
the ' great ruler.' At the end of them the author wrote ' by
these braunches above mentioned every understandynge man
may know how many honorable wor*ll* and worthy personages
. . . are descended from Helig ap Glannog.'

One of the principal individuals in the series connecting
Helig and Cunedda was Yarddur, or Jarddur, who had two
sons, Yerwarth and Madog. One paragraph in the *Notes*
purports to show that ' the right Reverend and Ryght. ho.
John Bishoppe of Lincolne, lord Keeper of his Majesties greate
seale of England,' was descended from Madog, but another
traces him back to Yerwarth.

The significance of these genealogical records depends upon
whether or not Sir John Wynn had anything to do with the
compilation of the *Notes* : if he had not, then the showing that
most of the ' pryme men within the country of Carnarvon '
were descended from Helig, may have been a counterblast to
the *History* in which Wynn traced the Gwydir family back to
' Gruffith ap Kynnan, Prince of Wales.' If, on the other hand,
Wynn did have a hand in the matter, the prominence given to
John, Bishop of Lincoln, may be attributed to the fact that
within the limits of the time during which the manuscript must
have been prepared, Wynn's son Owen was hoping to marry
the Bishop's niece. Sir John had been at pains to secure the
support of the Bishop, who had expressed surprise that Wynn
had done so little for his son [181a]. In any case (apart from the
Bonedd y Saint) none of the 'authorities' upon which the *Notes*

were founded carry us farther back than the sixteenth century, and that is a thousand years after the inundation is supposed to have taken place.

III

THE GEOGRAPHICAL IMPLICATIONS OF THE LLYS HELIG LEGEND

THE modern versions of the Llys Helig legend introduce geographical impossibilities and suggest that it was, at least in part, inspired by a desire to account for certain local place names. The story of Seiriol, the priest, whom the legend calls Helig's brother, and who, after the inundation, is supposed to have made a causeway from Penmaen-mawr to his chapel on Priestholm.

(a) ' Traeth Ell' and the ' Lavan Sands'

HAVING found that the *Notes to bee observed* are not to be commended for their reliability in respect of Helig's ancestry, we must now examine the story of the catastrophe which overtook him. Even without close study it is easy to see that it includes several features that challenge attention; consider, for example, the geographical conditions which are postulated as obtaining when the inundation occurred. The coastline is placed much farther north than its present situation —farther north even than a line connecting Great Orme with Penmon in Anglesey, and there is an allusion to a river (Ell), which divided Caernarvon from Anglesey and Anglesey from Flintshire. This river, as we have seen, becomes Dee in one copy of the *Notes to bee observed*, whilst a mid-nineteenth century Guide to Llandudno makes it Gell. [65].

The Ell is stated to have flowed between Penmon and Priestholm, thus, according to the author, making the latter to be part of Flintshire. This is a statement to which those who take the story of Helig at its face value attach great importance, because, they say, the remoteness of this outpost of Flintshire is proof that a great inundation *must* have taken place, resulting in the loss of a vast tract of land.

In his 1864 paper [63], C. R. Hall gave a sketch-map comparing the supposed pre-Helig geography with present day conditions, and on a first glance (Fig. 1) it seems reasonable enough; but if we examine the map more carefully we are led to ask whether it is likely that any subdivision of North Wales

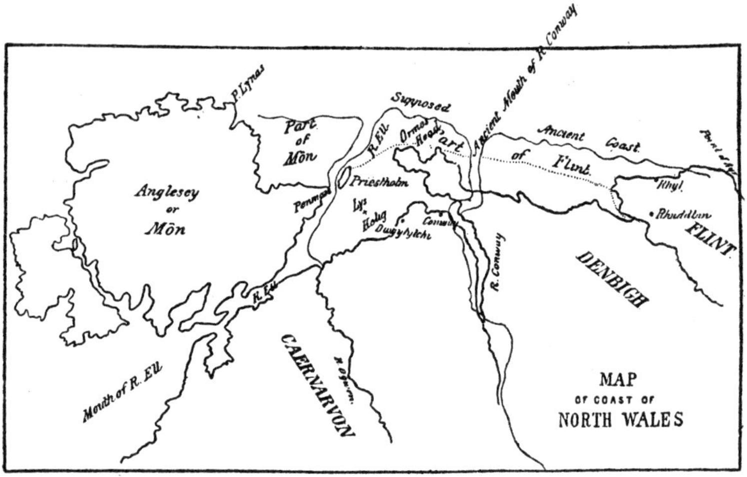

Fig. 1.   Map purporting to illustrate the ancient coast
of North Wales

Prepared by C. R. Hall [63] in 1864 as a reconstruction of the region in the
time of Helig ap Glannawg.

would make Flintshire an enormous belt of country stretching
from near Chester to Anglesey ; had there been such land when
the boundaries of shires or counties were determined it would
surely have been shared between Flintshire, Denbighshire, and
Caernarvonshire !

It is true that there *was* once land in the region concerned—
that the coast-line *did* once lie farther to the north than at
present—but those conditions obtained at a period much more
remote than the earliest during which Helig is supposed to have
lived and long before there was a territorial subdivision known
as Flintshire ; that shire was established (when the other shires
in North Wales were either established or confirmed) by the
Statute of Wales at Rhuddlan in 1284, several centuries after
Helig is supposed to have lost his palace.   When Domesday
Book was compiled the present Flintshire and a large part of
Denbighshire were parts of the great ' county ' of Cheshire.[165]

The tradition, often cited during discussions of the Llys Helig
problem, that Priestholm, now popularly known as Puffin
Island, was formerly regarded as part of Flintshire, does not, as
wishful thinking might suggest, point to a time when Flintshire

extended all the way from the Point of Ayr to Priestholm and so support the story in the *Notes* ; it is much more likely to have had its origin in that story. It is not an uncommon occurrence for there to be parts of a county isolated from the main territory, but not so far removed as Flintshire is from Anglesey.

The River Ell itself also introduces what at first sight appears to be a serious difficulty. Those who have tried to explain it [4b, 63] have usually regarded it as a continuation of the River Ogwen which enters the sea near Bangor and it figures as such in the maps by Hall and Ashton; but there never was any river Ell, or a Traeth Ell named after it ; there is, however, a common noun *traethell* meaning a strand or sand bank. Dafydd ap Gwilym used the word in the 14th century ; in a poem in which he sought safe passage across the Dyfi (Dovey) Estuary he described the waves as the mantle of the opposite shore (Mantell wyt i'r draethell draw) [5], whilst on Lewis Morris's Chart of ' Aberdovey Bay, Bar, and Harbour,' the sand-bank opposite the mouth of the Dyfi is named Y Draethell Goch. But the writer of the *Notes*, or someone from whom he copied, seems to have regarded Ell as a separate word and so got a name for the river necessary for his interpretation of the separation of Arfon from Anglesey and Penmon from Priestholm.

A probable reason for the suggestion that the mouth of the river lay between Penmon and Priestholm is that whereas the waters of Conway Bay are shallow the channel separating Priestholm from Anglesey is deep, and, as Thomas Pennant observed, ' is the common passage for ships to and from the road at Beaumaris.' [131a]

The acceptance of the stones called Llys Helig as the site of a human dwelling involves, as will be shown later, a subsidence to the extent of at least forty feet ; but if the land stood forty feet higher than it does now, the Menai Straits would not exist as a continuous channel. Soundings show that very little of the Straits carry water more than thirty feet in depth even at high tide, whilst a quarter of a mile from the central pier of the Tubular Bridge the rocky floor of the Cribiniau Channel, scoured free from sand and mud, is covered by less than ten feet of water at low spring tides.

The geological evidence shows that the development of the Menai Straits had been completed long before, not some centuries after, the coming of the Romans, and there is documentary evidence that Anglesey was already an island, separated from the mainland by a water-channel by no means easy to cross, when Suetonius, and after him Agricola, were engaged in the conquest of the island in the latter half of the first century A.D. [132]. In these circumstances we cannot admit a subsidence of anything like forty feet during or since the 6th century A.D. ; neither can we accept, as history or as geography, the part of the *Notes to bee observed* that is now under discussion.

The writer of the *Notes* urged in support of his story that those who survived the inundation and escaped to the hills ' made a great outcry, bewaylinge there misfortune and callynge unto God for mercy, the point of which hill to this day is called Trwyn (r) Wylfa, that is to say the point of the doleful hill or the mowrnynge hill.' Unfortunately, however, *Wylfa* does not mean wailing, and it would seem that the author had allowed his ingenuity to outrun his knowledge. *Trwyn yr Wylfa* means the point (or promontory) of the look-out, for Wylfa is a mutated form of *gwylfa*, derived from *gwylio*, to watch, and has nothing to do with *wylo*, to weep, or *wylofain*, to lament.

It was also stated that Traeth yr Lavan, the name given to the great stretch of sand which was supposedly one of the results of the inundation, was ' as much as to say *Traeth aflawen*, that is an unpleasant wharfe, because, ytt is . . . a fearefull and dismale objecte unto the eyes of thinhabitants, bryngynge them dayly in mynde how unhappy they weare to loose so fayre soe fruytfull and soe feartill a countrey.' *Aflawen* does indeed mean dismal or cheerless, but it is an adjective that might well be applied to the Lavan Sands in certain weather conditions without implying anything as to their origin.

Some writers have seen in Lavan a corruption of *oerlefain* meaning lamentation, whilst John Leland, the antiquary, who journeyed in the time of Henry VIII, nearly a century before the compilation of the *Notes*, referred to the sands as *Traeth ar Llevain* [156]—llefain meaning a cry or to cry, with dolefain meaning to cry or to shout. In his *Wanderings and excursions in*

North Wales (1836) Thomas Roscoe records that, ' since the [Lavan] sands shift continually they are not to be traversed without considerable danger. When the thick fogs of autumn or winter lie upon the ground the great bell of the village [i.e., Aber] presented for the purpose by Lord Bulkeley, is constantly rung, as a signal to direct the footsteps of persons landing from Beaumaris.' Before the bell was available it may well have been necessary to shout or cry out loudly.

It has also been suggested that the name originated in Llafan, which, signifying the edible sea weed used in making laver-bread, has come to mean sea shore or strand. This seems to be a quite plausible explanation, but as the meaning is not of importance in our present inquiry, the problem of its origin can be left for etymologists to solve.

The compiler of the *Notes* was no more fortunate in another attempt to explain the meaning of a place name when he suggested that ' *Traeth Mawr* hath his denomination from the ryver Mawr, which dischargeth ytt sealf through that washe into the mayne sea.' We have here a misconception similar to that noted in the case of Traeth Ell, for *Mawr* is an adjective (great) qualifying the noun *Traeth* (strand or spread of sand), and not the name of a river ; Wynn, at least, should have known Traeth Mawr well enough to have realized that it was the estuary of the River Glaslyn which enters the sea near Portmadoc. Part of the Traeth lay within his own domain, and in 1625, just about the time when the *Notes* were written he wrote to Sir Hugh Myddleton about a scheme for making an embankment to reclaim part of the estuary. A copy of the letter and Myddleton's reply thereto were printed in the 1878 edition of the *History of the Gwydir Family*. Leland, writing nearly a century earlier than Wynn, knew that ' Glesse Llinne Watar rennith at low water thorough the Traith Maur Warth, and deividith . . . Cairarvonshir from Merionithshire.' [156a]. Warth or Warthe also means a stretch of sand. In a letter from Sir Richard Bulkeley to Lord Treasurer Burghley, dated Beaumaris, 1590, there is a reference to ' Red Warthe in the County of Englesey.' It is now Red Wharf Bay.

Whoever was responsible for its incorporation into the *Notes*, there can be little doubt but that the mistaken derivation of Traeth Mawr was taken from Price's *Description of Cambria*, with which, as we have seen, the author was familiar. When dealing with the rivers of Wales, Price wrote : ' There are many other fair rivers of which some run to the sea, as Mawr at Traeth Mawr . . .' He seems to have arrived at this association by adding to a mistake previously made by Giraldus Cambrensis, who was born at Manorbier in Pembrokeshire in 1146, and in 1188 accompanied Baldwin, Archbishop of Canterbury, in a preaching crusade in Wales.

In his *Description of Wales*, Giraldus had a chapter entitled ' Of the two mountains from which the noble rivers which devide Wales spring,' and wrote, ' from the same mountains also the large river Maw, forming by its course the greater and smaller tracts of sands called the Traeth Mawr and the Traeth Bachan.' [46f]

A passage in his *Itinerary* (*the Itinerarium Cambriae*, for which he gathered the materials during his tour), shows that Giraldus had rather hazy recollections concerning the position of the river Maw, by which he meant what we now call the Mawddach which discharges into the Barmouth estuary, for he referred to the River ' Dissenith ' (i.e., Dysynni, which flows from Llyn Mwyngil at Tal-y-llyn) as lying between the River Maw and Traeth Mawr [46d]. In other words, he distinguished in this passage between Traeth Mawr and the River Maw, but made the Dysynni flow north of the latter, instead of, as it actually does, south of it.

It is also more than likely that it was a misinterpretation of place-names that made the author of the *Notes* describe Helig as Earl of Hereford and owner of a palace at Pwllheli. As to the former, Giraldus described Wales as extending from St. Davids to Ryd-helic, i.e., Rhyd Helig—or the Willow Ford—presumably what we now know as Rhyd Helyg-ar-Ŵy, a ford between Glasbury and Hay where the Wye forms the boundary between Radnor and Brecknock. Since there can be little doubt that the reference is to willows, it is difficult to see why the author of the *Notes* made Helig to be Earl of Hereford unless it was because he thought the *helic* in ' Rydhelic ' to be a personal

name, considered the locality to have been in Herefordshire'
and saw in the name an opportunity for the further aggrand-
izement of Helig with consequent increase in the prestige of the
' pryme men ' of Caernarvonshire. That Rhyd Helyg-ar-Ŵy is
actually on the Radnor/Brecknock border does not effect the
issue, for the Herefordshire of the Domesday Survey extended
farther west than the present county boundary. In any case,
the attribution illustrates the author's disregard for historical
accuracy, since the earldom of Hereford was not created until
several centuries after the time most frequently indicated as the
period during which Helig flourished.

Similarly, the *Notes* refer to *Pwllhelig*, instead of Pwllheli, as
though the name indicated an association with Helig instead of
being derived from *heli*, meaning brine.

Before leaving this part of the story we may note that the
special reference to Trwyn yr Wylfa as being in the lands of Sir
John Bodvel supports the view that Wynn had something to do
with the compilation of the *Notes*, for Bodvel was his son-in-law.

(b) *The Story of the Holy Priest, Seiriol, and his pavement*

If disregard for the realities of geography, past and present,
justify doubts concerning the supposed historical details in the
story of Helig, those doubts are not diminished by the inconsistencies in the continuation of the story, which relates to
Seiriol (Seirioel or Seirial in many early references to him) and
is as follows :

' Seirial, brother to Helig ap Glannog, was . . . head of the
religious house in Priestholme in Flyntshire, which house
was called Priestholme from Seirial . . . and in Welshe
sythense the inundacõn is called Ynys Seirial. This Seirial
hadd allso an hermitage att Penmen Mawr, and there hadd
a chappell where hee did bestowe much of his tyme in
prayers . . . From Priestholme to Penmen Mawr did Seirial
cause a pavement to bee made, wheruppon hee might walke
drye from his church att Priestholme to his chappell att
Penmen Mawre, the vale beynge very lowe ground and
wette, which pavement may att this day be discerned from

Penmen Mawr to Priestholme when the sea is cleare, yf a man liste to goe in a bote to see ytt.

' Sythence this greate and lamentable innundacōn the waye and passage beynge stopped in this straight in regarde the sea was come in, and did beate uppon the rockes att Penmen Mawre, this holy man Seirial, like a good heremite, did cause a way to bee beaten and cutte through the mayne rocke, which is the onley passage that is to passe that straight. This way leadeth from Dwygyfylchi to Llanvair Vechan, and is the kinges highway from Coneway to Bewmares, Bangor, and Carnarvon, and the onely passage that the kynges poste hath to ryde to and from Ireland.

' This rocke is a myle and a haulf in hight and very pendicular, especially beneath this way : the way begyninge att the sea shore within the parishe of Dwygyfylchi is cutt through the syde of a rocke still ascendynge untill you come to a cricke uppon the rocke called Clippyn Seiriall, and thence is cutt directly forward through the syde of a steepe hard rocke neither descendying nor ascendynge untill you come to Seirialls Chappell, beygne aboute a quarter of a myle from Clippyn Seiriall, and all that way is 200 yardes above the sea, over which yf either man or beaste should fall, both sea and rocke, rocke and sea, would strive and contend whether or both shoulde doe hym the greatest mischief.'

This account of the activities of Seiriol seems to have had its origin in a desire to explain the existence of the old road around the face of Penmaen-mawr, and it illustrates very well the inconsistencies so common in stories of its kind. It also illustrates the awe which the road inspired—an awe that continued into much more recent periods and is well indicated in many old engravings like that reproduced in Pl. 2B.

Apart from the fact that the cutting of a ledge in the extremely hard rock of Penmaen-mawr would have been an unnecessarily extravagant way of facilitating the walk from the mainland to Priestholm, as a glance at the map will show, the statement that the pavement from Penmaen-mawr to Penmon which preceded it was constructed because the ground was very low and wet does not accord with the picture of Helig's land

Pl. 3A. Joints in limestone on a foreshore   *Photo : F. F. Miskin*

The surface of a bed of limestone near Penarth, Glamorgan, illustrating the pavement-like appearance due to the joints which intersect the rock. Such surfaces, covered by shallow water and seen from boats, have been interpreted as paved causeways of human construction.

Pl. 3B. Cliffs of boulder clay near Aberystwyth   *Photo: J. Challinor*

illustrating the poor resistance of glacial deposits to erosion.

Pl. 4A.   Llys Helig on a falling tide   *Photo : F.J.N.*

The south-western corner of Llys Helig showing three of the lines and two of the angles of the supposed palace walls.

Pl. 4B.   Llys Helig on a falling tide   *Photo : F.J.N.*

A nearer view of the principal angle seen above. What appeared from a distance to be a straight narrow band is really a wide indefinite belt.

previously given in the *Notes*—an ' incomparable vale which did abound in fruytfullness and excell all other vales . . . in all fertility and plentifullnes.'

In fact, no one living when Seiriol is supposed to have been interested in this part of North Wales *could* have made a pavement to provide dry passage over wet ground from Penmaenmawr to Priestholm, because at that time almost the whole of the route was covered by the sea.

If we examine this part of the *Notes* more closely, it transpires that we can eliminate it altogether from our discussion of Helig and his lost land, for, in addition to the inconsistencies we have already noted, the references to Seiriol in various early genealogies speak of him as the son of Owain Danwyn, son of Einion Yrth, son of Cunedda Wledig. This would make him belong to the same generation as Maelgwn Gwynedd, who, according to similar sources of information, was contemporary with Caradog Freichfras, said to be Helig's great-grandfather. Even allowing for the inaccuracies in the genealogies, owing to the imagination of compilers and the errors of copyists, it is quite certain that if Seiriol is the name of a man and not of an imaginary character, he was not Helig's brother and is not likely to have been his contemporary.

The writer of the *Notes* tells us that since the inundation Priestholm had been called ' Ynys Seiriol,' but, in the 7th century it was still called by the name which is supposed to have been derived from Helig's father, for the *Annales Cambriae* record that, in A.D. 629, Caswallon was besieged on ' insula Glannauc ' [173a]. It is not until late in the 16th century that we find Seiriol associated with the island in literature, when Humphrey Llwyd wrote of ' The Isle Seirial (in English Priestholme) ' in his *Commentarioli Britannicae Descriptionis Fragmentum*, published in Cologne in 1570 and translated as *The Breviary of Britayne* by Thomas Twyne in 1573.

In his interesting, informative, but somewhat overcredulous book, *The Evolution of a Coastline*, William Ashton gave a map (here reproduced as Fig. 2) purporting to show the coastline and the roads from Caernarvonshire to Anglesey in the 5th century, and he even distinguished between ' roads ' and ' supposed

D

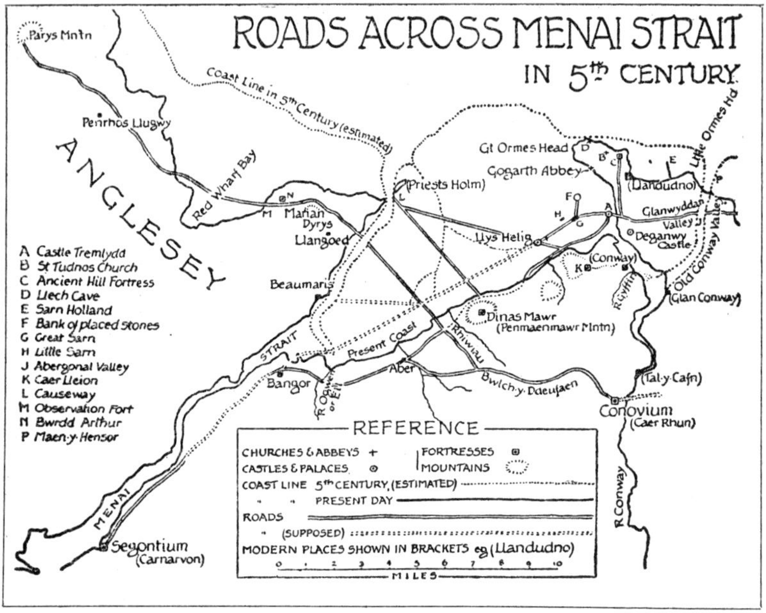

Fig. 2.   Map purporting to illustrate the roads
across the realm of Helig ap Glannawg

Reproduced from *The Evolution of a Coastline* [4a].

roads.' One of the ' roads ' is shown as running from Penmaen-
bach to ' Priest's Holm,' a distance of between six and seven
miles, with another from Penmaen-mawr to the island. There
is, however, not a shred of evidence to justify the claim that the
map represents land and roads that existed in the 5th century.
It is a diagrammatic illustration of the conditions postulated in
stories of people who are supposed to have lived in the area in
the early centuries of our era and has no more foundation in
fact than the stories themselves ; it is an indication of their
acceptance, not proof of their authenticity.

   In fairness to Mr. Ashton it must be recognized that he was
expressing views that were current when he wrote and that, in
some quarters, are still held. He went to great trouble to collect
information about and to make personal observations around
the Welsh coast but—and he was not unique in that respect—

he tended to take at its face value all that others had said or written, and so arrived at conclusions which were unsound because they owed more to wishful thinking than to reliable data.

It will be noticed that the map, Fig. 2, includes Llys Helig, although it purports to relate to the 5th century and the book in which it occurs suggests that the inundation which destroyed Helig's territory probably took place between 520 and 563 A.D., i.e., in the 6th century. The author explained that he thought it probable that the Llys was built by the Romans (on account of its rectilinear plan), and that Helig or one of his ancestors took possession of it after the Romans had withdrawn from Britain.

There is evidence to show that students of local history and topography were familiar with the contents of one or other of the manuscripts containing the story of Helig even before the appearance of Miss Llwyd's printed edition of the *Notes to bee observed*. In his *Cambria Depicta*, an illustrated account of a tour in North Wales published in 1816, Edward Pugh wrote of floating in a boat ' over the palace where tradition says one Helig Voel ap Glanog, a chieftain of the 6th century had great possessions extending far into this bay ; but which were suddenly overwhelmed by the sea. It is said that at a very low ebb, ruined houses are seen, and a causeway pointing from Priestholme Island to Penmaenmawr.'

Pugh claimed to have seen the causeway, which, he said, was two or three fathoms beneath the surface of the water and about nine feet wide : it was made of ' large massy stones cut into forms, of a light warm grey colour, in all respects like those of the adjacent isle.'

We cannot tell exactly what he saw, but the fact that it pointed from Priestholm would suggest that it was a submerged reef of Carboniferous Limestone, the rock of which the island consists. The regularly disposed bedding planes and joints which intersect the limestone might well have conveyed the impression of a pavement made up of large grey stones ' cut into forms.' Such pavement-like surfaces are often to be seen on foreshores where well-jointed rocks are exposed (Pl. 3A).

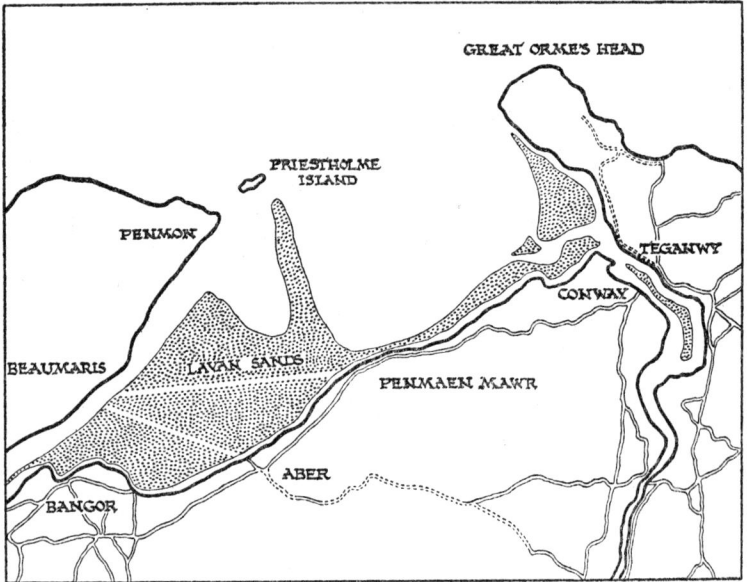

Fig. 3. The Lavan Sands in 1795
Simplified copy of part of the map of North Wales by John Evans of
Llanymynech. 1795.

Although, as we have seen, there can at no time have been
an artificial causeway or pavement extending from Priestholm
to Penmaen-mawr, Pugh regarded what he saw as proof that
the story of Helig was history, for, he added, ' From the certainty of the existence of this causeway, we may venture to give
credit to the existence of the remains of Helig's houses. Helig
after the awful visitation just related embraced a religious life,
and his twelve children followed his example.' Thus is tradition,
improved upon, made to masquerade as history.

The map of Wales published by John Evans of Llanymynech
in 1795 suggests a much more likely origin for the belief in the
existence of a submerged causeway than the ' massy stones '
seen by Pugh. On a modern map or sea-chart there is shown,
between Anglesey and the mainland, a roughly pear-shaped
shoal called Dutchman Bank, separated from the main Lavan
Sands by an open channel called Penmaen Swatch. The

pattern and limits of such shoals or sand-banks are not constant, and on Evans' map (see Fig. 3) a long narrow tongue, continuous with the Lavan Sands, projects from the direction of Llanfairfechan towards and almost as far as Priestholm. The general character of the map suggests that the delineation of the sand-banks, like that of the land features, was based upon observation or survey, and a person familiar with the story about a submerged causeway could not be blamed if he saw support for it in a sand-bank which at low spring tides had the shape and trend of the one which Evans depicted.

IV
LLYS HELIG : DOCUMENTARY EVIDENCE

THERE is no documentary record of an inundation in the Dark Ages that might have inspired the legend of Llys Helig. Early maps do not afford evidence of such an inundation hereabouts. Loss of land which has taken place during historical times is due to slow erosion, not sudden subsidence. The earliest allusions to Helig's lost lands either fail to locate them or else associate them with Cardigan Bay, suggesting that, as far as Conway Bay is concerned, the legend is an importation.

(a) *The search for historical and documentary evidence*

THE conclusion that they have neither historical nor documentary background, reached after our examination of what the *Notes* have to say about Seiriol, is confirmed when we try to discover the origin of the story, as now told, of Helig and his lost lands.

The catastrophe is not mentioned by any contemporary writer or in any early Chronicle that relates to the period in question. This, of course, is not surprising, for we cannot expect to find a record of an incident that never occurred ; the only reason for pursuing the inquiry in this direction is in order to discover whether or not there is any account of an inundation on a smaller scale that might have affected the region in which Llys Helig is situated, and so might have inspired either the legend or its association with this region.

No reference is made to such an event in *Brut y Tywysogion*, but it does not record happenings prior to A.D. 681, and the omission does no more than confirm the view that if Helig really lived at all it was in an earlier period. It will be remembered that in spite of the vagueness which exists concerning the century in which he lost his lands, the 6th is the one most frequently mentioned.

There is no record of the catastrophe in the *Annales Cambriae*, although they begin with an entry dated A.D. 453 and include references to natural phenomena such as an eclipse of the sun in 624, an earthquake in the Isle of Man in 684, and a hot summer in 721.

These *Annales*, in their present form, were almost certainly first written in the 10th century [91b], and although believed to have originated in South Wales they might be expected to have included a reference to so great a catastrophe as that which is supposed to have overtaken Helig ; their silence on the subject may be taken as significant for the whole period (from the 4th to the 9th centuries) that includes the various dates that have been assigned to Helig.

There are no relevant allusions in the *Anglo-Saxon Chronicle*, the records in which begin at the commencement of the Christian era, or in the Chronicles of *Florence of Worcester*, which begin with A.D. 450, but this is not necessarily significant because in whatever they had to say about Britain, these, and many similar works that have been examined although not enumerated here, seldom mentioned anything of importance about Wales : most of them were mainly concerned with affairs in England.

Gildas, whose works date from approximately A.D. 540-560, just about the time most in favour as the period of Helig's loss, makes no mention of an inundation. He was not an historian but introduced historical matter by way of illustrating his message, which, like the prophet Jeremiah's, was a warning that Divine retribution would inevitably follow persistent sin [177].

In the preface to his *Ruin of Britain*, Gildas gave instances from Biblical history of calamities that had overtaken the wicked, and in the book itself he severely criticised Maelgwn and exclaimed, ' why dost thou obtusely wallow in such an old black pool of crime.' He also reminded Maelgwn of God's warning, made through Jeremiah, that He would destroy the nation that did not repent.

In these circumstances it is difficult to believe that, had a catastrophe overwhelmed a region with which Maelgwn was associated, just before or about the time Gildas was writing, he would not have referred to it, and it seems reasonable to interpret his silence as an indication that no extensive flooding affected the North Wales coast during the middle part of the 6th century, and that Helig was not contemporary with Maelgwn. This is in accordance with the chronology of some of the genealogies which suggest that Helig came later than Maelgwn, but, as already indicated, every century that we come nearer to modern times increases the difficulty of accepting the story of a great inundation.

The History of the Britons (*Historia Britonum*) written (or rather transcribed from earlier manuscripts) before A.D. 820 by the Welshman Nyniaw, better known in literature as Nennius [169], is silent upon the subject of Helig, and Geoffrey of Monmouth also gives us no help although he drew upon other sources of information in addition to the *History* compiled by Nennius. He tells us about Cunedda Wledig and Maelgwn Gwynedd, but had nothing to say about Helig and Seiriol [57].

Another early chronicle in which we might expect to find a reference to a catastrophe of the magnitude of that we are now considering is the work known as the *Flowers of History*, by Roger of Wendover who was associated with the Abbey of St. Albans and died there in 1237. His work purported to be a history of the world from its creation until the time of his death and it was used by Matthew Paris in the compilation of his *Chronica majora*.

The greater part of Roger's work was a ' history ' of Britain : it tells of how the Saxons came in the 5th century, of King Arthur and his exploits, of a severe winter in A.D. 554 when wild animals and birds became unusually tame, and of ' Caretius ' whom the Saxons drove into Wales, which was described as a region ' set with dense forests, environed with deep marshes, and broken with high mountains.'

Roger derived his information from a great number of earlier works, but he made no mention of a man who suffered as a result of the sudden loss of a coastal area in North Wales, nor (it is mentioned now although its significance will not appear until later) of the inundation of an even larger area in what is now Cardigan Bay.

No useful purpose would be served by following this line of inquiry any farther. It is safe to say that there is no documentary evidence for a widespread inundation in Conway Bay during the Dark Ages.

(b) The ' evidence ' of early maps and of coast erosion

The evidence popularly adduced to prove that the sub-merged stones called Llys Helig are the site of an ancient homestead resolves itself into three principal kinds : the evidence of ' ancient documents ', the evidence of old maps, and the evidence of local coast erosion. The first of these has already been discussed and found wanting ; what of the others ?

In the second century A.D. Ptolemy of Alexandria wrote a geographical treatise which was accompanied by a general map of the world and several detailed maps of the better known parts of it. One of the regional maps (entitled Albion) related to Great Britain and Ireland. (Pl. 8A).

The original manuscript has not survived, but there are good grounds for supposing that the earliest known copies, which date from about 1400 A.D., give us a fair picture of the extent and accuracy of the geographical knowledge that was available to the Alexandrian. Accordingly, the maps which appear in manuscript copies and printed editions of his work have been cited as evidence of coastal changes since the beginning of the present era ; and because they were prepared long before the earliest of the dates associated with Helig, they have been compared with modern maps in order to demonstrate the supposed difference between the coast line of North Wales before and after the inundation which deprived the son of Glannawg of his land. [4d] (Fig 4).

Such comparisons are, however, unwarranted, for no Ptolemy map represents the details of any part of the British coastline with sufficient accuracy. They were built up on determinations (by the somewhat rough and ready astronomical methods then available) of the latitudes of a limited number of places, supplemented by travellers' notes concerning the mutual relationships of other places in respect of bearing and distance.

A map of the North Wales coast drawn according to Ptolemy's data would, on the basis of some of the early copies of his work, be a line connecting the estuary of the Dee with Braich-y-pwll at the extremity of the Lleyn Peninsula, or on the basis of other copies (for owing to the carelessness or incompetence of copyists the manuscripts vary) it would include,

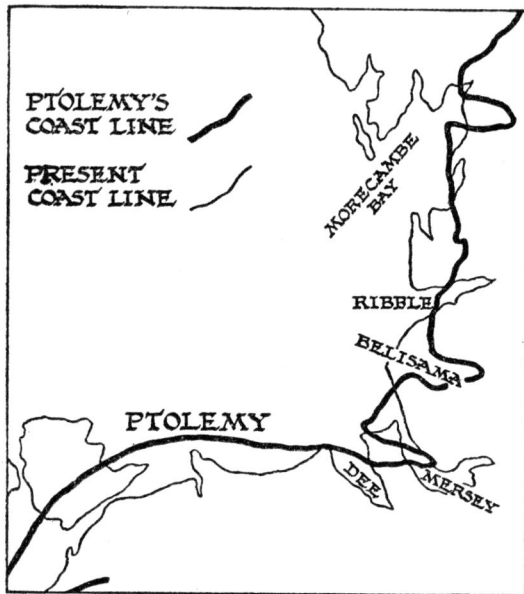

Fig. 4.   Supposed changes in the coast of North Wales

Sketch map purporting to indicate changes in the North Wales coast since the
time of Ptolemy, about 150 A.D. ; from *The Evolution of a Coastline* [4d].

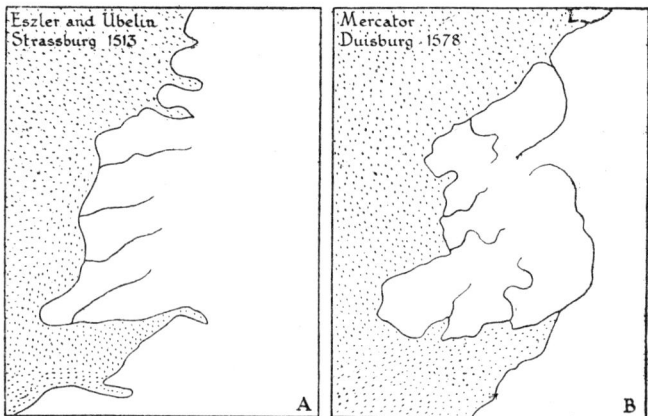

Fig. 5.   Wales on some of the printed editions of
Ptolemy's Maps

Maps compiled on the basis of information regarding the latitude and longitude
of a few places. The coastline was largely conjectural and varied with the
knowledge available at the time of publication.

between those two points, an indication of an estuary, probably that of the Conway (Fig. 10). The coastal details that are to be seen in many of the printed editions of the Ptolemy maps (Fig. 5) were introduced by later map-makers who had access to more and better information than was available to Ptolemy himself. His maps, therefore, whether in manuscript or printed, have no part to play in inquiries like that with which we are now engaged, unless there are good reasons for supposing that they give significant information, which in the case of the coast now under discussion they do not.

Indeed, if we were to accept the Ptolemy maps as criteria, we must consider the whole of Scotland to have swung round through an angle of 90 degrees since A.D. 150, for on the map of 'Albion,' the northern part (which, in outline, is clearly recognisable as Scotland) extends away to the east instead of to the north. We cannot here discuss the reason for this curious mistake, but realising that it exists, we shall appreciate the inadvisability of quoting Ptolemy in a matter affecting a seventy mile stretch of the Welsh coast for which he could indicate the estimated position of not more than three points.

That modern maps and the early printed maps of Wales (e.g., those by Humphrey Llwyd [117], Christopher Saxton, John Speed, and Herman Moll) differ in their delineation of the coastline is also of no significance in a matter such as that with which we are now dealing. Notwithstanding their pretensions to originality, those who published maps of England and Wales towards the end of the 16th century and throughout the 17th, almost without exception copied the coastlines and most of the other details from the maps made by Christopher Saxton in the fifteen-seventies ; but his maps were on too small a scale and were not sufficiently accurate to be used as evidence in a discussion involving a comparatively small encroachment of the sea. This is not to say that he was incompetent or that his maps are not deserving of high commendation ; it is because, judged by modern standards, the surveying methods and instruments available to him were somewhat crude. [116].

That Lewis Morris indicated some submerged rocks on one of the charts of the North Wales coast which he prepared at the request of the Admiralty in the years immediately following 1737, and named them *Llys Elis ap Clynnog* (Pl. 1B), only proves that he was aware of the story associating the rocks with Helig ; it does not prove that they were the site of his palace. In the text which accompanied the charts, Morris referred to ' Gwydd-no Goronhir ' and the submergence of ' Cantre Gwaelod ' in Cardigan Bay, but not to any inundation associated with his ' Llys Elis.' In his *Celtic Remains*, completed in 1757, he gave the hame as ' *Llys Elis ap Glanmor*, overwhelmed by the sea, as tradition has it, and buildings are pretended to have been seen under water.' [162].

The Glanmor was evidently a mistake, but after the appearance of Lewis's chart the ' Llys ' became a standard map-feature, e.g., *Llys Elis ap Clynnog* on the map of North Wales in the 1760 edition of the *Large English Atlas* by Bowen and Kitchin and *Llys Helig* on the earliest editions of the one-inch Ordnance Survey maps. The Lewis Morris charts were reproduced in 1801 by his son William, in *Plans of the Principal Harbours, Bays, and Roads in St. George's and the Britsol Channels, from Surveys made . . . by Lewis Morris, New Edition by William Morris, Shrewsbury, 1801*, and in the text relating to Conway there is a recommandation that a buoy should be placed on ' that patch of foul ground, called Llys Ellis ap Clynog.' The influence of this chart is seen in the *Llys Elisap Clynnog*, which, to this day, appears on Admiralty Charts.

An interesting variation in the site of Llys Helig is, as we have already seen, to be found in the *Map of Wales according to the Antient Divisions*, by William Owen, engraved in 1788 for Warrington's *History of Wales* and of which the relevant part is here reproduced as Pl. 1A. The authority for this location would seem to have been William Williams whose manuscript *History of Beaumaris* (1669) is mentioned on page 85 ; this tells of a flood from the mountains (not, be it noted, from the sea) that affected a great tract of ground about the beginning of the 6th century, and describes the inundated area as being triangular, with its apex opposite ' Llanvaes Friary.' ' At the utmost angular point,' the author continued, ' some stones are discoverable in the sands, which, according to tradition, was the residence of the Lord of the district named Helig Foel ap Glanog, and is still called Llys Helig ap Clynog. This Helig, and his father before him, were reputed to be the Lords and owners not only of this extensive tract but also of the whole Comot of Arllechwedd. It seems he and his family escaped with their lives, and ever after embraced religious lives.'

Since Williams was writing from Beaumaris, opposite which, at the extremity of the Lavan Sands, there was a patch of sand ' Dry at last qr. Ebb ' (*vide* Lewis Morris' Chart of Beaumaris Road), it is not difficult to see why he placed Llys Helig where he did.

Old maps, then, merely show that the name Llys Helig was in use in the eighteenth century—they are not proof that the stones are either the ruins of a Llys, or were in any other way connected with Helig.

Evidence of past and recent coastal erosion is frequently cited by those who accept the legend at its face value, but whilst the fact that, in places, the sea has undoubtedly extended its limits indicates that the site of Llys Helig was once dry land, it does not prove that the stones are the ruins of a palace.

There is a vast difference between the loss of land by *erosion* and the loss of the land by *subsidence*, and recent losses along the coast of North Wales are due to the former cause. During the last century or so, for example, land has been lost in the neighbourhood of Llanfairfechan—not because subsidence has allowed the sea to overflow it, but because there is, locally, a tendency for the action of the tides to cause a westerly migration of the materials of the beach. Similarly, owing to coastwise movement of sand and pebbles along part of the north shore at Llandudno, there is now a beach covered by water at high tide, where fifty years ago there was a turf-covered bank with a gradual slope towards the sea [4q]. There has also been erosion of a more serious nature on the Gogarth side of the Great Orme. This is the kind of coastal loss that, in the region with which we are concerned, is responsible for the numerous stories of old people who could remember living or reaping on sites now covered by the sea, or whose parents had recollections of so doing.

We cannot, however, account for the stones called Llys Helig and regard them as the remains of buildings by postulating long-continued erosion of this kind. Given sufficient time and the right kind of rock (and the easily eroded stony clays and gravels that fringe much of the coastline in this region are undoubtedly of the right kind), the sea can eat its way inland for a considerable distance, but in doing so it destroys the land surface, and the site of any building such as Llys Helig (had it existed) would have been completely obliterated, not simply lowered to the extent of more than thirty feet.

Since Pennant drew attention to a dateless, nameless epitaph in the churchyard wall at Abergele it has been cited as evidence that the sea has gained upon the land in North Wales within historic times [131b]. The stone bears a Welsh inscription to the effect that ' In the churchyard of Michael ' there reposed ' a man who had his dwelling three miles to the north ' ; this would imply an encroachment of the sea to the extent of more than two miles, for the church is less than a mile inland.

The inscription has been largely destroyed by weathering, but a copy accompanied by an English translation was made on a ' granite ' slab, the gift of Mrs. Taylor, wife of Archdeacon Taylor of Liverpool, and placed nearby. They are illustrated in Pl. 6A.

The original stone had no date but its characters indicate that it was executed in the early part of the 17th century. According to local tradition it is a copy of a still older memorial, but it is of no value as ' evidence ' because it is not in its original position. It has been built into a wall and neither the name of the man nor of the place where he lived is given. Had he been drowned in a great flood-catastrophe the fact would surely have been mentioned. In any case the stone has no bearing upon the problem of Llys Helig because the reference to St. Michael indicates a date not earlier than the 8th century, and most likely not earlier than the 12th, since when no great catastrophe involving the loss of a coastal strip two miles wide has taken place.

An interesting sidelight is thrown upon possible changes of level in North Wales by an Ordnance Survey study of the movements that have taken place in the vicinity of London [123]. Borings in the lower part of the Thames Valley show that the land surfaces of late Neolithic times, perhaps dating from about a little before 2000 B.C., are now from sixty to seventy feet below mean sea level, whilst Roman remains have been found on sites five or six feet below Trinity High Water Mark. This would suggest that since man came into the area the region has sunk at least seventy or eighty feet, and that in the last 2,000 years the inhabited land surface of Roman times has sunk about fifteen feet.

Comparison between two series of observations undertaken by the Ordnance Survey (the first between 1840 and 1860 and the second in 1921) shows that subsidence to this extent has not taken place all over the country. It shows that the south of Britain has tilted rather than subsided as a whole, for the amount of subsidence was found to increase with increasing distance in a south-easterly direction from Liverpool, reaching its maximum in the neighbourhood of London and the Thames estuary. During the period of about seventy years between the two surveys there has been a lowering of level in the Thames estuary to the extent of more than a foot, but in North Wales there has actually been a rise of about three inches. If, therefore, in the region of maximum subsidence, the land has sunk only about fifteen feet since Roman times, it is not likely to have sunk more than forty feet during the same period in North Wales, a region of minimum subsidence, and the stones called Llys Helig, cannot, therefore, represent a site that was habitable during the 6th century A.D.

Movements like those just mentioned take place extremely slowly, but Helig's land was supposed to have been devastated with appalling suddenness. It is, of course, true that sudden flooding can occur without sudden subsidence, e.g., at the end of a period of slow submergence if naturally built barriers, or dykes or dams erected to keep the water off the land were suddenly destroyed. We cannot, however, evoke this explan-ation in the present instance because it implies engineering knowledge, skill, and resources in the construction of dams to keep out the sea and of sluice gates or pumps to facilitate the discharge of river water from low-lying land, that cannot have existed amongst the inhabitants of North Wales at so early a period.

(c)   The situation of Helig's territory

The earliest references to Helig date from the 13th century. Some of them occur in copies of the genealogies of the saints (*Bonedd y Saint*), e.g., in the Peniarth MS. 16, where we have *Bodo a Gwynin, a brothen Sant, meibyon Glannauc m. helic voel odyno helic, gwyr heuyt a oresgynnwys moreutir,* i.e., Bodo, Gwynin, and Brothen, saints, sons of Glannauc son of Helig Foel of Tyno Helig, men also whose territory the sea overwhelmed [103].

This wording suggests that the sea overwhelmed the lands of Helig's sons as well as his own, and in this connection it is interesting to note that Brothen is the saint of Llanfrothen in the estuary of the Glaslyn, which until the erection of the embankment across the entrance to Traeth Mawr at the beginning of the nineteenth century was covered by the sea. Geologically speaking it was an estuary that had been drowned as a result of change in the relative levels of land and sea.

A statement similar to that in Peniarth MS. 16 occurs in a copy of such a list made by Gutun Owain in 1455.—*Bodo a Gweinin a Brothen, meibion Glannawc (ap Helic Voel) a Dyno Helic, gwyr a orysgynnod mor eu tir.* [100]. These and similar records, which, it may be noted, speak of ' Glannawc ' as the son (not the father) of Helig, associate the latter with Tyno Helig or Helig's Dale, and describe him as one whose lands the sea overflowed, but a similar record in the Hafod MS. No. 16 stops short at *Helyc voel otyno helyc,* and says nothing about the loss of his lands [99]. None of the references say where Tyno Helig was situated.

Sixteenth century copies of the genealogies are essentially like those just mentioned. One dating from about 1510, compiled by Sir Thomas ap Jeuan ap Deikws, [106] merely mentions the sons of ' Helig ap Glannoc,' whilst another, in the ' Book of Syr Hugh Pennant,' [108] of about 1514, includes the reference to lands overwhelmed by the sea.

Other ' information ' is given in the manuscripts left by Iolo Morganwg. In what he claimed to be a transcription of the

Pl. 5A.   Llys Helig on a low spring tide   *Photo : F.J.N.*

The bank of seaweed-covered stones increases in extent as the tide recedes. The two distant patches are not straight narrow bands, but wide oval patches like that in the foreground.

Pl. 5B.   Llys Helig on a low spring tide   *Photo : F.J.N.*

The central bank of stones depicted in the composite plan, Fig. 6.

Pl. 6A. Tombstones in Abergele Churchyard   *Photo : L. M. North*

Old memorial stone and modern copy cited as indicating recent encroachment
by the sea.

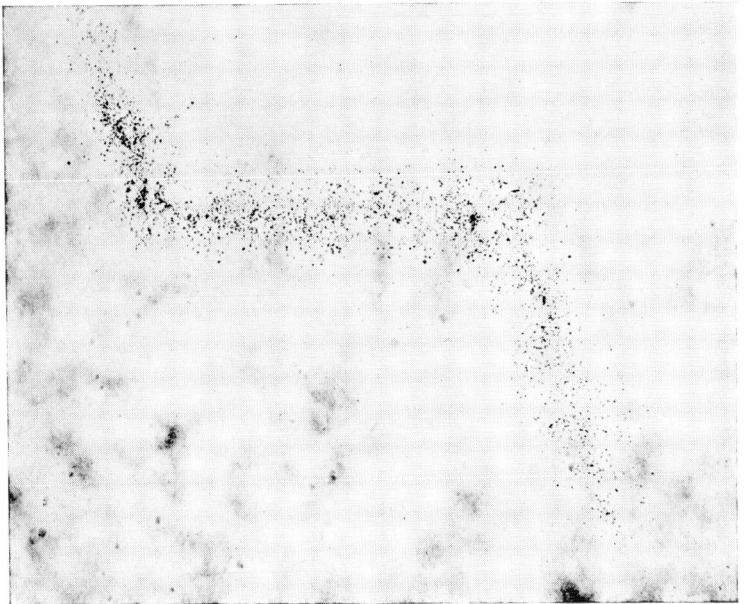

Pl. 6B.   Diagramatic representation of the seaweed
covered stones at Llys Helig

Fine ash sprinkled upon a card, about 21 inches by 26, to make a pattern
resembling that seen at Llys Helig (see also Plate 7).

' Genealogies of the Saints' from a manuscript (previously mentioned on page 35) of Thomas Truman of Pantlliwydd, we are told that Helig, son of Glannog, of Tyno Helig in the north, whose lands the sea overwhelmed, had twelve sons who were contemporary with Rhun the son of Maelgwn ; they became saints in ' Bangor Vawr ' in Maelor and some afterwards went to Bangor Cadvan in Bardsey. [179] We are also told on the same authority that Seiriol, the great grandson of Cunedda Wledig, was placed in charge of a college at Penmon founded by his brother Einion, King of ' Leyn ' [179c] and that he established Bangor Seiriol in Penmon. [179d] Other accounts (15th century and later) attribute the foundation of the religious houses at Penmon to Maelgwn. [51a, 101, 105-6].

From another series of genealogies, purporting to be from the ' Book of Thomas Hopkin, of Coychurch, which was one of the manuscripts of Thomas ap Evan of Tre-bryn, in the same parish,' [179e] Iolo claimed to have copied the names of five sons of Helig, ' the son of Glannog of the plain of Gwyddno, whose territory was overwhelmed by the sea.' Four are described as ' saints in Gwynedd from the Bangor of Bardsey,' while the fifth was ' Gwynwn, a saint of Ceredigion.' It is a pity that Thomas Hopkin's book cannot now be traced (if indeed it ever existed) for it associates Helig with Cardigan Bay, the site of one of the best known of the Welsh inundation stories —that relating to Cantre'r Gwaelod, the Lowland Hundred. This will be discussed at greater length in a later chapter.

The most remarkable of the relevant Iolo ' records ' are those in *A Chronological Account of Times and Remarkable Occurrences* ; this he claimed to have copied from a transcript of ' one of Caradoc of Llancarvan's Chronicles ' made by ' Watkin Giles of Pen-y-Vai.' [179b]. In the Welsh part of the *Iolo Manuscripts* the manuscript is attributed to Watkin Pywel, and since there was a Powel family at Pen-y-fai near Bridgend, it is probable that the reference to Giles was a mistake. In any case, this manuscript, also, is one that does not now seem to be forthcoming.

' In 331,' the chronicle was supposed to say, ' sea and land floods occurred coincidently, when the territory of Helig, the

E

son of Glannog of Tyno Helig, was inundated and irrecover-
ably lost. This territory lay between the estuary of the River
Clwyd in Arvon, and that of the Branck in the north Sea . . .
In 353, marshes in Gwynedd and Ceredigion were lost in
consequence of an astonishing sea flood, through which
many municipal places were destroyed.'

A discussion of the geography of the first of these passages
would be more laborious than profitable, and if we could take
the dates at their face value they would seriously complicate the
chronological aspects of our discussion ; they make Helig lose
his land more than a century before he was born, if, as the
Notes to bee observed claimed, his great-great-grandfather was
Llŷr Mereini—grandson of Cunedda Wledig.

Fortunately, however, we need not, nowadays, spend time in
trying to reconcile a statement made by Iolo with others with
which it does not agree, for as we have already had occasion to
note, whilst he may have been, in some respects, as the editor of
the Rolls edition of the *Brut y Tywysogion* called him, ' a
scrupulously faithful antiquary,' he was also a clever literary
forger [176] and if the passages we have just cited are not some
of his fabrications it is strange that he was so careless of many of
the originals that no one has seen them since.

We shall have occasion to refer to this aspect of Iolo's activity
again, and in the meantime it is sufficient to note that the
passages quoted from his ' chronicles ' include details not to be
found in any of the other early notices about Helig. They
relate to a period (the fourth century) which is earlier than is
covered by other reputed extracts from Caradoc's *Chronicles*—
earlier indeed than any that could have been included in a
chronicle that Caradoc wrote, for his story was to begin where
Geoffrey of Monmouth's ended—i.e., late in the 7th century.
At the end of the copy of Geoffrey's book in *The Red Book of
Hergest*, is the note, ' The kings that were from that time forward
in Wales, I shall commit to Caradog of Llancarvan, my fellow
student, to write about.'

We may note in passing, since we shall have other occasions
to mention it, that *The Red Book of Hergest* is one of the best
known early manuscripts in the Welsh language. It contains a

representative collection of the literature (except Theology and Laws) current in Wales at the close of the 14th century and early in the 15th, and is regarded as one of the oldest and most reliable records of a large part of the works of the Welsh poets from the 12th to the 14th centuries. It is so-called from its having once belonged to the Vaughans of Hergest Court in Herefordshire ; it is now in the possession of Jesus College, Oxford but housed at the Bodleian Library.

If further evidence were needed to show that the dated ' records ' in question, whether invented by Iolo or not, need not be taken seriously, it lies in the fact that, as Sir John E. Lloyd [88] and others have pointed out, there is no evidence to show that, if Caradoc really existed, he acted upon Geoffrey's hint that he should compile a history of the Welsh kings, and more than a little evidence to show that he was not the original author of *Brut y Tywysogion*. We are not therefore, called upon to try and explain away any chronological difficulties introduced by statements like these which Iolo claimed to have copied.

It might, indeed, seem to have been a waste of time and effort to have considered them at all or to have looked for confirmation of the story of Helig in any early document, but— reverting to our comparison between legends and an ivy-covered ruin—whilst we can, if we wish, ignore the adherent vegetation, there comes a time when it is desirable to remove it altogether so that the structure beneath may be as clear to the ordinary observer as it is to those who have trained themselves to interpret it while it was still obscured.

It is not a case of trying to show that there is no literary evidence for an occurrence that we know could not have taken place ; there can, of course, be no such evidence. It was, however, necessary to show that there are no records of an occurrence in historic times, that could have given rise to stories that ultimately grew into the one related in the *Notes to bee observed*.

Disregarding Iolo Morganwg's records as being, to say the least, unreliable, it will be noticed that none of the early references to Helig's land that we have already considered say where it was, but attention has recently been drawn to the

Latin translation of a Welsh Triad, preserved in a manuscript in Exeter Cathedral Library (MS. 3514), which is more explicit [79]. The MS in question includes a list of the six sons of Rhys ap Gruffudd ap Rhys, and it is associated with a Welsh Chronicle, both having been written (in the opinion of the late Robin Flower) about 1280.

The Triad commences ' There are three Kingdoms that were submerged by the sea,' and enumerates them as follows :

The Kingdom of Tewthi Hen, son of Gwynnon, King of Kaerrihog . . . between Mynwy [St. David's] and Ireland. No one escaped from it, neither man nor beast, except Teithi Hen and his horse, and for the rest of his life he was sick with fright.

The second Kingdom was that of Helig son of Glannawg that was between Cardigan and Bardsey Island and as far as Mynwy. And that land was extremely good and fruitful and flat . . . and stretched from Aber[ystwyth] to Lleyn and as far as Aberdyfi.

The sea submerged a third, the Kingdom of Rhedfoe son of Rheged.

We shall have occasion later on to mention submerged lands off the Pembrokeshire coast and another reference to a horse-man who escaped, and also to say something about the man referred to as Tewthi (or Teithi) Hen, but we have no clue concerning the location of the Kingdom of Rhedfoe, unless we can assume a geographical sequence in the three Kingdoms ; in that case the last named should be farther north than Cardigan Bay. The reference to Helig ap Glannog is, however, explicit, and makes his lost land include that to which more recent story-tellers have given the name Cantre'r Gwaelod—the Lowland Hundred : but this, in other early manuscripts, is associated with an entirely different set of personal names.

Thomas Jones of Aberystwyth who published the Exeter MS and discussed some of the implications of the Triad pointed out that although it occurs with the list of the sons of Rhys, it is an interpolation. It appears to have originated as a marginal note in some earlier copy and to have been incorporated into the main text when the Exeter copy was made.

The date of the earlier amended manuscript is not known, but it may well be such that its reference to Helig is the oldest that has yet been brought to light, *and it locates his lands in Cardigan Bay, not in the region with which the legend is now associated.*

The earliest reference that might be taken as associating Helig with the north coast of Caernarvonshire occurs in a 15th century poem [79] on The Court of Gwilym ap Gruffudd of Penrhyn, by Rhys Goch Eryri. The poet refers to an allusion by Taliesin to Gwilym's famous house on the bank of Traeth Helig (*yng nglan Traeth Helig*). Although none of the known poems attributed to Taliesin contains any mention of the house and the reference is neither positive nor detailed like the one in the Triad, it might, emanating from Penrhyn, be accepted as circumstantial evidence. It was left to the writer of 820D to place the scene of the legend indubitably in Conway Bay, either out of his own fertile imagination or because some such idea was current locally in his time.

We find, then, that most of the early statements relating to Helig mention a region called Tyno Helig without saying where it was. One of them—probably the earliest—locates it in Cardigan Bay, whilst by implication, a 15th century poem associates it with the region to which it was assigned by the writer of *The Notes to bee observed* and those who have followed him.

We have also found that there is no documentary record of an inundation in Conway Bay during the Dark Ages that might have given rise to such a legend, and we are forced to the conclusion that the modern story of Llys Helig is an importation —that an allusion to an inundation in another area was adapted to the geography of Conway Bay. Subsequently it was embellished with harrowing details of a terrified servant who rushed to tell Helig (or his harper) that the sea was advancing upon them ; of the servant's escape with the harper, or with Helig and his family (the accounts vary) ; and of Helig and a crowd of his frightened people rushing to Trwyn yr Wylfa, wringing their hands at the sorrowful spectacle they beheld.

In other words, it seems certain that what a few people have concluded—viz., that the legend has no foundation in local fact—is indeed correct, and that what many have accepted as fact—viz., that the remains of Helig's palace can be seen in the sea off Penmaen-mawr—is really fiction. There is no document-ary evidence to show that Llys Helig is the relic of an ancient palace, and since, also, there is no historical record of an inundation at any of the times when Helig was supposed to have lived, we are not called upon to look for his palace in any other part of Conway Bay.

At this point our inquiry bifurcates. We have, on the one hand, to try to discover what the stones called Llys Helig really are—for it is not enough merely to have shown they are not what they are usually claimed to be—and on the other hand we have to try to discover how the simple story in the *Notes to bee observed* grew into the elaborate modern *Legend of Llys Helig*.

The first of these tasks will be comparatively easy since we shall be dealing with natural phenomena, and Nature works in an orderly manner ; the second will be more difficult for it involves the imagination and the credulity of man. The one will be like reading the succession of stories in a palimpsest in which clear records are superimposed upon earlier, half-effaced ones ; the other will be like trying to decipher a series of records that have been fragmented and thoroughly mixed.

V

LLYS HELIG : A GEOLOGICAL EXAMINATION

AN examination of Llys Helig shows that the appearance of
walls is illusory and that the accumulation of stones is of glacial
origin. It consists of pebbles and boulders derived from Boulder
Clay deposited when stone-laden ice melted at the end of the
Ice Age, and may be compared with similar accumulations of
stones on the foreshore at Deganwny and near Penmaen-bach.
The change of level responsible for the submergence of the stones
was completed in prehistoric times.

(a) The site and the reputed walls

THE last few chapters have been somewhat iconoclastic
and our inquiry into the story of Helig can now enter
upon a constructive phase. We have not destroyed an old story,
but, by stripping away the modern decorative details, have
disclosed one that seems to have been imported from another
region. Having done so we find ourselves left with right-angled
lines of stones in the sea off Penmaen-mawr and under an
obligation to explain their likeness to the ruins of walls. If they
do not represent the site of Helig's palace, what, then, are they,
and how came they into their present position ?

The first detailed ' eye witness ' account of Llys Helig dates
from 1864 [63] and was written by Charlton R. Hall of Liverpool. The Rev. R. Parry, who accompanied him, had evidently
seen the ' History of Helig ap Glanawg ' in the *Cambrian
Quarterly Magazine*, because Hall says that Parry showed him an
' old magazine in which had been published a paper which
embodies the local tradition. The paper had been drawn up by
a Welsh Clergyman [and] a lady, a descendant of the clergyman . . . had it published in the Magazine I refer to, I think
about 1830, in order to put the tradition on record.'

Guided by the indication of the spot upon Lewis Morris's
chart (which, being a sea chart was more accurate in this
respect than the previously published land maps) Hall and four
others set out for Llys Helig one afternoon in August, and
eventually saw ' a mass of black seaweed upon the surface of the

water . . . running in regular lines.' He recorded that, by
putting his arm into the water, he could feel stones, which
seemed to show that the seaweed was growing upon a ridge that
had the appearance of being arranged 'just as the stones of a
wall would be after being thrown down by the action of the sea
until those on either side would support the rest.'

' There appears,' he reported, ' to be a centre part free from
stones' where the water was six or seven feet deep ; this he
interpreted as a court-yard or the interior of a large apartment.
He sketched a plan of the walls as he saw them (Fig. 6), and an
account which the Rev. R. Parry contributed to the local
newspaper added the observation that ' where the stones were
under water the seaweed made up for the deficiency and we
found no difficulty in tracing the whole.' He also described the
house as facing south and the garden as facing north, with a
tower in the middle, which was, he said, like all the ancient
Welsh towers, circular in shape. To Hall and those with him
the evidence seemed conclusive, and another step had been
taken in the conversion of legend into history.

The next visit of which we have a published account took
place in 1908, when W. Ashton, author of *The Evolution of a
Coastline* (1920), went with a local boatman at a time when
there was an exceptionally low tide. From his book we learn
that

' Three sides of a large square, with a large rectangular
recess at the south-west side, were seen to be well-defined by
straight and almost continuous lines of wall, for the most part
covered by a tall ribbon-like seaweed . . . These stones did not
vary six inches from the straight line. There were two
specially large stones, standing some 70 yards from the
eastern corner as if they had formed two pillars of a gateway.
A causeway of stones with perpendicular sides connected
these two stones with the eastern corner . . . It is quite impossible for anyone to view these 350 or more yards of strictly
rectangular remains and to entertain the slightest doubt as to
their having been human handiwork.' [4f].

He concluded, ' The fact that the site corresponds with that
indicated in the Wynn manuscript forms strong presumptive

evidence that this is the site of the palace of Helig ap Glanawg.'
This savours of wishful thinking because the Wynn manuscript
does not indicate the position more precisely than that it was
' two miles within the sea, directly over against Trwyn yr
Wylva,' and acceptance of the stones as those which Wynn had
in mind is not proof that they were the remains of Helig's
dwelling !

In the following year the site was again visited, this time by
members of the Llandudno, Colwyn Bay, and District Field
Club. They came to the conclusion ' that human hands had
laid the stones,' although Councillor L. S. Underwood, who was
one of the party, tells me that to him 'the stones did not suggest
actual walls but might have been regarded as the remains of
walls that had collapsed.' He expressed the opinion that ' the
whole of the site appeared to be more artificial than natural.'

In 1913, Horace Lees, familiar with the tradition and with
the findings of the previous expeditions, went to the spot and
found that ' The place consisted of wall-foundations to the
south and west,' with a bank of stones to the north and east,
enclosing a miniature lagoon. He described four straight
stretches of wall meeting at right angles, and stated that the
stones of the walls, although showing no sign of shaping or
squaring, were uniform in size. He came to the conclusion that
the walls were those of a courtyard into which cattle could be
driven in times of necessity, and expressed the opinion that,
' it is the great bank that wants investigation. Here it is that the
palace must have stood with all its buildings.' [86]

Lees gave a plan of what he saw (Fig. 6). It showed the great
bank of stones and the southern and western ' walls ' ; in 1920
Ashton reproduced it with the addition of the walls in the north
and east (which he himself claimed to have seen) and the site
of the inner round tower which Hall had described. This final
sketch has all the appearance of being a properly surveyed and
measured plan and would seem finally to have established the
shape and dimensions of the enclosure, whatever it may have
been, and whenever it was built.

That Ashton saw more than Lees, and that their combined
observations produced a plan very different from that drawn

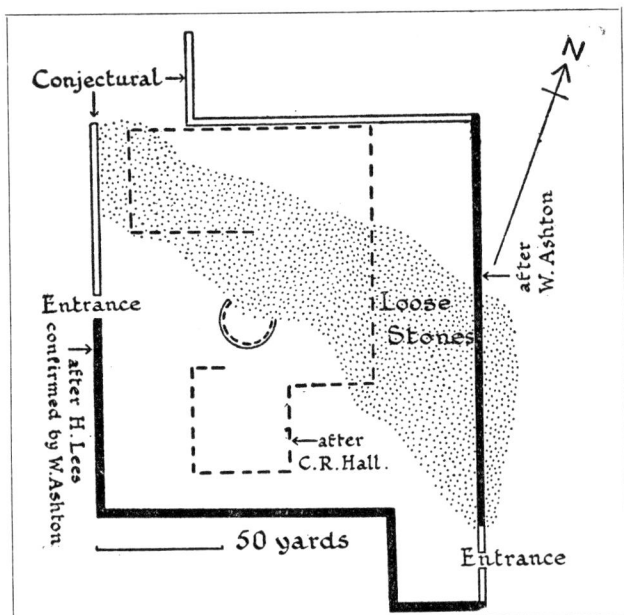

Fig. 6. ' Plans ' of Llys Helig compared

Plans prepared by C. R. Hall [63], W. Ashton [4g], and H. Lees [86] purporting
to depict the walls of Llys Helig.

previously by Hall, might be attributed to the difficulties
attendant upon the observation and measurement of features
more or less completely covered by water and indicated mainly
by the exposed extremities of long ribbons of seaweed ; but, to
the present writer, the only explanation which seems possible
after examining the site during the whole period of its gradual
disclosure and re-concealment by the fall and rise of a tide, is
that the differences are due to the fact that various observers
were attempting to reconstruct something which they expected
to see but which does not and never did exist.   There are,
indeed, ridges of stones, but they are not the remains of walls.

It cannot be asserted that the differences between the records
made by various investigators are due to the progressive
displacement of the stones of rectilinear walls by the action of
the sea, for, if so much change could have been caused in less
than a century it is not reasonable to suppose that any recogniz-

able traces of buildings or walls could have survived for more than a millennium.

It is true that as one approaches the site there is an appearance of straight narrow lines at right angles (Pl. 4A), but at closer quarters, and as the water recedes, exposing more and more of the seaweed (Pl. 4B), the lines resolve themselves into wide indefinite bands (Pl. 5), and, when the tide is at its lowest, into a formless jumble covering several acres. The appearance of straight lines and right angles at one state of the tide is an illusion resulting from the acuteness of the angle of vision consequent upon the low elevation of an observer standing in a rowing boat.

The way in which a sinuous, wide, and ill-defined band can give the impression of being made up of narrow straight lines meeting at right angles is illustrated in Pls. 6 and 7. One of these reproduces a photograph looking vertically downwards on to the surface of a piece of white card on which some fine ashes have been sprinkled to make a pattern that resembles the outline of one of the patches of seaweed at Llys Helig ; the others are from photographs of the same card taken at something approaching the angle of vision of an observer in a rowing boat.

Owing to the smaller size of the objects photographed the angle of vision in Pl. 7 is less acute than that of the observer in a small boat at Llys Helig, and the bands of ash appear to be relatively much wider in proportion to their length than is the case with the bands of the seaweed ; but in spite of this exaggeration there is a distinct suggestion of narrow straight lines meeting at right angles ; they would appear narrower still in a photograph taken from a level more nearly approaching that of the card.

Comparison between Pls. 4 and 7 will, it is submitted, show that there is nothing on the Llys Helig site to justify the drawing of rectilinear plans like those that have been published. The plans, and the impressions recorded by other observers who did not make plans, are based largely upon exposures of seaweed, for at no time are the stones themselves exposed to the extent which the plans or the descriptions imply. My own conclusion, after rowing to and fro across the site, observing the floor where the water was shallow, testing it with a pole where it was deep, and examining scores of such stones as could be lifted above the surface of the water, was that the whole area is covered with irregularly distributed stones, varying in size from huge boulders two or three feet in diameter down to pebbles no larger than walnuts with, here and there, patches of fairly clean coarse sand.

There is no regularity in the distribution of the stones that would support the view that they were walls or were derived from walls, even when allowance is made for the damage that walls are likely to have sustained during an encroachment of the sea and some centuries of exposure to ebbing and flowing tides.

It is true that a few of the stones were roughly rectangular in shape and, seen through the water, looked as if they might have been dressed blocks, the edges of which had been rounded as a result of attrition since they were submerged ; but it was found that such blocks always consisted of rock affected by well-defined bedding planes and joints, so that the shape and comparative uniformity of size are due to natural causes. The majority of the stones were, however, of no particular shape, having been derived from various kinds of rock (igneous and sedimentary) in which the distribution of joints and bedding planes did not favour the development of medium sized rectangular blocks. The edges and corners of all the stones had suffered much abrasion and there was nothing comparable with the angular fragments seen in screes and quarry debris.

It is impossible to avoid the conclusion that the variability in the composition, size, and shape of the stones is an indication that the source of supply included much-worn boulders and pebbles of many kinds of rocks and many different sizes—and this gives a clue to their origin and the means by which they were brought into the place where they are now to be seen.

(b) *The nature and origin of the sea-weed covered stones*

The stones at Llys Helig vary as much in composition as they do in size. There are sedimentary rocks—hard sandy mudstones and coarse grits of types common amongst the Cambrian, Ordovician, and Silurian rocks of Caernarvonshire—and there are several kinds of igneous rocks. Of the latter, the most abundant are rhyolites (lavas) and diabases (dark coloured crystalline rocks), both of types that are well-developed in Caernarvonshire, whilst the remainder are all of kinds that can be seen in the mountains to the south and west. There are no rocks of immediately local origin such as the Carboniferous Limestone which occurs at Great Orme's Head or the igneous rocks that make up Penmaen-mawr Mountain, whilst careful search failed to reveal any of the pinkish granite that some visitors claim to have seen. Some of the boulders do indeed appear to be pinkish in colour but that is due to an incrustation of algae.

There can only be one answer to the question—What can have been the origin of this assemblage of stones, so variable in kind and in size, so located, and rising from the sea floor just sufficiently for the seaweed that has established itself upon them to be exposed when the tide is at its lowest ? To a geologist the answer is obvious, but there are many to whom geology is little more than a name, and on that account we must now refer to what may appear to be an entirely irrelevant matter.

The last of the major episodes in the geological history of our country, and indeed of the northern part of the entire Northern Hemisphere, was characterised by the development of a very cold climate ; lakes and rivers became frozen and snow accumulated to such an extent that little else could have been seen over vast areas of continental size.

At one time, Britain north of the Thames and the Bristol Channel must have resembled the interior of modern Greenland and have appeared as an extensive ice-field, broken here and there by ' islands ' of rock where the tops of the higher mountains rose above the snowy wastes.

The period—the Glacial Period or Ice Age—was not one of continuous and uniform coldness for at times conditions improved and the ice temporarily disappeared from most if not from all of England and Wales ; but even when warmer conditions began to be permanently re-established and the ice finally retreated from the lower ground, the mountainous regions continued to be centres of snow accumulation, with tongues of ice—glaciers—moving slowly from them down the valleys.

During its progress the ice picked up the loose superficial material that constituted the soil and the subsoil, and it also became the repository for rock fragments that fell on to its surface from peaks and crags that remained as temporary or as permanent features of the snowy landscape. Such fragments tended to fall into cracks that developed in the ice as it moved along, and, accumulating in the lowest layers of the glaciers, they were rubbed one against another and against the rocky floor over which the ice moved ; as a result, their angular edges were worn away and they were converted into smooth pebbles that retained in a large measure the general shape of the original fragments, and did not, like typical beach pebbles, become more or less completely rounded or egg-shaped. If the nature of the material permitted, the stones were not only worn smooth but their surfaces acquired a polish ; in addition, many of them were covered with scratches or even deep furrows, made as they were rubbed against other stones embedded in the ice, or against the rocks over which the ice was moving [120].

When the stone-laden ice eventually melted it left behind widely spread deposits, variable in thickness, characterised by the heterogenous nature of their materials, and known to geologists as 'Drift.' Some of the deposits are of a gravelly nature whilst others consist largely of boulders and pebbles embedded in stiff clay : for them the term Boulder Clay is used.

The story of the Ice Age, and of the times when climatic conditions temporarily and locally improved, must be read in the appropriate text books [82, 172]. It is sufficient here to say that one of the centres of ice distribution in Britain was situated in North Wales, and that some of the superficial debris from the Snowdon area and other parts of Caernarvonshire was transported northwards, whilst ice from the Isle of Man, the Lake District, and the south-west of Scotland, also laden with soil and rock fragments, moved southwards across the site of what is now the Irish Sea [155].

Since some rocks are easily recognizable and are limited in distribution it is often possible to determine the place whence the glacially transported boulders were derived. Their present distribution in the boulder clay shows that some of the ice which came from the north rode over Anglesey and the Lleyn Peninsula, whilst some of it made its way into the Vale of Clwyd, or, crossing the low ground eastwards of the Clwydian mountains, penetrated into the heart of England. In the neighbourhood of Penmaen-mawr and Llandudno, however, the northern ice extended only about as far southwards as the line of the present coast ; here it met the ice-sheet which originated in the Welsh mountains, so that both contributed to the transport of non-local rock debris into the region with which we are more particularly concerned.

At the end of the Ice Age the land stood at a higher relative level than at present, and the coastline of North Wales was correspondingly farther out. The tract extending northwards from the present rocky hills was floored largely, if not completely, with conglomerations of stones and clay left behind at the melting of the ice, and the surface was irregular and hummocky owing to the uneven deposition of the material. In course of time (for reasons and with results that we shall have to consider later on) there were changes in the relative levels of land and sea, the net result of which was to cause the sea to encroach upon the land. Deposits of mud and silt (derived in part from the destruction of the hummocks and ridges of boulder clay, and in part from the material brought down by rivers) were laid down to build up a comparatively even floor that formed a wide coastal fringe. This became the basis of a land region upon which vegetation, including large trees, began to establish itself when submergence temporarily gave place to re-emergence.

The land conditions were not permanent. There were times when renewed change of level caused the submergence of the coastal plains, and their accumulations of vegetable debris, which had given rise to beds of peat, were covered with silt and mud ; at other times the sea retreated and exposed the surfaces of the new layers of silt, and land conditions again prevailed. On the whole, however, the movement for a long time after the close of the Glacial Period was such that the sea gained upon the land.

This period of oscillation corresponds broadly with the time that archaeologists include in their Mesolithic, Neolithic, and Bronze Ages. More will be said about these terms when it becomes necessary to consider the periods to which they relate, and it is sufficient here to say that the ages come between the Old Stone Age of cave-dwelling, hunting man, and the Iron Age which, in Britain, preceded and to some extent overlapped the Roman occupation. There is, as we shall see, ample evidence to show that man was well established in various parts of Wales whilst the changes were taking place, and to indicate also that the encroachment of the sea had nearly ceased by the end of Bronze Age times. As the sea gained upon the land the surface of the glacial and other superficial deposits in these coastal fringes suffered considerably from the eroding action of the waves.

The fine-grained constituents of such deposits would, in these circumstances, be washed away more readily than the heavier stones ; these would accumulate on the surface of the boulder clay that still remained, giving rise to heterogenous and unsorted assemblages of boulders and pebbles—exactly like those which occur on the site called Llys Helig. There can, indeed, be no doubt but that the ' Llys ' consists of the debris of denuded hillocks or ridges of glacially transported material resting on a surface that has been submerged.

An excellent illustration of what Llys Helig originally was can be seen just north of Degannwy, where glacial deposits are in process of erosion (Pl. 12A). The low cliff exposes a section of greyish boulder clay—the Drift of North Wales origin—covered by some of the reddish brown Drift brought by the ice that had travelled across the site of the Irish Sea, the whole being covered by blown sand. The older (Welsh) Drift contains many boulders, some of them of considerable size, as well as innumerable smaller pebbles, whilst the newer (Irish Sea) Drift, deposited by ice which had travelled farther from sources of supply, is conspicuously less crowded with stones.

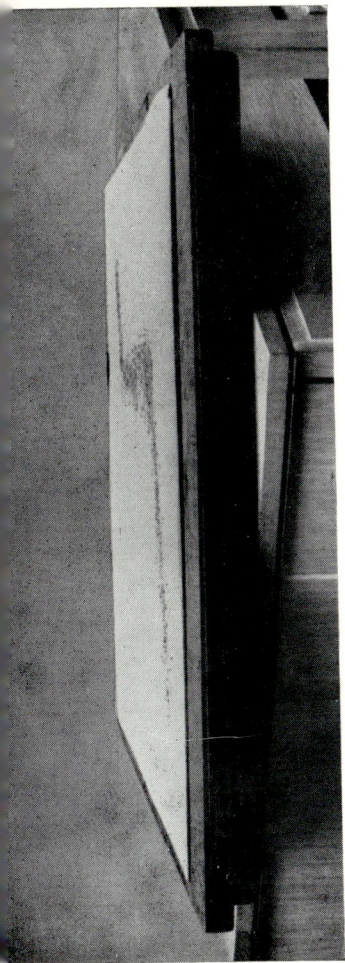

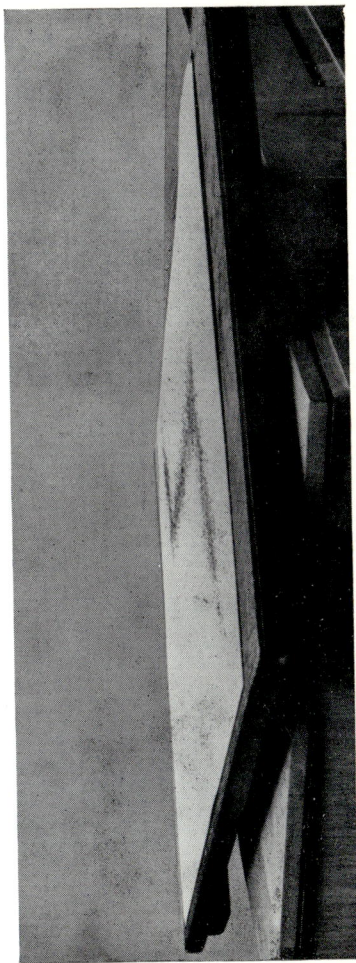

Pl. 7. Explanation of the appearance of straight walls at Llys Helig

Photographs of the card illustrated in Pl. 6 showing that when viewed at a low angle the bands appear to be narrower and straighter than they really are. The angle of vision of an observer in a boat at Llys Helig is even more acute and the bands correspondingly narrower and straighter.

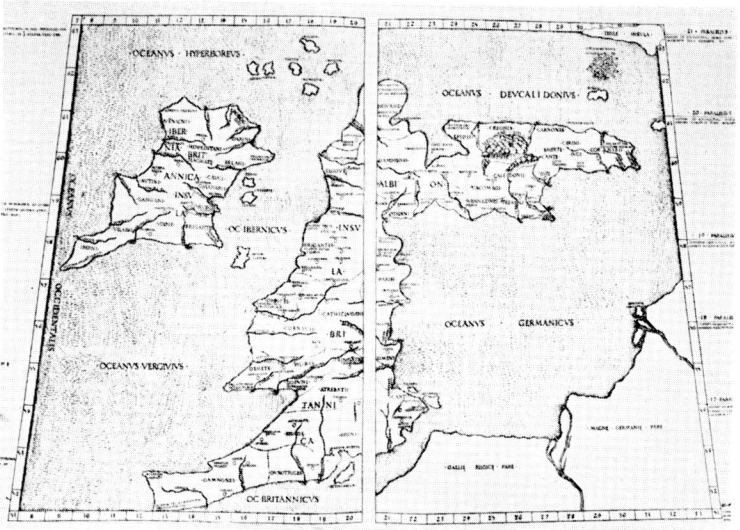

Pl. 8A.   Ptolemy's ' Albion '

The map of Albion from the Rome edition of Ptolemy's *Geography* (1490).

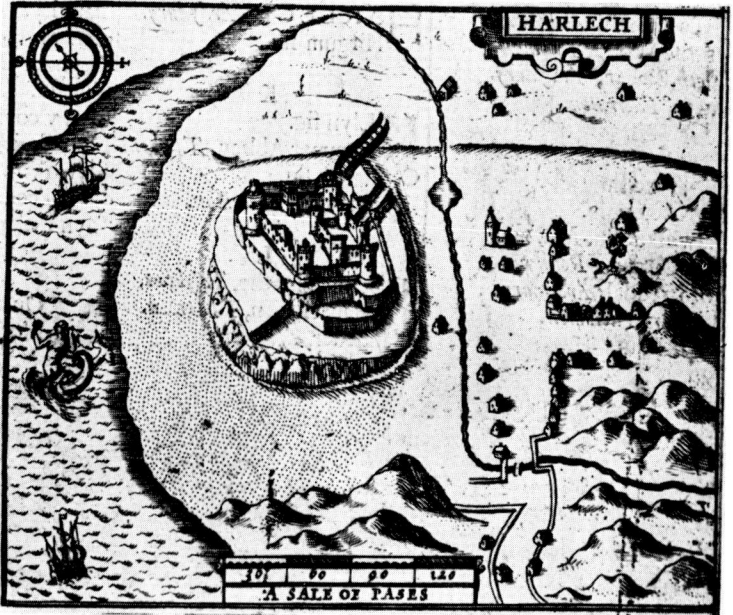

Pl. 8B.   Harlech in 1610

Plan of Harlech from John Speed's map of Merionethshire, 1610.

On the foreshore at Degannwy there is an accumulation of stones representing the pebbles and boulders that were in that part of the mass that has already worn away ; some of the stones are very large like the most conspicuous ones at Llys Helig, but the majority are small, and are scattered about, just as they are on the legendary site, with no tendency to sorting according to size (Pl. 13A). The whole patch of stony foreshore opposite the cliff that has been cut in the hillock of boulder clay is distinctly higher than the beach on either side, and if, in time, the fine-grained components of the remainder of the mass should be removed by the action of the waves, and the land were to sink so that the site became covered to the same extent as Llys Helig, we should have a stony patch rising just sufficiently above the surrounding sea floor to attract attention at low spring tides.

Many of the stones in the Degannwy cliff display the striated surfaces characteristic of rocks known to have been associated with glaciers, but the fact that none such were seen at Llys Helig is not an indication that the material is not of glacial origin, for even if the scratches had survived the attrition to which the stones were subjected as they were isolated from the deposit in which they occurred, the stones are now too encrusted with algae and other marine organisms for such survivals to be easily discovered. Patches of stones similar in nature and origin to those at Degannwy, are to be seen in the Black Rocks near Penmaen-bach, illustrated in Pl. 13B.

Thus ends the first part of our bifurcated inquiry ; briefly its results are as follows : Llys Helig is not the ruin of a human habitation, but an accumulation of stones brought together during the Ice Age and exposed in their present position as a result of erosion and submergence. There has, indeed, been an encroachment of the sea in the area to which the legend relates, but though it took place in comparatively recent geological times it was completed long before any of the periods during which Helig is supposed to have lived.

Looked at in one way this chapter might be regarded as ending our story. It has been shown that the reef called Llys Helig cannot be the remains of the palace of Helig ap Glann-

F

awg and an alternative explanation has been suggested. It has been shown that the legend in its modern form is largely of modern origin and that it is not likely to have originated in the area to which it now relates—but, as the wise son of Sirach said, ' When a man thinketh he hath finished then he is but at the beginning ; and when he ceaseth, then shall he be in perplexity.' (Ecclesiasticus xviii, 7). Indeed, the studies described in these five chapters are more in the nature of a prolegomenon—the real story of the legend has yet to be written.

On the face of it, Nature's operations seem to be directed mainly towards destruction. Cliffs disintegrate under the buffetting of the waves, mountains crumble into screes and rivers wash away their banks—but these operations are really first steps in construction ; they are the preparation of material for subsequent operations, for the building up of new rocks, and the development of new landscapes. Similarly, in taking the modern Llys Helig legend to pieces the object has been to prepare material from which to select for an experiment in reconstruction.

VI

THE LLYS HELIG STORIES : ORIGINS AND ASSOCIATIONS

THE expression ' Llys ' Helig was introduced in the 18th century, and may have first appeared in a manuscript, now lost, that was written between the compilation of the *Notes to bee observed* and their first appearance in print.

Some of the embellishments introduced by the writer of the *Notes* appear to have been inspired by pamphlets published in 1607 after floods had occurred in the estuary of the Severn. Later writers incorporated details from legends relating to palaces submerged in lakes that were attracting popular attention early in the 19th century.

(a)   The origin of the modern versions of the story of Helig's lost lands

IN making his suggestions about the significance of the ancient fort upon Penmaen-mawr the writer of the *Notes to bee observed* began his remarks with ' by tradicõn we receive it from our forefathers ' ; his explanation of the Meini Hirion began with ' ytt should seem that . . .', and in explaining the ' Carneddi ' he said, ' we must onely rely upon tradicõn.' There are, however, no such reservations in his stories of Helig and Seiriol ; the statements are positive and unqualified : ' In his [Helig's] time happened the great innundacõn ' ; ' his people did run upp to save themselves ' ; ' Seirial, brother to Helig ap Glannog, . . . did cause a pavement to be made,' and so on.

In references to Helig there is no suggestion of popular belief or tradition ; the events were recorded as if they were history, but, as we have seen, we can find no authority for such statements amongst the early manuscripts that were being studied and copied at the time—one of considerable activity in the study of ancient records—nor do we find that the persons or the events were mentioned by earlier topographical writers whose works had by then been published or were known in manuscript. John Leland, who was Librarian-Antiquary to Henry VIII, for example, in the account of his journeys made in the fifteen-thirties [156b] mentioned the story of lost lands between Aberdyfi and Towyn, which the ' se ful many a yere syns hath clene devourid,' but he said nothing about an equally devastating inundation in the north.

Price's *Description of Cambria now called Wales*, written about the middle of the 16th century, also says nothing about a great incursion of the northern sea, although there are paragraphs about the rivers and the territorial subdivisions of Wales.

That Humphrey Llwyd did not have occasion to mention the matter in his translation of the *Brut y Tywysogion* is not particularly significant, because that group of records does not purport to begin until late in the 7th century, but it is significant that he did not refer to it in his *Commentarioli Britannicae Descriptionis Fragmentum* which was published in Cologne in 1570, and of which a translation by Thomas Twyne was published in 1573 under the title of *The Breviary of Britayne*. Although the *Breviary* related to Britain as a whole more than one third of it was devoted to Wales ; mention was made of matters such as the election of Maelgwn Gwynedd as King about 540, of legends like that of St. Winifred's Well and of the ' Ile Seirial (in English, Priestholme),' but there is nothing about the sudden loss of large parts of the coastal areas of Wales. The significance of Llwyd's silence upon the subject of Helig is increased by the fact that he was a Denbigh man, and his works and his maps show that he was familiar with the geography, history, and folk-tales of North Wales.

This failure on the part of earlier and contemporary writers to mention the story suggests that, in the form in which it is given in the *Notes*, it was not widely known in North Wales in the 16th century, and that, in all details other than the personal name and the reference to land lost by inundation, it may have been, in large measure, if not entirely, either copied or invented by the writer of the *Notes* or by some one with whom he was in communication.

It also transpires that, in the 17th, 18th and early 19th centuries the story was known only to such people as studied and copied old manuscripts, e.g., people like Humphrey, Bishop of Bangor, the clergyman, David Lloyd, whose access to the MS 820D we have already mentioned, and William Williams, a schoolmaster, who in 1669 wrote a *History of Beaumaris*. The manuscript of that history was once in the possession of Paul Panton of Plas Gwyn in Anglesey, but it seems now to be lost, although Fenton quoted from it in his *Tours through Wales*. It illustrates very well an early stage in the embellishment of the story and of the way in which it began to acquire historical status.

Williams tells us that the story of Helig

' gains the more credit because there are ruins of old Walls to be seen in that place to this very day at Equinoctial tides. And because wrought and carved free Stones and Iron barrs of Windows and other Irons belonging to buildings have been found there. And the Compiler of this history hath been told by antient people of Ty Mawr (now the Mansion house of Robert Coytmore Esqur, not far distant) that they had seen Iron barrs of Windows and other Irons come from thence. Moreover, there is a place called Yr Wylfa upon the Sea side, not far from Dwygyfylchau Church, which signified the place of weeping. For when the sea by God's secret Judgmt. had leave to transgress its antient bounds, and to fall upon Helig ap Clynog's house, the Houshold made hast towards the Hills, and upon a Hillock in sight of the place, seeing House &c. overwhelm'd by the Sea, they could not chuse but lift up their Voices and weep ; whence the place is call'd Yr Wylfa to this day.'

It is not possible now to discover what the ' antient people ' really saw, but more tangible evidence must be forthcoming before we can accept the statement that carved freestone or iron bars were found on the site called Llys Helig. Even if such objects had been found they are not likely to have been what they were supposed to be. Pieces of dressed stone might, indeed, have been found on the sea floor in some part of Conway Bay if they had been dropped from ships conveying materials for a medieval building—a castle or a church. Freestone used for mullions, window casings, and fireplaces in Caernarvon Castle so closely resembles certain sandstones of Triassic age near Chester as to make it difficult to suggest any other place of origin for them, whilst the *Register of Edward the*

Black Prince includes orders for stone to be taken by sea from Chester, for repairs to Conway Castle in 1347 [135].

The story of Helig was seldom mentioned in print during the 17th and 18th centuries. It is not, for example, to be found in Robert Vaughan's *British Antiquities Revived* (1662), although that book refers to the ' large Plaine extending itself between the Countyes of Carnarvan, Cardigan and Pembroke, long since swallowed up by the sea : ' neither is it to be found in the augmented edition of Powel's *Historie of Cambria* prepared by W. Wynne in 1697, nor in P. Yorke's *Royal Tribes of Wales* (1799).

In the *Observations on Several parts of . . . North Wales*, based upon tours made between 1769 and 1773, William Gilpin recorded that Mr. Myddleton, Rector of St. Georges near Denbigh, showed him a Welsh manuscript a translation of which ran thus :

' In the year 813, the *castle of Treganwy*, was burnt by lightning ; and in the year 823 it was rebuilt. It was afterwards reduced by the Saxons, and destroyed. This castle stood within the present floodmark, opposite to Penmaenbach ; and the road from Rhyddlan-castle passed though it. . . . Hence the road ran in a straight line to the palace of Elis Clynog, which lay about a mile from Priestholm island. This palace once commanded a very beautiful vale, now totally flooded, and known by the name Lavan Sands. For about the time that the castle of Treganwy was destroyed by the Saxons, the sea broke in upon this country, and overflowed all the lands of the vale, which became a sandy beach, and took the name of Lavan, or lamentation, from the melancholy cries of its suffering inhabitants. It is said that two persons only escaped from the palace of Elis Clynog.'

These allusions to Elis Clynog illustrate the extent to which manuscripts like those with which we are concerned are interrelated and the way in which mistakes are not only carried forward but also improved upon. William Williams in his *History of Beaumaris* (1669) wrote of Helig ap Clynog, one of Lewis Morris's charts of about 1740 has Elis ap Clynog, Mr.

Myddleton's manuscript, Elis Clynog, and the modern Admiralty Chart, Llys Elisap Clynnog !

The geographical conditions mentioned in Mr. Myddleton's manuscript, but not the date, were incorporated by William Owen into the *Map of Wales according to the Antient Divisions* which he prepared for Warrington's *History of Wales* (1788). The map, part of which is reproduced in Pl. 1A, puts ' Llys Helig ab Glanog, over flowed in the 6th century,' at the apex of a large triangular ' Lavan Sands,' that is, much nearer to Priestholm than to Penmaen-mawr, and where William Williams put it in his *History of Beaumaris* (1669).

Whichever way we examine the story there seems to be no escape from the conclusion that although a man named Helig may have lived in Wales sometime during the first few centuries of the present era, the popular story of the circumstances in which he lost his lands is neither history (because an inundation such as it postulates could not have taken place within the limits of the time during which Helig is supposed to have lived), nor genuinely ancient legend (since it was not until the 17th century, more than a thousand years after the events to which it relates are supposed to have happened, that the story began to acquire even the bare outline of its present form).

Whatever part the common folk—the peasantry, the vulgar —may have played in preserving the germ of the story, it is to educated writers that we owe its elaboration and its survival. Gilpin, for example, did not hear it in a farmhouse, he read it in a manuscript preserved in a Rector's library.

We have seen that certain manuscripts available to the compiler of the *Notes to bee observed* provided him with the foundation for his story of ' Helig ap Glannog whose lands were overwhelmed by the sea,' and we can also hazard a guess as to what inspired him to add the details about the fruitful lands and the distress of the dispossessed inhabitants. In 1607, only a few years before the time when the manuscript was written, a particularly devastating flood affected large areas on both sides of the Bristol Channel.

An account of it was published in a twenty-five-page pamphlet, ' Printed for W.W. and to be solde in Paules Church yarde at the figure of the Grey hounde.' It had the following quaintly informative title :

Lamentable newes out of Monmouthshire in Wales, contayning the wonderfull and most fearefull accidents of the great overflowing of waters of the saide Countye, drowning infinite numbers of Cattell of all kinds as Sheepe, Oxen, Kine and Horses, with others ; together with the losse of many men women and Children, and the submersion of xxvi Parishes in January last 1607.

It described how ' in the month of Januarie last past upon a Tuesday, the sea, being very tempestuously moved by the windes, overflowed his ordinary Bankes and did drowne 26 Parishes adjoyning on the coast side, in the foresaide Countrey of Mon-mouth-shire, the particulars whereof doe followe ; all spoyled by the greevous and lamentable furie of the waters.'

Then followed the names of the parishes that were affected, and some details of the damage done to cattle, corn, and houses, after which the narrative continues,

' the foresaid waters having gotten over their wonted limittes are affirmed to have runne at their first entrance with a swiftnesses so incredible, as that no Grayhounde could have escaped by running before them. And they yet cover twenty foure miles in length, and foure and more in breadthe, which if the water were quite gone againe are not to bee recovered within the space of five or sixe years to bee so serviceable ground as formerly they have beene ; yea and there is no probabilitie that that part of the Countrey will ever be so inhabited againe in our age as it was before this floud, howsoever it hath heretofore bene reputed the richest and fruitfullest place in all that Countrey.'

A woodcut illustration shows men and animals struggling in the water from which the upper part of a church projects, and there are records of some unusual personal experiences :

' Further, among other matters, these things are related as certaine truths. As that a certaine man and a woman having taken a tree for their succour and espying nothing but death before their eyes : at last among other things which were carried along in the streame, perceyved a certain Tubbe of great largeness to come nearer and nearer unto them untill it

Fig. 7.   The Severn Floods of 1607

One of the several contemporary illustrations of floods affecting the low-lying lands on either side of the Severn estuary.

rested upon that Tree wherein they were. Into which (as sent unto them by God's providence) committing themselves they were carryed safe untill they were caste uppe uppon the drie shoare. . . . Another little childe is affirmed to have been cast upon land in a Cradle in which was nothing but a Catte, the which was discerned as it came to the shore to leape from one side of the Cradle unto the other, even as if she had been appointed steresman to preserve the small barke from the waves furie.'

Then, after references to other catastrophes which were sent as judgements, and exhortations to repentance as a means of averting similar occurrences, the author (the Rev. William Welby) concluded :

'Let us thinke upon the judgements which God hath inflicted upon others for their vices, that so wee may be the more averted from the like offences. . . . The Lord of his mercie grant, that wee may learne in time to be wise unto our owne health and valuation, least that these water flouds in particular, proove but forerunners unto some fearfull calamities, more generall.'

Details relating to the effects of the flood on the southern side of the Channel were given in another booklet, entitled :

Newes out of Summersetshire, 1607. A true report of certaine wonderfull overflowings of Waters overthrowing and bearing downe whole townes and villages and drowning infinite numbers of sheepe and other cattle. . . . Printed at London by W.J. for Edward White, and are to be solde at the signe of the Gunne, at the North doore of Paules.

This also included an illustration (reproduced as Fig. 7) which, although somewhat larger than the one in the *Newes out of Monmouthshire* was related to it. The upper part was copied from the other (or vice versa), whilst the lower part depicts a few extra animals, mostly sheep, and a baby floating in a cradle. We shall have occasion later on to recall the last of these items.

The Summmersetshire pamphlet also refers to the length and breadth of the affected land, to the ' lamentable spectacle it was to beholde,' and to people who fled ' up to a hill some half a myle from the Towne, where . . . they reposed themselves,' and from which on the next day, ' they beheld their houses . . . in the water.' Such a flood, the author said, ' could not but bring much losse to the poore inhabitants, yet to increase it, their corn fields . . . are toombed and buried in the huge grave of waters.'

The floods were also described in a pamphlet preserved in the Library of Edward Harley, 2nd Earl of Oxford. It was called

God's warning to his people of England by the great overflowing of the Waters of Floudes lately hapned in South-Wales, and many other Places. Wherein is described the great Losses and wonderfull Damages that hapned thereby ; . . . Printed in London, for W. Barley and J. O. Bayly, and are to be solde in Gratious street, 1607.

The author observed that ' since the generall dissolution of the whole world by water, in the time of Noah, never the like inundation of watery punishment then hapned,' and he referred to the rapid approach of the waters, the destruction they caused, and the consequent impoverishment of the people that were affected [129].

It would seem, therefore, that the details of these extensive floods were widely known in the years immediately preceding the compilation of the *Notes to bee observed*, and the general picture given by the *Notes* as well as some of their details are such as to render not improbable the suggestion that the writer had one or more of the pamphlets in mind when he set about the preparation of his own manuscript.

The Monmouthshire pamphlet described the area affected as ' reputed the richest and fruitfullest place in all that countrey,' and the Harley pamphlet speaks of the ' overflowing of the seas in divers and sundry places of the realm whose fruitfull valleys (being now overwhelmed and drowned with theise most unfortunate and unseasonable salt waters) do foreshow great barrenes to ensue after it.'

Of the victims' escape the latter said,

' But as soone as the people . . . perceived that it was the violence of the waters of the raging seas, and that they began to exceed the compasse of their accustomed boundes, and making so furiously towardes them, happy were they that could make the best and most speed away, many of them leaving all their goods and substance to the merciles waters, being glad to escape away with life themselves. Many of them might see, as they stood upon the tops of high hills, their cattle perish . . . and their barnes . . . which was no small griefe to them. . . . Thus God suffred many of them to escape his yrefull wrath.'

The Summersetshire pamphlet spoke of the ' lamentable spectacle ' and of people who saved themselves by hurrying to a neighbouring hill, and all of them referred to the length and breadth of the land that was affected.

These expressions are very reminiscent of the *Notes to bee observed*, but, tempting as it is, the suggestion that the compiler of the *Notes* may have been familiar with the pamphlets describing the 1607 flood requires support before we can admit it even as circumstantial evidence.

Fortunately, a large series of ' Wynn ' documents is preserved in the National Library of Wales [181] ; from some of these it appears that during 1607 Sir John frequently corresponded with relations and acquaintains in London, and one paper in his hand-writing contains instructions about purchases to be made there on his behalf. Although undated, it was, by reason of its associations, assigned to the year 1607 by the compiler of the Library's Calendar of the Wynn papers.

Amongst the items asked for were ' Camden's Britannia with maps ' and ' some rare books as you can lyght on.' Now the first edition of Camden's *Britannia* to include maps appeared in 1607, published by George Bishop and John Norton of The Bell, St. Paul's Churchyard ; two of the flood pamphlets were also published from addresses in St. Pauls Churchyard—The Grey hounde and the Gunne—whilst the third emanated from Gratious Street, not far away, and they all appeared in 1607. Even if they cannot be regarded as rare in the sense of being choice or notable, the pamphlets were sufficiently curious to have attracted the attention of anyone visiting the booksellers in and near St. Paul's Churchyard with a roving commission to look for out-of-the-way publications.

If, as there is no reason to doubt, Wynn had something to do with the *Notes to bee observed*, although not actually writing the copy that has come down to us, there would seem to be good grounds for suggesting that reports of the 1607 floods initiated the first stage in the development of the simple statement about Helig's lands being overwhelmed by the sea, into the modern story of Llys Helig. This is all the more likely because parts of the coast of Denbighshire were also affected, though less seriously, by the floods. They are mentioned in a letter from John Lloyd of Vaynol to ' My verie loving Coosin Sir John Salusburie Knight at llewenie '—one of the Llewenny papers preserved in the National Library of Wales. The letter is dated February 5th, 1606 (1607 by present reckoning because at that time the legal year began on March 25th), and with its contractions expanded it runs as follows :

' Sir John, it is not vnknowen vnto you howe that the sea
banke at Abergeley is broken and so it is to the vorryd and
howe it is come over a greate parte of our cuntrey and hath
don much harme and is like to doe more vnles some good
meanes may be had for the preventing of yt, in regarde
whereof wee the neighbours have agreed that the best gent
in the cuntrey Justices of peace and others shall meete at
Abergeley vppon Tuesdaie next by Xen of the clocke, and to
make view and survey of the decayes of the sea banke there.
And I for my parte haue vndertaken to giue you notice
thereof and to praie you to take the paines to repaire thither
at the tyme aforesayd that you may be an eye wittnes of the
iminent danger there. Wee do meane to be peticioners to his
Majestie and to the highe Court of parliament to be releeved.
Your presence there shall do greate good . . .' [22].

There are passages in the 1607 flood-pamphlets that recall
Arthur Golding's translation, published in 1567, of Ovid's
Metamorphoses. In this country Ovid was widely read and
greatly admired in late medieval times. Dafydd ap Gwilym
acknowledged his influence and Shakespeare borrowed largely
from him, so that it is by no means unlikely that the clergyman-
author of the *Lamentable Newes* was familiar with Golding's
translation. If this were the case the reference to Helig's people
running up to the top of a neighbouring hill, as well as some of
the other details, were inspired by a poem written at the
beginning of the Christian era, for Ovid died in A.D. 18.

In the section of the *Metamorphoses* dealing with the creation
of the world and the story of the flood the following lines occur :

The floods at random where they list through all the fields
     did stray ;
Men, beasts, trees, corn, and with their gods were churches
     washed away.
If any house were built so strong against their force to stand,
Yet did the water hide the top, and turrets in that pond
Were overwhelmed . . .
Some climbed up to tops of hills, and some rowed to and fro
In boats . . . another sits a fishing in an elm. [164].

It is interesting, when trying to discover the source of the information which authors incorporated into their writings, to note the extent to which one has been influenced by another, not only in regard to material, but also in the phrases used to present it, even when there may be no question of intentional plagiarism.

(b) Llys Helig and some lake legends

A modern version of the Llys Helig story is given by Professor T. Gwynn Jones in his *Welsh Folklore and Folk-customs* (1930) :

' The lord of Tyno Helig was Helig ap Glannawg. He had a daughter who was beloved by a young man of low degree, whom she would not marry because he did not wear a torque of gold.

' He killed a nobleman and brought his torque to her. She sent him to bury the body lest the crime be discovered. When he was digging a grave, a voice cried thrice, "Vengeance will come." He fled in terror and told the maid what he had heard. She sent him back, telling him, if he heard the cry again, to ask what time the retribution should come. He does so, and the reply is "In the time of children, grand-children, great-grand-children and great-great-grand-children." "We shall then be dead," said the maid, when she heard this.

' They were married and lived to see the fourth generation of their descendants. All their descendants attended a great banquet. A servant, in fetching wine from the cellar, noticed that it was half full of water in which small fish swam about. She went and told the bard, who at once departed, taking with him the servant. As they were leaving, the waves swept over the palace. Next morning Tyno Helig had disappeared.' [81].

This version differs in several important respects from those we have already had occasion to mention, and we are entitled to ask when and how the differences originated, but before doing so we may note, that this is the only occasion on which fish swimming in the cellar are introduced into the story. The idea may well have been suggested by a passage in Andrew

Marvell's *Character of Holland* in which, referring to floods in that country, he wrote :

The fish oft-times the burgher dispossest.

The other differences are more significant and in order to appreciate them we have to turn our attention to another class of inundation story.

In *Celtic Folklore*, Sir John Rhŷs wrote, ' It is an ancient belief in the Principality that the lakes generally have swallowed up the habitations of men,' adding, ' as in the case of Llyn Syfaddon and the Pool of Corwrion. To these I proceed to add other instances, to wit, those of Bala Lake, Kenfig Pool, Llynclys, and Helig ap Glannog's territory including Traeth Lafan.' [145a]. His version of the Llys Helig story had more in common with the one extracted from Miss Costello's book than with one given by Gwynn Jones ; he summarised it as follows :

' A calamity had been foretold four generations before it came, namely as the vengeance of Heaven on Helig ap Glannog for his nefarious impiety. As that ancient prince rode through his fertile heritage one day at the approach of night, he heard the voice of an invisible follower warning him that "Vengeance is coming, coming." The wicked old prince asked excitedly "When ?" The answer was, "In the time of the grand-children, great-grand-children and their children.' Perchance Helig calmed himself with the thought that, if such a thing came it would not happen in his lifetime. The conclusion of the story is on familiar lines and speaks of a feast, of a servant going to the cellar to fetch liquor (in this case, mead), of the harper who alone could be warned of the impending danger, so that, those two apart, all the occupants of the palace were drowned, ' by reason of their intoxication.'

Rhŷs gave as his authority a quotation from *Y Brython*, 1863, which purported to have been taken from a work on the environs of Conway (*Aberconwy a'i Chyffiniau*) by Owen Jones, but, he said, he had been unable to trace the book. He associated the Llys Helig story with others in which inundations were involved, and we must note what he said about them before proceeding farther with our principal inquiry.

The version of the story associated with Llyn Syfaddon (Llangorse Lake) in Brecknockshire, to which Rhŷs referred, was first printed in full in *the Cambro-Briton* in 1821, where it was described as being copied from a manuscript formerly in the possession of Huw Thomas. This means that it must have been written before 1714, the year in which Thomas died, having bequeathed his manuscripts to Edward Harley, Earl of Oxford. By profession a herald, but by inclination an anti-quarian, Thomas had collected materials for a history of Brecknockshire. [78d].

The manuscript containing the Llyn Syfaddon story is now in the British Museum (Harleian MSS 6381) and before it was given to the public in full a summary had appeared in *The History of the County of Brecknock* by Theophilus Jones (1809) [78a] and *The Cambrian Traveller's Guide* (1813) [114a], whilst an account in Welsh was printed many years later in *Y Brython* (1863) [93].

The story in the Huw Thomas manuscript was described as *The Legend of Llyn Savathan,* and it tells of a great and beautiful lady who was the heiress of all the land now covered by the lake. She was courted by a young man whom she could not accept because he was too poor. ' The youth, in his despair,' the story continues, ' meets a carrier with a great charge of money, . . . whom he not only robs but murders, and burieth in the place for fear of discovery.'

The lady, acquainted with the circumstances, would not marry him until he had visited the grave at night in order to appease the ghost who was reported to be troubling the place. Whilst at the grave ' he heard at midnight a voice cry aloud, ' Is there no vengeance for innocent blood ? ' and another voice answer, ' Not until the ninth generation.' He told the lady what he had heard, but, she said, ' Before that time we shall be rotten in our graves, therefore we will enjoy ourselves while we may.'

Years afterwards, when they were old, they invited all their offspring to a feast, and at the height of it, ' there happened the most terrible earthquake which, opening her merciless jaws, swallowed them all up alive, not one soul of them escaping (I

Pl. 9. Llyn Cwm Llwch in the Brecknock Beacons

The small lake nestles beneath the cliffs on the right.
(Air Photograph by Major G. W. G. Allen. Reproduced by permission of the Ashmolean Museum).

Pl. 10A.   Cairn on Mynydd Epynt   *Photo : G. C. Dunning*

after excavation involving the removal of a low mound of earth covered by a
layer of stones. [25]

Pl. 10B.   Part of a stone circle on Mynydd Epynt   *Photo : G. C. Dunning*

Of thirty stones only twelve were visible before excavation ; the remainder had
fallen and were covered by soil and turf. [25]

presume by reason of their drunkenness not being able) and were immediately covered over with this great deluge of water.' It was, it will be remembered, 'by reason of their intoxication' that the people failed to escape in the version of the Llys Helig story which Rhŷs quoted.

It is on the authority of Iolo Morganwg that a similar tale is told of Kenfig Pool, a lake in the dunes near Porthcawl in Glamorgan. Rhŷs said of it : ' The original, from which I translate is . . . as I fancy, in Iolo's own words ' [145c].

Much condensed the story is as follows : A plebian was in love with Earl Clare's daughter, but she would not marry him because he was not wealthy. Seeing the agent of the lord of the domain coming home with his lord's money he murdered the man and stole the money, after which the lady married him. A little later a voice was heard to say, three times, ' Vengeance is coming,' and in answer to the question ' When ? ', said, ' In the ninth generation.' ' There is no need for us to fear,' agreed the married couple, ' for we shall be under the mould long before.'

In due course, the vengeance came, but in this story it was witnessed by a descendant of the murdered man, who, going towards the city, saw that it had been replaced by a large lake with three smoking chimneys projecting above the surface, whilst the gloves of the murdered man were floating upon the water [179g].

The Bala Lake story cited by Rhŷs was a translation from an article published about 1860 in Hugh Humphrey's *Llyfr Gwybodaeth Gyffredinol*. It tells of how

' Tradition relates that Bala Lake is but the watery tomb of the palaces of iniquity, and that some old boatmen can . . . hear at times a feeble voice saying "Vengeance will come, Vengeance will come," and another voice enquiring 'When will it come ? ' The first voice answers, "In the third generation." Those voices were a recollection over oblivion of an oppressive and cruel prince who used frequently to hear a voice saying "Vengeance will come," but he always laughed the threat away with reckless contempt. One night a poor harper . . . was ordered to come to the prince's palace. About midnight, when there was an interval in the dancing

G

and the old harper had been left alone in a corner, he suddenly heard a voice saying in a sort of a whisper in his ear,
"Vengeance, Vengeance." He turned at once and saw a
little bird hovering above him, beckoning him, as it were, to
follow.' [145d].

The story then tells of how the bird enticed the harper away
from the palace and up to the top of a hill. When at length the
harper decided to return to the feast he lost his way in the dark,
but at daybreak when he looked in the direction of the palace
he could see no trace of it ; the whole tract below was a lake,
and his harp was floating on the calm surface of the water.

To this series we must add the story, also in *Celtic Folklore*,
relating to Llynclys near Oswestry. It was taken from *Y Brython*
for 1862, where there is a Welsh version which Rhŷs summarized
as follows :

' The Llynclys family were notorious for their riotous
living, and at their feasts a voice used to be heard proclaiming
"Vengeance is coming, coming," but nobody took it much
to heart. However, one day a reckless maid asked the voice
"When ?" The prompt reply was to the effect that it was
the sixth generation : the voice was heard no more. So one
night, when the sixth heir in descent from the time of the
warning last heard was giving a great feast . . . the harper
went outside for a breath of air ; but when he turned to come
back, lo and behold, the whole court had disappeared. Its
place was occupied by a quiet piece of water, on whose waves
he saw his harp floating, nothing more.' [145e].

The floating object seems by now to have become an essential
ingredient in the story. It was a cradle in the 1607 flood
pamphlet, gloves in Iolo's Kenfig story, a harp in Bala Lake and
Llynclys, and, as we shall see later, to complete the cycle, a
cradle and a glove in one of the stories of Llyn Syfaddon.

VII
LLYN SYFADDON AND KENFIG POOL

A MAJOR step in the development of the mid-nineteenth century versions of the Llys Helig story was taken between 1813 and 1835 and can be attributed to the publication of the story of Llyn Syfaddon (Llangorse Lake) and of a translation of *Hanes Taliesin*. Other additions were derived from Iolo Morganwg's story of Kenfig Pool and the synthesis was completed by Wmffre Dafydd, in 1862.

The prototype of the Llyn Syfaddon story could have been inspired by circumstances connected with the formation and physical attributes of the lake, but the modern story is mostly of modern invention.

Seventeenth century writers mention a 'sunken city' in Kenfig Pool in Glamorgan, but there is no earlier authority for Iolo Morganwg's detailed story of the inundation.

(a) *Modern mixtures of old tales*

OUR enquiries have shown that the oldest known version of the story of Helig's palace is the one given in the *Notes to bee observed*. That manuscript, written soon after 1620, was known during the 18th century to a few of those who studied old documents but did not become accessible to the general public until it was printed in 1831.

It records, as if they were actual happenings and not merely tradition, that the lands of Helig ap Glannog were overwhelmed by the sea and that he and his people escaped by going to a nearby hill, from which, with sorrow, they surveyed a scene of devastation ; but even that simple story was an expansion of a still simpler statement, first found in 13th century manuscripts, to the effect that the lands of Helig were overwhelmed by the sea.

If we seek to discover the origin of the additional details included in the *Notes to bee observed*, and to trace the steps by which the story there told has developed into the many elaborate tales that have been current in recent years, the lake stories related in the previous chapter indicate the lines along which we can proceed.

Although first printed in summary in 1809, and in full in 1821, the Llyn Syfaddon story, in the version given by Rhŷs, had been committed to writing by about 1700 [125]. The existence of a legend of some sort relating to the lake was known to William Camden in 1586, for in his *Britannia* he referred to an 'ancient tradition that where the lake now is, there was formerly a City, which being swallowed yp by an earthquake, resign'd its place to the waters.' [10a]. He gave no indication that he knew what the legend was, but suggested that the city might have been the Loventium (Luentinum), mentioned by Ptolemy as one of the cities of the Demetae. This is now considered to have been a bad guess and Loventium is identified with a site near Llanio station, a few miles south of Tregaron, apparently for no better reason than that the names slightly resemble one another ; they are not related by derivation.

As told in Huw Thomas's manuscript, the story regards the inundation as retribution for a murder committed by a poor lover anxious to marry a rich girl ; a mysterious voice referred to vengeance, and the calamity was foretold nine generations in advance.

This is quite different from the original Llys Helig story, which purported to be a simple record of fact involving a man whose name appeared in ancient pedigrees ; it was obviously intended to be regarded as a legend and did not pretend, by including either names or dates, to have an historical background. Indeed, the writer of the Harleian Manuscript 6831— the sole extant authority for it—admitted that ' For confirmation of this story we can cite no history ; but this is the general tradition of the whole country and is common almost to every child here. Yet I must confess there are told so many fabulous and nonsensical stories of this parish that they make the truth of this story also to be called in question.' It is significant that he described the story as being common almost to every *child*, not every *person*. This would put it into the category of nursery tales—which, oft repeated and long surviving, are not usually presented as history although, in some cases, they may preserve the germ of an old and forgotten tradition relating to a person that really lived or to events that actually occurred.

It is possible to make suggestions concerning the way in which the Llyn Syfaddon story may have originated, but in order not to interrupt the continuity of our present enquiry they will be reserved for later paragraphs.

It will be remembered that Rhŷs gave as the authority for the version of the Llys Helig story which he quoted a work called *Aberconwy a'i Chyffiniau* (Aberconway and its environs) by Owen Jones, which, he said, he had not been able to trace. His failure in this direction is quite understandable because no such work exists, but amongst the essays in *Y Traethodydd* (Vol. XV) for 1859 there is one entitled *Aberconwy a'i Henafiaethau* by the Rev. Owen Jones, and another, unsigned, called *Beaumaris a'i Chyffiniau*.

The latter mentions ' Helig ab Glannawg ' and the former gives his story in some detail. It has extracts that were obviously taken from one of the printed versions of the *Notes to bee observed*, but it attributes the calamity to Helig's wickedness. It includes the reference to Vengeance (Dial a ddaw) and to the fact that it was coming in the time of the children, grand-children, and great-grandchildren of the person who was to be punished— this in answer to an inquiry by Helig himself. It would seem that Rhŷs had taken at face value information given verbally by someone who had seen the essays in *Y Traethodydd* but whose recollections had grown dim.

Aberconwy a'i Henafiaethau, however, only takes us back to 1859 and has no real significance in the history of the development of the legend ; its story of Helig is essentially the same as that given in 1835 by Robert Williams in his *History and antiquities of the Town of Aberconwy and its neighbourhood*.

Williams gave an outline of the story as it was in the *Notes to bee observed* stage, and said that it was still recorded in the traditional tales of the neighbourhood ' with the following additions ' :

' It had been prophesied four generations previously that vengeance would overtake the family of Helig ab Glanawg for the crimes of his ancestors. *Dial a ddaw, dial a ddaw,* was continually heard, although uttered by an invisible being ; *yn amser dy wyrion, neu dy orwyrion* was the appointed time, and the inundation was so sudden, that the servant, who, in going to the cellar to draw liquor, first observed the water, had only an opportunity of warning the harper of his danger, when all the others were overwhelmed by the flood in the midst of their festivities.'

The additions mentioned by Williams had, apparently, come into the picture so recently that their adventitious character was not in doubt. They were not current when Edward Pugh published his *Cambria Depicta* in 1813 and referred to Helig Voel ap Glannog, whose great possessions, extending far into the sea from Priestholm, had been suddenly overwhelmed.

There is nothing in what Pugh wrote in 1813 that could not have originated in the *Notes* and in copies of the early genealogies, but between the appearance of his book and that by Robert Williams on Aberconwy the story of Llyn Syfaddon had been printed in *The Cambro-Briton*, and it is difficult to see, in the extended version of the Helig story mentioned by Williams, anything more than a composite tale, made by grafting on to the original local tradition some of the circumstantial details of the legend of the Brecknockshire lake, with the addition of a reference to a harper ; this last may have been suggested by the story of Taliesin's visit to the court of Maelgwn at 'Dyganwy,' for *Hanes Taliesin* (the reputed personal history of the ancient bard) had recently been published in the *Cambrian Quarterly Magazine* (1833), with a translation by Wm. Owen Pughe—known before 1806 as Wm. Owen [138].

It was in this stage of its synthesis, with the cries of 'Vengeance' and references to the harper and the servant who went to the cellar, that the story was retold by Miss Costello, in 1845, in the form given in an earlier chapter as typical of the mid-nineteenth century versions.

*   *   *

There can be little doubt but that Iolo's story of Kenfig was also a local adaption of the Llyn Syfaddon legend. He gave no indication concerning the authorship or date of the manuscript from which he purported to have copied the story, but in the preface to the *Iolo Manuscripts* it is stated that, ' The collections from which the MSS were collected were made about the

beginning of the present century by E. Williams . . . with the
intention of forming a continuation of the Myvyrian Archaiology ' [179]. This was a collection of Welsh texts published
by Owen Jones (Owen Myfyr, a well-to-do furrier living in
London) in collaboration with Wm. Owen Pughe and Iolo
Morganwg, the last of whom contributed some items of his
own invention. All three men have been described as ' in-
curably romantic, and for them the line was very faint between
what was true and what they wished to believe.' [175].

The final volume of the original edition of the *Myvyrian
Archaiology* was published in 1807 [75] and since the ' legend of
Llyn Savathan ' had been referred to in Theophilus Jones'
Brecknockshire in 1809 and printed in The *Cambro-Briton* in 1821.
Iolo, who lived until 1827, could well have seen either or both,
There is nothing in the *Myvyrian Archaiology* or in the volume of
Iolo Manuscripts to suggest that Iolo had consulted the original
Huw Thomas manuscript, which at that time was in the British
Museum. That manuscript seems, indeed, to have remained
almost unnoticed until printed reference had been made to it.
Even Lewis Morris was apparently unaware of its existence, for
although, in his *Celtic Remains* (1757), he mentioned ' Llyn
Llynclys, a town swallowed up,' ' Llyngwyn, a pool in Radnor-
shire, where tradition says a town was swallowed up,' ' Cantref-
y-Gwaelod, overflowed by the sea,' and Llys Elis ap Clynog, he
had nothing to say about Llyn Syfaddon.

Edward Lhuyd indicated, in his additional notes to Gibson's
edition of Camden (1695), that he knew of a tradition associating a sunken city with ' Pwhl Kynffig,' but he gave no details
[10b]. Lhuyd was contemporary with Huw Thomas and may
have heard of or even have seen the manuscript with the Llyn
Syfaddon story, but it has yet to be shown that anyone earlier
than Iolo Morganwg had committed a detailed Kenfig story to
writing, and we have yet to learn who, or what, if not his own
fertile imagination, was his authority for introducing local
colour by making the rich heiress to be the daughter of a Clare,
one of a family of influential people in Glamorgan during parts
of the thirteenth and fourteenth centuries. His reference to
gloves floating on the water was an appropriate touch in view of

the period at which the crime is supposed to have been committed ; but even that was not an original notion.

When the story of Helig appeared in *Cymru Fu* in 1862, [17] under the title *Traeth yr Oerlefain*, some details from Iolo's Kenfig story had been superimposed upon the already composite version as told by Miss Costello ; it was not the sins of Helig which precipitated the calamity but a murder committed by a poor man who wished to marry a rich girl—in this case Helig's own daughter. The form which the warning of vengeance is alleged to have taken suggests that the author, Wmffre Dafydd, had been inspired by Iolo's story and not by the original Llyn Syfaddon legend as given in the Huw Thomas manuscript, whilst the reference to the servant who went to the cellar suggests the influence of the article in *Y Traethodydd* by Owen Jones. This had been printed three years, and the *Iolo Manuscripts* twelve years, before the appearance of Wmffre Dafydd's essay—periods sufficiently long for their contents to have become known in a general way, even to people who were not familiar with the works in which they appeared.

It transpires, therefore, that the modern version of the Llys Helig story, cited in *Welsh Folklore and Folk Customs*, originated in 1862 ; it was compiled by Wmffre Dafydd and was a piece of story-writing rather than a stage in the development of a genuine folk tale.

As in Iolo's story, so in Wmffre Dafydd's, an alteration was made to suit the new locality to which reference to a murder was to be introduced, for it was not money but a golden torc (torque) that was stolen. A torc is a personal ornament, either a circular hoop or a spiral armlet made by twisting ribbon-like strips of metal, and a golden one is a very likely object to have suggested itself as a possession appropriate to a person of importance living in North Wales in some remotely distant past.

When Wmffre wrote, three such ornaments had been recorded from North Wales—two of them well within the memory of people then living. The first was discovered near Harlech in 1692 and was described in the notes which Edward Lhuyd contributed to Gibson's 1695 edition of *Britannia* [10c]. It is preserved at Mostyn Hall. The others were found in the early part of the 19th century—one near Holywell in Flintshire in 1816 and the other on the slopes of Cader Idris in 1823 [137]. Two other finds of torcs have been recorded in recent years, one near Rhayader consisting of four spiral armlets and the other, near Knighton, of three. They are now in the National Museum of Wales. Had they been discovered during the legend-building period we are now considering it is more than likely that a torc would have been introduced into the Llyn Syfaddon legend !

The article in *Y Brython* from which Rhŷs took his version of the Llys Helig story was an account of the Llandudno district by O. Parry, and the author had evidently seen the then recently published little volume in which Halliwell brought the *Notes to bee observed* to the notice of the world at large, because, in addition to the details he had culled from *Aberconwy a'i Henafiaethau* he gave an extract from the pedigree of Helig.

With the appearance of the versions in *Y Brython* and *Cymru Fu* the embellishment of the Llys Helig story came to an end for a time but the influence of Iolo's Kenfig story continued to make itself felt in other directions. It is impossible to avoid the conclusion that it was the basis of the Bala Lake and Llynclys stories in the forms cited by Rhŷs. The latter's authority for the Bala story was, as we have seen, an anonymous article in the *Llyfr Gwybodaeth Gyffredinol*. In the absence of any indication that the story had been previously associated with Bala Lake, it is difficult to see in it any more than a local adaptation of Iolo's Kenfig story, or at least of Iolo's material. Bala Lake, it should be noted, has an older legend introducing Tegid Voel and his wife Ceridwen, but that forms no part of the sequence with which we are now concerned. We shall have occasion to mention it later on.

The authority for the Llynclys story cited by Rhŷs (see p. 98) is a letter in *Y Brython* entitled *Chwedlau y Llynoedd*, by Cynddelw [30]. The writer was Robert Ellis of Llanrhaeadr ym Mochnant, a Baptist minister who did much to popularise antiquarian subjects ; he said that the story was 'told by old people forty years ago.' Dates given in circumstances like these are notoriously unreliable, and it is not uncharitable to

Cynddelw's memory to suggest that what he was told was, in this case also, a local adaptation of Iolo's Kenfig story, and most likely of its ' Bala ' version. There was the same kind of conversation about Vengeance, and although a much less elaborate reason was given for the harper's absence from the hall when the disaster took place, his harp floated on the waters when all else had disappeared.

(b) *The Llyn Syfaddon (Llangorse Lake) Story : possible origins*

Although the Llyn Syfaddon story as told in the Huw Thomas manuscript is almost certainly a 17th century compilation, it may well have been inspired by recollections of certain miraculous powers which the lake was once supposed to have possessed, or else by some earlier story of an inundation the details of which had been forgotten.

As to the first of these possibilities, Giraldus Cambrensis recorded that

' The lake also (according to the testimony of the inhabitants) is celebrated for its miracles, for it sometimes assumed a greenish hue, so in our days it has appeared to be tinged with red, not universally, but as if blood flowed partially through certain veins and small channels. Moreover it is sometimes seen by the inhabitants covered and adorned with buildings, pastures, gardens and orchards. In the winter, when it is frozen over, it emits a horrible sound, resembling the moans of many animals banded together, but this perhaps may be occasioned by the sudden bursting of the shell [i.e., of the ice] and the gradual ebullition of the air through imperceptible channels.' [46b].

Leland, familiar with ' Giraldus book caulled Itinerarium Cambriae,' for he mentioned its account of the lake, also described the variable colour of the water, but, with characteristic perspicacity, was able to suggest a cause for the pheomenon, '. . . on the one side [of Llin Seuathan] wel nere the ripe is a kinde of weedes that goith alonge the Llin, wherein the spaune hath socur, and also the great fische. At great windes the water doth surge there marvelusly. Lleueny cummith through this lake, no great river, and after great raine is perfightly seene of redde color in the middest of the lake ' [156c]. In another passage he gave the additional information that ' after a great reyne Lleueney cummeth owt of the montaynes with such a rage that he bringethe the color of the dark redde sand with hym, and ys sene by the color wher he violently passeth thorowgh the mere.'

We can now see why Giraldus or his informants spoke of the appearance of blood flowing through veins and small channels ; the description was based upon observation and was not merely a legendary attribute of the lake. On its way to the lake the Llyfni river flows over a deposit of dark red sandy clay—a product of the disintegration of the surrounding rock, the Old Red Sandstone—and becomes turbid with red mud. The velocity of the river water when it enters the lake is such that it flows for a considerable distance before it loses its identity and so appears as a red band in the otherwise clear water. Other small streams flowing into the southern end of the lake come directly from the rocky outcrops ; they carry a smaller burden of suspended material and are relatively clear.

Leland also referred to the noise that was sometimes to be heard at Llyn Syfaddon : ' After that it is frosen and with thaue beginnith the breeke, it makith such a noise that a man wold thinke hit a thunder.' Such a phenomenon may well have given rise to the stories of vengeful voices crying in the night.

Whether the real and imagined attributes of Llangorse Lake —it will be convenient to use the modern name when referring to the lake and Llyn Syfaddon when referring to the legend— had anything to do with the birth of the legend or not we are never likely to know, but they do at least show that the lake was essentially the same in the time of Giraldus as it is now. From this it follows that if the story was inspired by circumstances connected with the origin or subsequent history of the lake it must have been handed down orally from a time long before the 12th century until the end of the 17th. This is unlikely, but to be unlikely is not to be impossible, and our next step is to inquire into the mode and date of the origin of the lake.

It has been found that the levels at which rock occurs all

around Llangorse Lake are such as to indicate that most of the water lies in a shallow basin excavated in the Old Red Sandstone ; this would suggest that the basin originated as a result of the scouring action of ice during the Glacial Period, and that the lake came into being immediately or soon after the disappearance of the ice. We have already considered the conditions which obtained during the Ice Age, and it is apparent that a lake formed at or soon after the end of that era cannot have inspired a legend based upon the destruction of a princely habitation. In terms of human chronology the time was early in the Old Stone Age, when men had to be content with the shelter afforded by bushy arbours or by caves ; besides, there is nothing to show that man had by then penetrated into this part of Wales.

The rock basin that forms the nucleus of the site is not responsible for the full depth of the lake—28 feet in its deepest part—because near the northern end there are post-glacial deposits of clay and gravel. These have raised the level of the outlet, thus increasing the size and depth of the lake which at this end now extends beyond the limits of the rock basin in which it originated [67]. If this enlargement of the lake, or any stage in it, took place fairly quickly as a result of the damming of the outgoing streams due to the deposition of material transported during a storm of exceptional violence or a period of unusually wet weather, it would have affected habitations that had been erected on the shores of the original lake. In such circumstances personal recollections of the event may have been passed on from generation to generation, eventually to be elaborated into a legend with details suggested by the mode of life of peoples much more recent than those affected by the floods.

Events such as those postulated must have taken place in prehistoric times because although there are likely to have been changes of level and area due to the alternation of wet and dry cycles it is unlikely that there has been notable permanent increase in size since the beginning of the present era. On the contrary the extent of level marshy land southwards and north-westwards of the lake suggests that any progressive change that may have taken place in historic times has tended to reduce the area of the water.

In 1925, a ' dug-out ' canoe was recovered from the mud on the bottom of the shallow northern part of the lake. [37] It had been skilfully hewn from a single oaken log, and was studied by Sir Cyril Fox, who came to the conclusion that although nothing was found to indicate its date ' it is not unreasonable to associate it with the island, wholly or in part artificial, which is situated on the same shore of the lake 500 yards away.' This is the island marked *Bwlc* on the 6″ Ordnance Survey map, and excavation [24] ' showed that it was of the crannog class, being largely composed of stones held in place by piles.' [37a]

Crannog is the term given to the stockaded islands erected in ancient times, mostly in the lochs of Scotland and Ireland. An important example is the lake village at Glastonbury. They were built up on the bottom of the lake and so differ from typical pile dwellings, like those of Switzerland, whose platforms are supported by piles.

The canoe and the crannog in Llangorse Lake suggest an island home, but nothing was found on Bwlc to indicate the period of its occupation. ' Many such,' wrote Fox, ' are known to have been occupied in the Early Iron Age, but they were in use both earlier and much later, as might be expected from the exceptional security which the inhabitants of the lake-dwellings would enjoy . . . The absence of any objects definitely of medieval character on the Llangorse crannog suggests that its occupation ceased before, at the latest, the thirteenth century.'

Leland, it will be remembered, was impressed by the fact that ' at great windes the water doth surge there marvelusly,' and if strong winds happened to coincide with a higher-than-usual water level it would have been by no means impossible for homes on a crannog to have been flooded or even destroyed ; this would also apply to homes built on the shores of the lake itself. In the circumstances, if the legend in the Huw Thomas manuscript is not an imagined tale it may well have been inspired by vague references to a catastrophe of that nature, and the buildings and gardens which, according to Giraldus, the inhabitants sometimes saw upon the waters, may well have originated in almost forgotten stories about homesteads on the crannog—and these may have existed at any time between the Iron Age and the thirteenth century.

This, until comparatively recently, was as far as it was possible to go in speculating about the Llyn Syfaddon story ; that we can now go farther provides an interesting illustration of the way in which new kinds of evidence may open up new lines of inquiry.

Rhŷs suggested that the name Syfaddon ' is probably of Goidelic origin . . . [and] we are at liberty to suppose that it was the name of the wicked princess in the story, and that she was the ancestress of a clan once powerful on and around the lake, which lies within the Goidelic area.' [145h]   The Goidels in Wales were invaders from Ireland.

We are never likely to be able to determine how near to the truth this supposition may be, but we can at least say that if a person named Syfaddon did once exist, it was not an experience of hers that the Huw Thomas legend describes, for the mode of life implied in it belongs to a more recent period than that of the Goidels, and there is nothing in the legend to indicate that the lake was named after a person. But, as we discovered in our study of Llys Helig, however much a story may be embellished, its ' core,' if as a genuine tale it ever had one, is only concealed, not destroyed ; and even if we have to reject the palace of the princess from the Llyn Syfaddon story there may still remain a basic fact in which the story originated.

Pursuing the suggestion that the legend may have been of Goidelic origin, it would appear that if vague references to a sunken ' city ' had really been current in the area from a time so remote that no recollections of its details had survived, a physical change which may actually have taken place at about the beginning of the Iron Age is more likely than any other known or inferred happening in the history of the lake to have given rise to a story like that in the Huw Thomas manuscript.

It has long been realised that certain kinds of fossils throw light upon the climatic conditions which obtained in past ages, and the evidence of fossil plants, particularly of the pollen

grains which are present in beds of peat, has made our knowledge of the conditions which obtained in the prehistoric
human eras much more precise than it used to be.

Pollen is the dust-like material, usually yellow in colour,
which, discharged from the anthers of flowers, causes germin-
ation of the ovules in the same flowers or others of the same
species. Insects are responsible for the carriage of pollen to the
appropriate organs of many plants but from trees it is usually
distributed by the wind : in such cases it may be scattered far
and wide with the result that most of it falls upon the ground or
into lakes and rivers.

The outer coverings of pollen grains are highly resistant to
decay and many kinds are almost indestructible under any of
the natural conditions in which they are likely to come to rest.
Consequently, the pollen of trees of past ages and even of species
that may be locally extinct may be preserved in the peat that
has accumulated over the years in boggy places. The levels at
which the grains occur in the peat are related to the order in
which they were scattered over surfaces that have been buried
one after another as the thickness of the vegetable debris
increased.

Fortunately, pollen grains, which have distinctive surface
markings, and can, within certain limits, be identified, can be
isolated from the peat by drastic chemical reagents, which
destroy most of the ordinary plant debris but leave the pollen
grains almost or quite unharmed. This being the case they
provide information concerning the identity of the trees that
existed in the area in former times, their relative abundance,
and the way in which the general assemblage has changed with
the passage of time.

The picture placed before us by studies in this field is as yet
by no means complete, for not all pollen grains are equally
resistant to decay and those which do remain cannot usually be
identified more closely than by reference to the genus to which
the plant belonged, but there are often other identifiable
fragments which provide supplementary information, and in
spite of its limitations, pollen-analysis makes it possible to
reconstruct in outline the forest history (and therefore, to some

extent, the climatic changes) in the areas where peat has been preserved. It shows, for example, that, speaking generally, the climate of Britain during Bronze Age times tended to be relatively dry whilst wetter conditions prevailed during the succeeding Iron Age.

From a study of certain bogs on the high ground south of Craig y Llyn, the culminant ridge of Blaenau Morgannwg, the hill region of Glamorgan, and of pollen grains found in association with a bronze cauldron recovered from the peaty bottom of Llyn Fawr at the foot of the escarpment, H. A. Hyde has been able to indicate the essential stages in the physical history of the lake. [39]

The cwm in which the lake is situated was formerly occupied by a small glacier, the moraine of which formed a dam across the mouth of the cwm and so provided a hollow in which water could accumulate. The lake almost if not completely disappeared during the dry phase which extended into the Bronze Age, but refilled when wetter conditions returned as the Bronze Age gave place to the Iron Age, say about 500 B.C. It was soon after this that the bronze and iron objects constituting the Llyn Fawr 'hoard' [14] were thrown into the lake or into the swampy bog that represented an early stage in its re-formation. Twenty three objects, including sickles, socketed axes, a sword, and two large cauldrons were found in 1910-11 during the conversion of the lake into a reservoir, and their presence in the peat suggests that the refilling of the lake took place well within the limits of human experience.

There is no evidence upon which we can reconstruct in so much detail the history of Llangorse Lake, but the two lakes are sufficiently near together for both to have been subjected to the same general climatic conditions, although, owing to the considerable difference in aspect and elevation the actual rainfall may have been, as it is now, less at Llangorse than at Llyn Fawr—it averages about 60 inches per annum around Llangorse and over 80 around Llyn Fawr. If Llangorse lake also shrunk during the dry period and expanded when wet conditions again prevailed, human beings could have been there to see the changes.

It transpires, then, that there *were* changes in late prehistoric times which could have provided the foundation for a story of a sunken city or palace in Llangorse Lake, but in the absence of some entirely unpredictable discovery it can never be more than a suggestion—the time gap between the incident and the Huw Thomas manuscript is too great and the connexion between them too intangible to encourage the hope that we shall ever be able to bridge the one or trace the steps in the other. We must be content to recognize that although the stories now told of Llyn Syfaddon are modern inventions or compilations, the history and characteristics of the lake are such as to have created the air of mystery in which legends are born. The story of Kenfig Pool, however, owes nothing either to the circumstances in which the lake originated or to any air of mystery that has surrounded it. The City of Kenfig was overwhelmed by sand, not by water.

Before leaving them we should note that the Llyn Fawr discoveries provide an excellent illustration of the way in which additions to knowledge are often made when they are least expected. When the hoard was discovered in 1911 the technique of pollen analysis had not been developed and the customary cleaning to which the objects were subjected removed any pollen or other minute plant-fragments that may have been attached to them. Fortunately, one of the cauldrons and a sword, put away in a box and forgotten, did not come into the possession of the National Museum of Wales until about 28 years after their discovery. By this time the importance of pollen analysis had been recognized, and it was found that the objects were still partially coated with a thin layer of the deposit in which they had been embedded. Although this, when carefully brushed off, most of it from the cauldron, amounted to less than one fifth of an ounce in weight, it provided information relating to the whole hoard that could not have been obtained except through a medium like this.

(c) The ' sunken city ' in Kenfig Pool, and some other lake legends

Iolo Morganwg's story of Kenfig Pool does not support the view that ' it is an ancient belief in the Principality that lakes generally have swallowed up habitations of man.' It is, rather, an illustration of the desire to elaborate a story of which no more than an indication of its character has survived.

Although situated amidst sand dunes, Kenfig Pool contains fresh water because it results from the impounding of surface waters resting upon impervious glacial deposits. Its early history is wrapped up with that of the local dunes, and we have more than a little evidence to show how and when they were formed.

Along certain parts of the Pembrokeshire coast blown sand rests upon an ancient soil contemporary with that which, along many other parts of the Welsh coast, is associated with peat beds occurring near to or below sea level, or with occurrences on the foreshore of fallen trunks and even the standing stumps of trees, sometimes described as submerged forests.

It will be convenient to deal at a later stage with the nature and significance of these relics of the vegetation of a past age and with the terms used to describe the subdivisions of pre-historic time ; it is sufficient here to say that the situation of the blown sand in Pembrokeshire indicates that here, at least, the sand accumulated after Neolithic or New Stone Age times. [84] Similar evidence from many other parts of the coast from Pembrokeshire to Glamorgan, has been set forth in detail by L. S. Higgins in *An Investigation into the problem of the sand-dune areas on the South Wales Coast.* [66]

At Laugharne the dunes were developing in Late Bronze Age or Early Iron Age times [11] ; at Merthyr Mawr they were forming during Early Iron Age times [38], whilst stone implements and other human artefacts, found on occasions when the sand has been locally blown away to expose the original surface, show that the area between Kenfig Pool and the sea was occupied by man during one or more of these prehistoric ages. [54]

That the dunes in western Glamorgan had became stabilised by early historic times is indicated by the fact that the so-called Via Julia, usually attributed to the 1st century A.D., passed through the area now affected by the sand, which would not have been the case had there been reason to anticipate that the route was in danger.

When documentary records began to accumulate after the Normans came, there is nothing to suggest that the sand in the Kenfig area was regarded as a source of danger, or even of annoyance. Conditions cannot have been alarming in the 12th century, for, some time before 1152, a castle of sorts was built on natural soil and gravel on the site of a later castle that is now engulfed by sand, [147] whilst the original church of St. James had been built before 1154. [12] In 1184 the port of Kenfig accommodated 24 ships, [53] so that the estuary could not then have been sand-choked. All this goes to show that during the 12th century there was neither immediate danger from moving sand, nor any expectation that difficulties were likely to arise from its presence in the area.

During the 13th century conditions changed rapidly and for the worse ; by 1262 it had become necessary to erect a new church, St. Mary Magdalene (hence the village name, Mawdlam) on higher ground farther inland [66b] ; by 1316 certain pastures had been overwhelmed by the sand [53a] ; and there is documentary evidence of the existence of the pool in 1365, for in that year two men were summoned to attend the church to answer to a charge of illegal fishing in Kenfig Pool and Avan Water. [53f]

Evidence pointing to a sudden encroachment by sand in the 13th century comes also from the Margam Burrows a little farther north. The Margam Charters refer to the Hermitage of Theodoric near the mouth of the River Avan, but not after about A.D. 1249. This suggests that it had ceased to function, and that the building was overwhelmed suddenly is indicated by the fact that, when discovered, the ruins were buried to the depth of the upper storey, and a clay partition, 3 inches thick and plastered with mortar on each side, was found still standing supported by the sand. [53a] So fragile a structure would have crumbled and fallen had it been exposed for any considerable time in a ruined building.

The pool most likely occupies part of the original estuary of the River Kenfig and results from the blocking of the river mouth by sand, giving rise first to a marshy tract and then to a lake—but this was after the establishment of the castle and churches. As the mouth of the river was pushed steadily farther north towards its present position communication with the lake was maintained by a stream flowing northwards past the old town. Both the shape of the pool at its northern end and the ' slacks ' in the dunes suggest that it may originally have had an outlet in that direction. The former existence of such a stream is suggested by a charter of Thomas Despenser [53c] dated 1397. It speaks of a stream ' which used to run from the southern to the northern water of Kenfig,' i.e., from Kenfig Pool to the estuary of the Kenfig River, and called it the Black River, a name which survived until modern times in Gwter-ddu.

It appears, then, that a small lake, which came into existence in the 14th century on the site of a marsh created by encroach-ment of the sand, gradually assumed something approaching its present size, after which the sand moved across and obliter-ated the stream which drained it. That such diversion is possible is illustrated by the way in which, within living memory, the sand of Merthyr Mawr Warren, only a few miles from the Kenfig dunes, has moved across a stream, caused the death of trees originally on the far side, and compelled the water to seek an entirely new channel.

To round off the story of the pool—we find that by 1480 the Via Julia had been abandoned and a new road made further inland. By 1485 a new St. James Church had been built by the side of this road and when Leland went there in 1538 he saw ' a little village on the east side of Kenfig, and a castel, booth in ruine and almost shokid and devourid with the sandes that the Severn Se ther castith up.' In 1660 a Survey and Presentment describing the ' Town and Burrough of Kenffig ' included a statement to the effect that ' the sand had overcomed (time out of mind) a great number of dwelling houses ' [53e]. Since then the sand has again become stable in parts and a new road to Port Talbot has been made along the course of the old Via Julia.

These inquiries into the origin of Kenfig Pool have not been undertaken in order to discover whether there is any historical foundation for Iolo's story—we know that there is not but in order to see whether it is likely that any tradition relating to its origin was associated with the lake in times long past. The available evidence seems to be entirely against such a notion.

Just when Kenfig Pool first acquired the tradition of a sunken city we cannot now determine, for although many 17th and 18th century writers referred to one none of them gave any details. The reference made by R. Warner, in the account of his *Second Walk through Wales* (1797) is typical. ' Equally void of credit,' he wrote, ' is the popular tradition of a city having formerly stood on the spot which the lake now occupies : this is a fable common to many places.'

By the time Kenfig Pool began to be mentioned in documents, the stories of Helig and of Seithennin (whom we have yet to meet) were already misty memories of a distant past and the crannog in Llangorse Lake had long been deserted ; but the nineteenth century had dawned before the details of a Kenfig inundation story were given to the world, and then it was a clumsily conceived story with no valid claim to be regarded as a folk-tale.

Living as he did in Glamorgan, Iolo must have been familiar with the ' ruined city of Kenfig ' and the pool amidst the sand, and his reference to smoking chimneys may well have been suggested by recollections of sand blowing around exposed fragments of the buildings that had been overwhelmed during the formation of the dunes. One is certainly reminded of chimneys by a distant view of the remains of the castle. There is nothing in the lake itself to have suggested the existence of sunken ruins, and soundings show that even when the water level is highest the maximum depth is nowhere more than 12 feet.

All that we can discover about them suggests that the modern stories which are told of Llys Helig and Kenfig Pool, (and the same applies, as we shall see later on, to the modern stories of Bala Lake and Llynclys) are not survivals of an ancient tradition concerning the lakes of Wales. The last two came into being about the middle of the 19th century, and the first two only a little earlier—well after 1800. All of them seem to have been influenced directly or indirectly by a story told of Llyn Syfaddon, but that only carries us back to a little before 1700 and its origin is doubtful.

We can now see the danger of drawing conclusions from collections of apparently related legends without first of all assessing very carefully their validity as evidence. In introducing the Llys Helig story here quoted on page 94, Gwynn Jones wrote, ' Another detailed inundation story is that of Tyno Helig ' [81a], adding, a few pages later, ' A tale told of Llyn Syfaddon, Brecknockshire, corresponds exactly, to the Tyno Helig story.' Actually, however, the detailed story in question only goes back to 1862 ; its correspondence with the Llyn Syfaddon legend is due to the fact that it resulted from the fusion of that story with an earlier, simpler, inundation story centred upon Llys Helig, supplemented by a reference to fishes, introduced no doubt, because it was the sea that was involved and not the water spewed out during an earthquake.

In the case of Kenfig Pool, if there ever was an old local legend on to which the lake story was grafted, we know nothing of its details, but in Iolo's version the local touch was provided by introducing the Clares, and the novel element was the smoke coming from the chimneys of buildings that had been overwhelmed. The treasures and dishonest lover are recent additions to the stories of Conway Bay and Kenfig Pool, and throw no light upon the former geographical distribution of really old tales.

Reference was made in an earlier chapter to Llyn Gwyn or Llyngwyn, a small lake south-east of Rhayader in Radnorshire, of which Lewis Morris wrote, ' here tradition says a town was swallowed up.' The name may indeed, like Llynclys, suggest the Welsh verb *llyncu*, to swallow, but it has not yet been possible to discover when and how this tradition originated. It does not appear to have become a popular folk-tale. There is, on one side of the lake, a semicircular earth-work of which the two ends are about 40 yards apart. It rises from 18 to 20 feet above the surrounding ground level and from 10 to 12 feet above the area which it encloses, but its origin has not been satisfactorily explained. It cannot have been built for defence since the site is so situated as to be open to attack, but it has been suggested (without supporting evidence) that it may have been of monastic origin, in connection with fish breeding and preservation.

One thing, however, is certain—the earthwork is more recent than the lake, for its well-finished ends show that it does not represent the surviving half of a circular enclosure that has suffered erosion or submergence. The idea that a town has been swallowed up is quite untenable, and even the local tradition, mentioned in the Radnorshire volume of the Cambridge County Geographies, that the earthwork ' marks the spot where an important town used to be,' is open to the objection that about one seventh of an acre is rather a small site for an important town !

The thesis developed in this chapter is that the similarity between the stories with which we are now concerned does not indicate that they represent, in their modern forms, survivals of ancient folk-tales once widely distributed in Wales but are, rather, evidence that an old story has travelled in comparatively recent times and has grown whilst doing so. In many cases the versions which ultimately appeared in print were concocted by essayists, and we have no means of assessing the part which local country folk may have played in their conception and preservation.

VIII
SOME VARIATIONS OF THE PRINCIPAL TALES

THE nineteenth century history of the Llyn Syfaddon story illustrates the gradual introduction of new material, often by intermingling with other classes of story (in this case the story of water sprites) and the stories of other lakes, e.g., Llyn Cwm Llwch.

A story about an inundation affecting Llynclys near Oswestry was known in the 16th century, but it concerned a wicked king and was quite different from any of the modern versions, which originated in a ballad written by a local gentleman early in the 19th century.

(a) Llyn Syfaddon and Llyn Cwm Llwch

IN reviewing the stories that have contributed to the modern version of the legend of Llys Helig we have considered only those forms—usually the earliest which had been committed to writing—that influenced the tale, but there were other forms as well, and, for obvious reasons, reference to them has been reserved until the principal stories had been told.

Here, for example, is another Llyn Syfaddon story, as given in *The Mythology and Rites of the British Druids*, by Edward Davies (1809) :

' The site of the present lake was formerly occupied by a large city ; but the inhabitants were reported to be very wicked. The king of the country sent his servant to examine into the truth of this rumour, adding a threat, that in case it should prove to be well-founded, he would destroy the place as an example to his other subjects. The minister arrived at the town in the evening. All the inhabitants were engaged in riotous festivity, and wallowing in excess. Not one of them regarded the stranger, or offered him the rites of hospitality. At last, he saw the open door of a mean habitation, into which he entered. The family had deserted it to repair to the scene of the tumult, all but one infant, who lay weeping in the cradle. The royal favourite soothed the little innocent. In this situation the stranger passed the night ; and whilst he was diverting the child he accidently dropped his glove into the cradle. The next morning he departed before it was light, to carry his melancholy tidings to the king.

' He had just left the town when he heard a noise behind him like a tremendous crack of thunder mixed with dismal shrieks and lamentations. He stopped to listen. Now it sounded like the dashing of waves : and presently all was dead silence. He could not see what had happened, as it was still dark, and he felt no inclination to return into the city, so he pursued his journey till sunrise. The morning was cold. He searched for his gloves, and finding but one of them he presently recollected where he had left the other. He determined to return for that which he had left behind. When he was come near to the site of the town, he observed with surprise that none of the buildings presented themselves to his view. . . . The whole plain was covered with a lake. Whilst he was gazing at this novel and terrific scene, he remarked a little spot in the middle of the water : the wind gently wafted it towards the bank where he stood ; as it drew near he recognised the identical cradle in which he had left his glove. His joy on receiving this royal favour was only heightened by the discovery that the little object of his compassion had reached the shore alive and unhurt. He carried the infant to the king, and told his majesty that this was all which he had been able to save out of the wretched place.'

In recounting this story Davies said ' The old story of its formation [i.e., of the lake] is not totally forgotten. I recollect some of its incidents, as related by an old man of the town of Hay,' and many years later the same version was given as the ' story of Llangorse Lake,' in The Folk-lore and Folk stories of Wales, by Marie Trevelyan. [166] It is, however, altogether different from the story told in the manuscript which Huw Thomas had, and it neither fits into the sequence of inundation stories relating to lakes in Wales, nor, as far as I have yet discovered, was it committed to writing before Edward Davies included it in his book about Druid Mythology.

In its beginning the story told by the old man of Hay resembles a version (to be mentioned in a later chapter) of the

Llynclys legend describing the destruction of the palace of
Benlli, and one cannot help feeling that vague echoes of that
story, as told by Nennius, had been supplemented by memories
of sermons about the destruction of Sodom and Gomorrah, and
about the discovery of the infant Moses. The integration may
indeed have been first effected in a sermon intended to dis-
courage sin by enlarging upon the results of indulging in it,
and as far as our present knowledge goes we cannot regard the
story as an ancient Legend of Llangorse. We can, however,
see where Iolo Morganwg may have got the idea of the gloves
which he introduced into his Kenfig story, for *The Mythology and
Rites of the British Druids* was published whilst he was collecting
the material which was subsequently printed as the *Iolo
Manuscripts* !

Yet another Llangorse story was told by William Howells in
his *Cambrian Superstitions* (1831),

'Llyn Savadhan,' he wrote, 'is a curtain o'er a scene, a
lesson unto man, and the winding sheet of many a fair corse.'
According to tradition, ' There stood a palace on the spot
now occupied by the lake. The lord was a dissipated and
sacreligious man who oppressed the peasantry.' One evening
he had summoned two bards to play at a party, and at
midnight ' a loud clap of thunder (far louder than the terrible
noise which the lake makes when its ice cracks) shook the
foundation of the palace . . . a voice was heard to say
' Vengeance is come.' . . . The minstrels saw a hand beckoning them ; they followed their guide for some distance but he
disappeared, and on looking towards the palace they saw
that, it too, had disappeared ' and an expanse of water lay
bubbling on the spot where it had stood.' [68]

It does not seem to have occurred to the originator of the
story that it was hardly necessary to create a lake approaching
400 acres in extent in order to destroy a palace, but in repeating
it Howells most likely did so with his tongue in his cheek, for he
also wrote ' Traditions, it is pretty generally known, are relics
of heathenism, or popish superstition . . . most of them [are]
popish blarney.' [68a]

This ' superstition ' serves to remind us how little we really

now about the ultimate origin of some of these said-to-be-old
stories. It includes elements which we have already encountered
as current before Howells' book was published, e.g., the bad
overlord, the clap of thunder, and the noise made by the ice,
but there are also other familiar elements, which, as far as I
have been able to discover had not previously appeared either
in manuscript or print, e.g., the expression ' Vengeance is
come,' the harpers, and the hand which beckoned away from
the impending disaster. Are we then to regard his story as one
of the sources of those we have already discussed ?

It looks as if he had come across a story including elements
which, apart from his own references to them, we have only been
able to trace back to Robert Williams and to 1835, and we are left
to wonder if such a story was ever committed to writing, and if
so whether a copy still lies unnoticed in some private library.
We have here an illustration of the fact that the importance of
a work does not necessarily lie in the degree of erudition is
displays. Taken as a whole, *Cambrian Superstitions* is more
amusing than reliable, but it either proves the existence of a
story including the expression ' Vengeance is come ' at least four
years before it was incorporated into a printed reference to Llys
Helig, or else it is to Howells that we owe the now familiar
phrase. There is, indeed, a reference to vengeance in the Huw
Thomas manuscript but it was in the form of a question, not an
assertion or a threat.

A version of ' The legend of Savaddon Lake ' given in
Folklore for 1908 illustrates very well the way in which a story
may receive additions implying a precision to which the earlier
writers never pretended. It tells us, quite objectively, that
Llangorse lake was formerly called ' Savaddon Lake ' after the
city of that name, ' a town identified with the Roman Loventium,' which lies buried beneath its waters ; an amplification of
this form of the story, given in *Legends and Folk-lore of South Wales*
a school reader published in 1931, opens with the very positive
assertion that, ' In the time of the Romans, the city of Savaddan
was ruled over by a very high spirited beautiful princess called
Gwenonwy.' [150]

Briefly, the remainder of the story in this version is as follows :

of many who desired to marry her, the princess would conside
none save Gruffydd of Bronllys, son of a neighbouring prince
Although of gentle birth he was poor and Gwenonwy could no
marry him because she had promised her father she would no
unite herself to anyone who was below her in rank or in riches
She told Gruffydd to go out into the world to gain wealth and
honour by fighting, and to return in a year and a day.

His journeys brought him more fighting than money, but a
the end of the specified time he decided to return to Gwenonwy
On the way he stopped at a monastery known as Bryn-yr-allt
on a hill overlooking the Lake 'Savaddon', and sought lodging
for the night.

Whilst in bed he heard monks in an adjacent room talking
about the Prior who was expected back on the following day
bringing with him gifts from Howell, Prince of Cwm-du
Seeing in this an opportunity to secure the wealth he needed
Gruffydd set out next morning, hid in some bushes by the side
of the road along which the Prior would have to travel, killed
him, and took the treasure.

He told Gwenonwy what he had done and she sent to the
Priory for monks to come and perform the wedding ceremony
Unfortunately for Gruffydd, however, some of the monks had
gone to meet the Prior and had found him mortally wounded
by the roadside ; before he died he told them who it was that
attacked him.

The Prior's successor, Owen, performed the ceremony, but
condemned Gruffydd for his crime and Gwenonwy for her
acquiescence in it. He foretold that punishment would follow
' in the fourth generation from now.' Infuriated by what she
regarded as an insult, Gwenonwy ordered the Prior to be cast
into prison, there to remain until the fourth generation, after
which, if his prophecy were not fulfilled, he was to be put to
death by burning.

In due course a great-grandchild was born, and when the
baby was 40 days old and no catastrophe had befallen them, a
feast was arranged at the palace and the now aged Prior was
brought before the company. He repeated his warning that
vengeance was at hand unless the guilty ones repented—a

warning which, in the version we are now considering, assumed the now familiar form 'Vengeance will come'—and he was taken to the top of a tall tower which was set on fire. As the fire burned a grey mist settled over the valley and, when it had cleared, the town and its environs had been replaced by a lake.

One of the monks standing by the side of the lake saw something floating upon the water, and on rowing towards it found it to be the cradle with the infant son of the last princess of Savaddon. (It is not explained how a boat happened to be so conveniently available in a place where hitherto there had been no water ; perhaps it was miraculously created with the lake !) The child was taken to the monastery where he was reared and ultimately became a monk and built a hut on the edge of the lake : the church of Llangasty was named after him, the monks having called him Gastayn.

The authority for the version of the story given in *Folklore* was Mr. Isaac Hughes of Treharris, 'who stated that it is as given to him by an old resident.' The age of the resident is not mentioned, but if we suppose him to have been 70, and to have heard the story when he was a child, we are only taken back to the middle of the 19th century, by which time, as we have seen, writers were busy mixing and supplementing the inundation tales of earlier days.

We have no means of discovering exactly how or by whom the circumstantial details and names in Isaac Hughes' version of the story were added, but one has the impression that so sophisticated a tale was produced by one who had read many books, and either deliberately or involuntarily jumbled what he had gleaned.

The reference to Loventium suggests the influence of an early edition of Camden, and, in his poverty and adventures (although not in his crimes) Gruffydd reminds us of the early 12th century Gruffydd ap Rhys, 'forlorn scion of an ancient race of kings,' [91c] who rebelled against Henry I and the Normans who had occupied what should have been his territory.

Giraldus Cambrensis mentions a story with a miraculous event associating Gruffydd with Llangorse Lake. In convers-

ation with Henry I, Milo Fitzwalter told of how, one da
when he was walking on the shores of the lake with Gruffydd a
Rhys ap Tewdur, ' upon the approach of the rightful princ
[i.e., Gruffydd] the birds of the lake joined in concert, and b
the clapping of their wings seem to testify an universal joy
[78b]. The foregoing quotation is from Theophilus Jones'
History of the County of Brecknock (1803), and Richard Col
Hoare's translation of Giraldus was published in 1806, so tha
whoever originated the story which found its way into *Folklor*
had ample modern material to inspire or to stimulate hi
imagination.

The reference to Bronllys in Mr. Hughes' story also suggest
the influence of Giraldus. Describing the death of Mahel d
Newmarch, whilst on a visit to Walter de Clifford at ' Brendlai
Castle,' Giraldus records that the building caught fire anc
Mahel was mortally wounded by a stone which fell from the
top of the principal tower. He despatched messengers to recal
the Bishop of St. David's, whom he had persecuted, and expressed the opinion that too severe a vengeance had been meted
out to him, for he had not been given time to repent. [78c]

These references to a death associated with a fire and a high
tower, and a church dignitary who had been ill-treated,
confirms the view that the version of the Llyn Syfaddon story
which Mr. Hughes provided for *Folklore* was not a current
folk-tale but was compounded of the vague recollections of an
imaginative nineteenth century reader.

Another modern story associated with Llangorse Lake
suggests the possibility that it will contribute to an inundation
yet to come ! It is given in *The Welsh Fairy Book*, by W. Jenkyn
Thomas, a book which proved so popular that it has been reprinted at least eight times between its first appearance in 1907
and 1952 [163]. The story relates to Llyn Cwm Llwch and is
too long to quote in full but the following summary will serve
our purpose :

At the foot of Pen-y-Fan, the principal peak of the Beacons
of Brecon is a lake called Llyn Cwm-llwch, overhung by
frowning precipices. . . . In very ancient times there was a
door in a rock hard by, which . . . disclosed a passage leading

to a small island in the centre of the lake. This island was, however, invisible to those who stood upon the shore.

People who went to the island were hospitably received by the fairies who lived there. Resentful at a guest who took away a flower, the fairies closed the door and for hundreds of years it could not be found. One day the local people planned to drain the lake to see if the fairies had left any treasure behind, and they dug a trench thirty yards deep (it can be seen to this day). Just as they had got to the point when another blow with the pick would have broken the bank and let out the water there was a flash of lightning and a peal of thunder, and from the lake there arose a gigantic man who warned them that if they disturbed his peace he would drown the valley of the Usk, beginning with Brecon Town.

As he disappeared he made some reference to the token of the cat. This was explained by one of those present. One day, when young, he had to drown a cat that belonged to an old woman. He tied a stone about its neck and threw it into the water.

The next day he went to Llyn Syfaddon to fish, and saw there the cat floating in the middle of the lake. He was frightened because he knew that the lakes were miles apart, and no stream flowed from one to the other.

The local people concluded that there was some mysterious connection between the lakes, and that if they tried to drain the small one the large one would feed it and cause its vast body of water to be discharged over the whole of the adjacent country. Accordingly, they left the trench unfinished [163c].

As far as I have been able to discover, the essential parts of the story now associated with Llyn Cwm Llwch—those relating to the central island, the fairies, and the warning given to the people who set out to drain the lake—first appeared in print in 1809 when Davies included the story in his *Mythology and Rites of the British Druids*, and there is nothing to suggest that it exists in an earlier manuscript.

Davies, however, did not indicate the identity of the lake any more than that it was ' in the mountains near Brecknock,'

adding ' I recollect a Mabinogi or Mythological tale respecting
this piece of water.'

Those who mentioned Llyn Cwm Llwch in their Tours
variously described it ' a fair well spring,' ' a small brackish
pool, being only a deposit of rain-water and sometimes perfectly
dry,' and ' a large lake of immeasurable depth,' [67a] but it was
not until the end of the 19th century that we have any authentic
record of the story as told by Davies being specifically associated
with it. When answering inquiries by Sir John Rhŷs about the
identity of the lake, Mr. Ivor James, sometime Registrar of the
University of Wales, wrote, ' The lake you want is Llyn Cwm
Llwch, and the legend is very well known locally.' [145u] No
authority for the identification was given, and it is necessary to
bear in mind that Lewis Morris cited Llwch as a word used
in Carmarthenshire and Brecknockshire to signify a lake [110]
and that, in his additional notes on Brecknockshire in the 1695
edition of *Britannia*, Edward Lhuyd mentioned that amongst
the lakes associated with sunken cities was ' Llyn Lhan Llwch
in Caermarthenshire ' [10b].

In the version of the story which came to the notice of Mr.
James the warning was given in a Welsh couplet which he
translated as follows :

> If I get no quiet in my place,
> I shall drown the town of Brecon.

Now Llyn Cwm Llwch is very small—only about 130 yards
by 80, and 18 feet deep when the water is at its highest level—
and it seems very unlikely that even credulous folk of pre-
nineteenth century days could have seen in so small a body of
water a potential danger to Brecon about five miles away. It
looks as if a possible catastrophe that had been associated with a
larger lake, perhaps Llyn y Fan Fach farther west, had been
foisted upon the little pond nestling under Craig Cwm Llwch,
for although differing in size the two lakes are similar in
situation, in nature, and in origin. Each lies in a cwm at the
base of the great northwards facing escarpment of Old Red
Sandstone, and in each the water is dammed back by the
debris deposited by a small glacier that once occupied the Cwm
[67]. In each, also, the natural outlet is a gully cut, mainly in

the glacial moraine, by water which flows out of the lake, and this might have suggested the possibility of draining the lake, as well as the notion that if the barrier were to be cut through by natural agencies damage might be done by the escaping waters. We shall meet with a similar fear, that disaster might follow an attempt to drain the lake, in connection with a story told of Llyn Barfog near Towyn.

Llyn y Fan Fach has been mentioned in this connection because it figures so prominently in local lake legends, but another possible (and perhaps more likely) origin for the notion that the overflowing of a high-level lake might give rise to floods in the valley below is found in one of the Harleian Manuscripts (No. 7107) in the British Museum to which my attention was drawn by the Rev. J. Jones-Davies. An unknown author, writing about 1695, recorded of Llyn y Fan Fawr, the companion lake to Llyn y Fan Fach, that in 1687, ' a large part of the rock shelveing above it, on Saterday December the tenth, fell down into the poole makeing the water overflow all the land about it, doing greate mischief to the Country and caused the river Uske to breake over its banks in a most dreadfull manner.'

It is by no means improbable that in the thaw after a severe frost a great rock fall may have caused the lake to overflow, but it would not have affected the valley of the Usk. In existing circumstances the stream flowing from the lake carries its water into the Tawe, and even if an unusually high surge could have carried water over the ridge of glacial deposits at the northern end it would have entered one of the headwaters of Afon Hydef, four miles or so away from its junction with the Usk.

The association of a legend relating to a possible flooding of the Usk valley with something that happened at Llyn y Fan Fawr would be just another illustration of the way stories grow by accretion, and the writer of the seventeenth century manuscript was speaking for the future as well as for our time when he continued : ' of the aforesaid poole . . . are tould many rediculous stories not worth recitall.'

We are left in doubt as to who introduced the connexion between the small high-level lake and the larger low-level one at Llangorse, if indeed there ever was one in genuine local lore ;

I

perhaps some one realized that since so small a sheet of water could not in itself give rise to serious floods, some additional source of supply had to be invoked if the tale was to appear even remotely credible, and the well-known larger lake was selected for the purpose, regardless of the fact that it lay about 1400 feet below the level of the one it was supposed to have the power to feed, and about 8 miles away from it on the other side of the River Usk !

The story of the cat is, of course, nonsense, but the idea that Llyn Cwm Llwch might have some subterranean outlet is not so ridiculous as might at first appear, because although there is usually water running into it, it often happens that none appears to be running out. This, however, is not because there are underground fissures, as there might be if the lake were situated on the outcrop of a rock like the Carboniferous Limestone, but because, even when its level is too low for there to be an issuing stream, the water seeps away through the permeable gravelly deposits of the dam to which the lake owes its existence, and appears again at the surface considerably lower down the valley.

The reference to the man who came out of the lake was, in all probability, inspired directly or indirectly by a passage in the Mabinogi of *Branwen the Daughter of Llŷr* (to which we shall give more attention later on). In explaining how a certain cauldron came into his possession Brân said that he saw a huge yellow-haired man coming out of a lake, carrying the vessel on his back.

Taking all things into consideration, especially its complete disregard of local geography, the story of Llyn Cwm Llwch seems, like the modern versions of some of the other legends we have considered, to be a literary effort compounded of several stories rather than a real local folk tale.

Before leaving this group of lakes it is interesting to recall that, of the stories associated with Llyn y Fan Fach nearly all, like the Llyn Cwm Llwch story, involve some disturbance of the surface of the water—the emergence of a gigantic hairy man [145n] or the rising of a beautiful water nymph [145g]. Whilst the stories themselves may be variants of well known and widely distributed legends their association with either or both of the lakes could have been due to a rarely manifested physical phenomenon which, like the weird noises heard on the shores of Llangorse lake, attracted the attention of persons wandering in the vicinity.

Shepherds and others visiting Llyn y Fan Fach have from time to time reported spontaneous disturbances and upheavals of the water and there is no reason for doubting the accuracy of the reports. As we have seen, the water is dammed back by glacial deposits which, being permeable, allow some of it to escape. If, on occasion, layers of silt should temporarily seal the floor of the lake, water already in the debris beneath might continue to drain away and create a partial vacuum in the interstices. When, in due course, the sealing layer gave way, air would escape and disturb the surface of the water for no reason that would be apparent to an observer on the shore. It is not difficult to imagine that such an occurrence, in days less sophisticated than those in which we live today, would remind a surprised and probably somewhat frightened observer, or someone to whom he recounted his experience, of stories like those which came to be associated with the lake.

(b) Llynclys : the old legend and the modern ballad

It is, perhaps, understandable that large and well known lakes like Bala (with an area of nearly 1,100 acres) and Llangorse (nearly 400 acres) should have had their legends, even if they were imported ones ; the same applies, in some measure, to Kenfig Pool, which although much smaller, covering only about 70 acres, is still a sizeable sheet of water ; but it is reasonable to ask why so small and little-known a lake as Llynclys should have been singled out for a similar distinction. It covers less than 6 acres, and although indicated it is not named on the popular edition of the one-inch Ordnance Survey Map. The lake lies near the Welshpool road about three miles south of Oswestry, and if one may judge from its representation on the early Survey maps (e.g., the edition of 1837) was even smaller before railway construction affected the drainage in the vicinity.

The answer is that there was a still older story associated with the lake—a simple tale, devoid of those details which appeal to the popular imagination. By the 19th century it had been forgotten except by those who read books like Llwyd's *Commentarioli* and its translation *The Breviary of Britayne* (1573), in which alone it had been printed, or by those who had dim recollections of having heard an account of what Llwyd wrote. In such circumstances it would have been quite natural, when interest in flood legends was revived early in the 19th century, for the Kenfig or Bala stories to have reminded someone that Llynclys once had something of the kind. This is how Llwyd told the story late in the 16th century :

> ' Let us now come to *Powys*, the second kyngedome of Wales, which in the time of German Altisiodorensis, [i.e., St. Germanus of Auxerre] which preached sometime there, agaynst Pelagius Heresie . . . The kynge whereof, because he refused to heare that good man, by the secret and terrible judgement of God, with his Palace, and all his householde, was swallowed up into the bowels of the Earth, in that place, whereat not farre from Oswestry, is now a standing water, of unknowne depth called Lhunclys ' . . . [167a]

In telling this story Llwyd explained that he regarded the name (Llynclys) as meaning the place of the devouring, implying that it was given to the lake because it stood on the site of a dwelling that had been swallowed up, but although the name is derived from *llyncu*, to swallow, and *llys*, a court or palace, the nature and situation of the lake indicate that such a legend is not likely to have originated in recollections, however dim, of circumstances associated with its formation.

Llynclys Pool (as it is called on the 6" Ordnance Survey Map) fed a small stream that flows into the River Morda, which is a tributary of the Vyrnwy. It lies in a slight hollow floored by relatively impervious superficial deposits brought thither by ice during the Glacial Period or by the waters that resulted from the melting of the ice as that Period came to an end, and it received the drainage from gravelly deposits also of glacial origin that rise to higher levels around it. In other words it is

a relic of the Ice Age and existed long before the time of St.
Germanus or any other Christian father. Even if it had wholly
or partially dried up and had been refilled or extended before
or soon after the beginning of the historic era, its site, before it
was a lake, would have been a water-logged marshy tract, and
not one on which even the most primitive of dwellings would
have been erected, to say nothing of the residence of a person of
importance. It was too small and too open to observation to
have been a safe retreat like some of the elevated tracts in the
marshes of Fenland.

Llwyd's reference to St. Germanus suggests the direction in
which we may look for the origin of the tale. There is nothing
in any of the accounts of Germanus of Auxerre about an incident
involving a king who lived where Llynclys now stands, but
Nennius mentions a city which was destroyed by fire because its
king, a wicked tyrant, refused to admit St. Germanus to it.
Llwyd was wrong in speaking of St. Germanus of *Auxerre*, for the
saint of whom Nennius wrote was a native of Armorica who
became Bishop of the Isle of Man [51b]. He did not come to
Britain until A.D. 462, after the death of his namesake of
Auxerre whose visits were made in 429 and 447, principally
with a view to helping the British clergy to combat the teaching
of Pelagius. This included the notion that it is possible for a
man to live without sin, solely by obedience to the dictates of
his own reason and in the absence of any assistance from God, so
that from the nature of his mission, Germanus of Auxerre
would have associated principally with professing Christians
and is not likely to have wished to visit a wicked king.

Nennius tells of a visit made by *his* Germanus to the iniquit-
ous and tyrannical Benlli, King of Powys. The king refused to
admit the holy man to his city and harshly treated the messenger that was sent to him. One of the king's servants entertained
the messenger who told him to come away from the city (or
citadel) and, with his nine sons, to fast all night, not looking
around whatever might happen to attract their attention. That
night ' fire from heaven ' consumed the city and all who were
therein. [169a]. A fuller account of ' this monkish story ' as
Lewis Morris called it, and a discussion of the identity of

Germanus and of the sources of the information drawn upon by
Nennius will be found in *The Lives of the British Saints* [51d], but
the foregoing summary is sufficient for our present purpose.

There is no mention of Llynclys in this story, and Benlli is
described as reigning over Iâl, a region between Ruthin and
Mold, eighteen miles or so north of Oswestry, not three to the
south of it ; this being the case it is significant that one of the
hills in the Clwydian Range, Moel Fenlli, has a hillfort on the
western part of its summit about 1674 feet above sea-level [43]
whilst the church of Llanarmon yn Iâl in an adjoining parish,
with a holy well, Ffynnon Armon, preserves the name Garmon,
derived from Germanus—and these are the names of the two
principal characters in the story.

The hill-fort on Moel Fenlli has an encircling rampart of
earth and rubble, and since no remains of habitations are
visible within the stronghold it is probable that they were huts
of wattle-and-daub or of wood. A fire that might have destroyed buildings of that nature is as likely to have been due to lightning or some other cause associated with a storm as to human
carelessness or malice.

Excavations on the site have yielded potsherds and glass of
Romano-British manufacture, together with coins and articles
of lead, iron, and brass [34]. These, and other objects found by
accident, ' show that the stronghold was occupied by a large
native population, say from A.D. 100—400 . . . but the hill fort
would seem to have continued to be inhabited rather longer
than the date proved by the relics,' for the fourth century coins
might well have been in circulation until the middle of the
fifth. [42]

The archaeological evidence, then, suggests that the
occupation of the site came to an end at about the time which
tradition assigns to the attempts made by Germanus to visit
Benlli, whilst literary evidence suggests that the story had been
committed to writing within 150 years of the event it purported
to record, for the *Historia Britonum* which Nennius edited at the
close of the eighth century is believed to have been originally
compiled about the year 600—in other words, tradition and

archaeological evidence converge to a degree that seems to point to more than coincidence.

Plausible as this explanation may seem, however, we have to recognise that we have no proof that the story has anything to do with an event that actually took place in the region to which it is supposed to relate. The messenger, the one hospitable household, the warning that those destined to escape should on no account look back, and the fire from heaven, may be no more than echoes of a sermon describing the destruction of Sodom and Gomorrah.

It is easy to understand why flood should have been substituted for fire, when the calamity had to be associated with a lake in a valley instead of a group of wooden buildings near the top of a hill. It is common folk-practice, when something required in a story is not locally available, to introduce something else that the locality can supply.

The modern versions of the Llynclys story are entirely different from those we have just considered. As an example we may take the one given in *Legends and Folklore of North Wales* [151]. It might, of course, be argued that a school reader need not be taken seriously in a discussion like this ; but, in fact, it is highly probable that such works are largely responsible for many dogmatic assertions by adults who have forgotten when and whence they obtained their information.

The Llynclys story as told in the book just mentioned is as follows :

' At Llynclys, not far from Oswestry, there is a very deep pool known as Llynclys Pool. The name means "swallowed court."

There was once a king who held his court at the spot where the pool now stands. Now at this court there was a clerk called Clerk Wylan, who was renowned for his knowledge and cunning.

The queen of the court was also famous, but for her beauty not for her cunning. Other men envied the King his lovely wife, but, strangely enough, he did not seem to be happy with her and people wondered why.

At last, after he had been married for about nine years,

the king told Clerk Wylan, in secret, how he had found the queen. "It was when I was out hunting upon the hillside one day" he said, "she is not of human origin at all. She is of the underworld. She only married me on condition that I allowed her to be away from me one night in every week, without asking her where she went or why."

Then said the wily Clerk, "I think I can give back your peace of mind if you will hand the queen to me. Also you shall give me a tenth of your cattle every year, and a tenth part of the wine in your wine-cellar."

The king agreed to these terms. Accordingly, Wylan hurried away to a cave in the rocks where he knew there was an entrance away down to the land of fairies. He began to recite magic spells and thus attracted the queen inside the cave. At once the beautiful lady was changed into the grimmest, ugliest, old hag that could ever be imagined.

"Now our spells have clashed," she said, "I was once a witch but I had the power to change myself into the most beautiful of women for six nights out of seven so that I could attract the king. But on the seventh day of each week I must become again the hideous hag you see before you. My husband has betrayed me into your hands. That I know. Now you shall keep me, and him will I punish".

Then, in the words of the ballad :

> Down went the king and his palace and all,
> And the waters now o'er it flow,
> And already in his hall, the flag reeds tall
> And the long, green rushes grow !

That was how the pool received the name of Llynclys, "swallowed court".' [151]

This story differs in many of its details from the ballad upon which it purports to be based. That, written by J. F. M. Dovaston early in the 19th century [23], begins :

> Clerk Willin he sat at King Alaric's board,
> And a cunning clerk was he,
> For he'd lived in the land of Oxenford,
> With the sons of Grammarie.

It then tells of how the king was worried because his queen, in accordance with a promise exacted when she married him, used to leave him on one night in seven and gave no account of her actions whilst she was away.

Clerk Willin promised, in return for ten oxen to be given annually to the monks at Whiteminster, to remove the cause of the king's distress. He went to a certain cave, and by means of magic discovered that the queen, on each seventh day, had to become the ugly ogress he saw there.

When the queen realised that she had been discovered, she said :

> Our power is pass'd, our spells have clash'd,
> No charm can our fate redress,
> And a penitent void for life art thou,
> And I, a grim ogress.

The fate, as indicated by the lines already quoted, involved the swallowing up of the king, his palace, and all associated with it.

Discussing the ballad and the story it tells, Rhŷs expressed the opinion that it was not clear how much came from the legend, and how much from the poet's own muse [145,0]. Had he seen the original publication he would have had no doubt on the matter. Although, as a native of West Felton near Oswestry, Dovaston had ample opportunity for becoming familiar with local lore, the preamble to his poem does not encourage us to set much store by it. He explained that

' Llunck-llys Pool is a small but beautiful lake . . . near Oswestry. The name in Welsh signifies *Sunk Palace*, and the vulgar have a firmly-believed superstition . . . corresponding with the catastrophe of this ballad. . . . In the summer months fishing parties of ladies and gentlemen frequently spent the day on it in a boat with music and refreshments ; for one of such occasions this ballad was hastily written when my ingenious friend Mr. T. Yates . . . suggested a more fanciful and perhaps more accurate derivation of the name, Llyn-glas, the Blue Lake.

The story of the vulgar is here enlarged by a very slight hint taken from Burton's *Anatomy of Melancholy* when he treats of Incubi and Succubi.' [23a]

Circumstances like these would seem to have favoured the creation of an imagined ballad rather than the versification of an ancient story, and in any case Dovaston only claimed that his verses were related to a superstition ' corresponding with the catastrophe of this ballad ' ; he made no claim concerning the events which led to the catastrophe.

In his account of this version of the Llynclys story, Rhŷs pointed out that whilst it was difficult to see any reason for the introduction of a king Alaric, Willin was a reference to Croes Wylan, which was a stone, supposed to be the base of a cross, a little way out of Oswestry on the north side (actually it is on the south side—so is Llynclys). This, of course, implies that in Dovaston's time it was locally supposed that Croes Wylan was Wylan's (i.e., Gwylan's) Cross, named after a person, and there are, indeed, in the parish of Llansanffraid in Montgomeryshire, not many miles away, a Trewylan (formerly Trefwylan), a Beddwylan, and a Gweirglodd Wylan—a homestead, a grave, and a meadow of Gwylan, apparently named after a person, but such evidence as there is suggests that whatever may have been the original meaning of Croes Wylan, the local popular interpretation in the early part of the 19th century—when Dovaston wrote—was Cross of Weeping or Wailing, not the Cross of Wylan, a person.

In his *History of Oswestry* (1855) W. Cathrall stated on the authority of Samuel Roberts, author of a short-lived periodical entitled *Oswald's Well*, that

' Croeswylan received its name Croes Wylan, the Cross of Weeping, during the plague period [i.e., about 1559]. People resorted to it with superstitious reverence. . . . During the plague the market was held at Croeswylan, so that the people from the country places should not visit the town and thereby suffer from the infection.'

It has also been suggested that the interpretation Cross of Wailing might be supported on the grounds that if St. Oswald met his death at Oswestry, as some people believe, the cross may have marked the place where people mourned and prayed for the souls of those killed in conflict. [149]

There are several other Weeping Crosses in Shropshire and

the names have been explained in various ways. Mr. J. L. Hobbs, Shrewsbury Borough Librarian, tells me that one near Shrewsbury on the Wenlock-Bridgenorth road is supposed to have been connected in some way with the ceremonies of the medieval church, perhaps the Rogationtide ceremony, when, it is said, it was customary to bewail one's sins.

We are, however, not really concerned with the problems which these various interpretations raise. They have only been mentioned in order to show that when the ballad of ' Llunck-llys Pool ' was written the local belief of the ' vulgar ' was that Croes Wylan meant the Cross of Wailing, and that Clerk Willin was a character introduced by the poet.

Dovaston acknowledged having taken a 'very slight hint' from the reference, in Burton's *Anatomy of Melancholy*, to *incubi* and *succubi*. Burton's notes include the following :

 ' Water-devils are those naiades or water nymphs which have been heretofore conversant about water and rivers . . . Paracelsus hath several stories of them that have lived and been married to mortal men, and so continued for several years with them, and after, upon some dislike, they have forsaken them . . .

 Olaus Magnus hath a long narration of one Hotherus, a king of Sweden, that, having lost his company as he was hunting one day, met with these water-nymphs or fairies.' [9]

Although described as slight those hints were sufficient to have provided Dovaston with the plot for his ballad, and, taking all the available evidence into consideration one is left with the impression that it is useless to try to discover what exactly was the local story current at the time he wrote.

It is by no means unlikely that, although aware that there was a story associated with the lake, he knew no more about it than what Humphrey Llwyd had written some two hundred and fifty years previously, namely, that it had something to do with the sudden submergence of a palace and its occupants. In the circumstances a ballad based in large measure upon a theme suggested by Burton's *Anatomy of Melancholy*, and written by a country gentleman who was a Master of Arts and a

Barrister of the Middle Temple, on an occasion when, on his own telling [23b] :

> Our banquet is spread on the boat's flat head,
> And our cool wine drawn from the hold,
> And we make good fare of the pike,

cannot be regarded as a folk story relating to the pool of Llynclys.

It is a pity that Rhŷs did not see the preamble to the volume in which Dovaston's poem was published, for, taking citations from it at their face value, he was inclined to regard what he called the ' substratum ' of the verses as being much older than the ethical motive in the Llynclys story as related by Humphrey Llwyd ; so indeed it was, but it was in no way related to Llynclys in particular or to Welsh folklore in general.

Dovaston was either unaware or thought it unnecessary to mention that the story of Hotherus, who got lost when hunting and met a water nymph, was one of numerous forms of an almost universal theme—the association between a fairy wife and a mortal husband. It had long been popular on the Continent, especially in France, Germany, and Spain, and was rewritten many times in the 15th and 16th centuries after a certain Jean d'Arras, had (in 1387) added a few conceits of his own to those he had been able to collect, and produced a romance called *Le liure de Melusine en frācoys* [52].

The story was that of *Melusina*, in which a Count of Poitou, having adopted the youngest son, Raymond, of a poor relation, was accidentally killed by him in an encounter with a boar, after they had been separated from their companions whilst out hunting. The grief-stricken young man wandered in the forest until he came across three beautiful maidens sitting near a fountain. He told one of them of his misfortune and she advised him to go home as if nothing had happened, expecting that when the Count's body was discovered it would be presumed that he had died in conflict with the boar. Raymond persuaded the maiden, Melusina, to marry him, which she agreed to do on condition that she was to be allowed to spend one day a week, Saturday, in complete seclusion. On that day Raymond was in no circumstances to intrude upon her privacy on pain of losing her for ever.

Melusina, having magical powers, built a large castle for herself and her husband and in due course they had several children ; but one day, as a result of gossip concerning his wife's weekly non-appearance, Raymond set out to find her and surprised her bathing : the lower part of her body had become that of a fish or serpent. At first the wife gave no indication of her knowledge that her secret had been discovered, but after somewhat distressing incidents that do not concern us here she bid Raymond farewell and left him for ever. Afterwards she used to reappear around the castle before the death of one of the lords.

The similarity in essentials between this story and parts of Dovaston's ballad is obvious enough, but we are not here concerned with the origin of the legend of Melusina—with its possible connexion with mermaids, and ultimately with the Mermen, which were among the sun-gods of the Chaldeans and Assyrians (half fish, half men, for it was supposed that the sun set into the sea and rose again from the land in the morning)— because it was educated writers of the nineteenth century, not simple peasants of a long past age, that associated the legend with a Welsh locality.

Another version of the Llynclys story, compounded from fragments of several others and given in the modern *Welsh Fairy Book* already mentioned, [163b] provides an illustration of the way in which folk tales lose their identity and throw the folklore picture out of focus, as it were. A tale entitled *The Swallowed Court* begins in this way : ' Benlli, a wicked Prince of Powys had been married a long time.'

Then follows a story, based in the main upon Dovaston's ballad, in which we are told that ' about nine years after Benlli had wedded the Maid of the Green Forest, he invited, amongst others, a learned clerk whose name was Wylan, to a feast' and finally, that ' Llynclys or Swallowed Court was the name given to the water which overwhelmed Benlli and his palace . . . When the surface is smooth, towers and chimneys can be seen at a great depth in the lake.' Askew Roberts, author of *The Gossiping guide to Wales* (1872) also mentioned the local belief that when the water was clear enough the remains of the palace

could be seen, but, he added, ' Unfortunately, there never
appears to have been a day when the water was clear enough.'

The Llynclys legend is included in Georgina F. Jackson's
collection of Shropshire folk tales published in 1883, [8] where
the authority given is ' an old MS history of Oswestry, preserved
in the British Museum.' The ' old MS,' however, is not so very
old since what it has to say about Llynclys was derived from
Humphrey Llwyd's brief reference to it.

(c) Llyn Gwyn, Llyn y Maes, and Bala Lake

In Miss Trevelyan's *Folklore and Folk Stories of Wales* (1909)
Llyn Gwyn is credited with a story entirely different from that
suggested by Lewis Morris and by William Camden, both of
whom referred to it as occupying the site of a submerged town.
' A curious story,' we are told, ' is attached to Llyn Gwyn ' :

St. Patrick passed it on his way to visit St. David. He was
accompanied by another saint, and when they reached this
lake one of them suggested resting awhile. This was done,
and during the halt the saints discussed religion. Coming to a
controversial point, the men grew irritable, and St. Patrick
was very angry. Several Welsh people overheard the
religious quarrel and expressed surprise and annoyance.
St. Patrick in spite turned them into fishes. One of the party
was a woman who was transformed into a white lady. She
was often seen accompanied by flashes of light. On account
of this insult to St. Patrick the sun never shines upon the lake
but during one week of the year. [166b]

The authority given for the story was the *Cambrian Superstitions* by William Howells ; he, however, located the lake in
Glamorgan, not in Radnorshire, and made the conversation
take place between St. David himself and St. Patrick. This
would be a convenient location, since St. David would have
passed through Glamorgan on his way from Menevia to
Caerleon, but, unfortunately, there does not seem to be, or to
have been, any lake in Glamorgan called Llyn Gwyn.

The handling of the story provides an example of the way in
which so-called tradition arises, for the more recent version
makes St. Patrick and the unknown saint quarrel, and speaks

of the conversion into fishes as if it had been a punishment for those who, overhearing the quarrel, expressed surprise and annoyance. Howells, however, says nothing about a quarrel and attributes the irritation of the onlookers to the fact that they were annoyed with St. Patrick for ' leaving Cambria for the Isle of Erin.' It only wants another writer to take this latest version of the Llyn Gwyn story at its face value and quote it in a new book of Welsh Folklore, and posterity will have yet another ' ancient tradition.'

In *Folk-lore and Folk Stories of Wales* there is an inundation story associated with Llyn y Maes, a small lake by the side of the railway, about two miles NNE of Tregaron, where a tongue of the local Silurian strata projects into the bog, Cors Goch Glan Teifi. Rhŷs said of the lake, ' there is a tradition that a village once occupied the place of its waters,' [145b] and the *Cambrian Traveller's Guide* speaks of ' Llyn y Maes, where tradition says that Tregaron once stood,' [145b] but *Folk-lore and Folk Stories of Wales* is more specific [166a] :

' A similar story [i.e., similar to Iolo's Kenfig story which had just been quoted] is told of Llyn y Maes, a beautiful lake near Treflyn, in Cardiganshire. Its name means the lake of the field, which according to tradition covers the ancient site of Tregaron. The people of this old place were very wicked and went to excesses in all ways. Most of their time was spent in revelry, feasting, hideous orgies, and incessant forms of every kind of pleasure known in those days. Many times had the people been warned that the place would be destroyed by fire and flood if they did not cease their wickedness, instead of which they gew worse as the years passed. One night, when the revelry was at its height, lightning caused a fire to break out, and flood followed, completely overwhelming the place. Not a person escaped, for those who were not burned were drowned. [A.B.] '

It is difficult to see in this story any more than another local adaptation of the account of the destruction of Sodom and Gomorrah, either directly applied to Llyn y Maes or imported from some other place which had already acquired such a legend. I cannot find that it was committed to writing before

1909, and the initials A.B., given as the authority for it, were stated to signify ' Clergymen and Dissenting ministers, and men whose itinerary professions give them opportunities of hearing folk stories.' In the circumstances the chances of discovering more about the previous history of this particular story are very remote.

The Kenfig story told in the same book is as follows :

' Kenfig pool near Porthcawl, Glamorgan, has a tradition attached to it. A local chieftain wronged and wounded a Prince, and the latter with his dying breath, pronounced a curse against the wrongdoer. The curse was forgotten until one night the descendants of the chieftain heard a fearful cry : ' Dial a ddaw ! Dial a ddaw ! ' (Vengeance is coming). At first it passed unnoticed but when the cry was repeated night after night, the owner of Kenfig asked the domestic bard what it meant. The bard repeated the old story of revenge : but his master, to prove the untrustworthiness of the warning, ordered a grand feast, with music and song.

In the midst of the carousal the fearful warning cry was repeatedly heard, and suddenly the earth trembled and water rushed into the palace. Before anybody could escape, the town of Kenfig with its palace, houses, and people, was swallowed up, and only a deep and dark lake or pool remains to mark the scene of disaster. In the early part of the nineteenth century traces of the masonry could be seen and felt with grappling irons in the pool. The sands nearby cover many old inhabitations.' [166a]

The authority given for this story was the *Iolo Manuscripts*, page 207, but (as comparison with our own page 97 will show) it is an entirely new story, with only one feature in common with Iolo's—the reference to the vengeance that was to come. It is a salutary warning against accepting anything as reliable because one has seen it in print, or even because an authority for it has been cited. We are reminded of the suggestion made by Rhŷs himself, that the greatest of all the difficulties that beset the student of folklore is ' the hopeless fashion in which some of these who have written about Welsh folklore have deigned to record the stories which were known to them.' [145k]

Although written for children, the opening paragraph of a little book called *Tales from Welsh Legends and History* (published anonymously in 1907) gives a clear and concise summary of the development of folk tales that is worth repeating.

' Before there were many written or printed books,' it says, ' people tried to keep great men in mind by telling stories about them.   As one man repeated stories to another, mistakes were made and at last there came to be tales of wonderful things that could not have happened just as the stories tell them.'

That mistakes leading to diversification should have been made in the old days is understandable enough, but there can be no justification for the introduction of variations as a result of careless copying or deliberate modification by modern authors.   There is, of course, nothing to be said against the creation of imagined tales, but when an old story, known to be associated with a particular locality is altered to suit the writer's fancy or convenience, it should not be cited as the legend of this and that person and place ; neither should a story be given a ' local habitation and a name ' in order to provide a legend for a locality reputed to have one, when, in fact, the details are quite unknown.

One cannot help feeling that, in most cases, the legends actually current amongst the country folk, before modern authors began to ' write them up,' were simple tales with a minimum of circumstantial detail—tales like that which George Borrow heard as he walked by the side of Lake Bala with a local lad.   The latter mentioned ' old Bala ' and on Borrow asking what that meant the reply was :

' It stood in the old time where the lake is now, and a fine city it was, full of fine houses, towers, and castles, but with neither church nor chapel, for the people neither knew God nor cared for Him, and thought of nothing but singing and dancing and other wicked things.   So God was angry with them, and one night, when they were all busy at singing and dancing and the like, God gave the word, and the city sank down into the Unknown, and the lake boiled up where it once stood.' [6]

K

A story like this may well have grown out of recollections of local inundations like those mentioned by W. Bingley in *A tour round North Wales, performed during the Summer of 1798.*

' The overflowings of this pool [i.e., Bala Lake]' he wrote, ' are at times very dreadful ; but this seldom happens, except when the winds rush from the mountains, when they drive the waters before them, even over the great part of the Vale of Edeirnion, rising in stormy weather very suddenly from the joint force of the winds and mountain torrents, sometimes eight or nine feet in perpendicular height and almost threatening the town with destruction.'

As a glance at the map will show, Bala lies at the end of a lake well stituated to be affected by south-westerly gales. If the story which Borrow recorded is not related to dim recollections of great storms, need we look any farther for its origin, and for the origin of the story which *The Folklore and Folk Stories of Wales* associates with Llyn y Maes, than to dramatic sermons by old-time preachers in days when printed books were either non-existent or were available only to the privileged few ? The towers and castles beneath the waters of the lakes are always ' said to be seen,' or ' used to be seen '—never actually ' seen.'

IX

CANTRE'R GWAELOD,
OR THE LOWLAND HUNDRED

THE story of Cantre'r Gwaelod, like that of Llys Helig, is an elaboration of a 13th century reference to the loss of land by inundation. It began to assume its modern form in the 17th century and was further embellished in the 18th, but the details of the modern version are of 19th century origin.

The Sarnau—stony banks extending for considerable distances into Cardigan Bay—which have been indicated as the remains of dams built to keep the sea out of Cantre'r Gwaelod are natural ridges, and it is suggested that the modern conception of Caer Gwyddno and the many fair cities of Maes Gwyddno were inspired by sea charts and maps.

(a) *The foundations of the story and its elaboration*

WE have already had occasion to note that the references to Helig in various genealogies merely say that his land, Tyno Helig, was overwhelmed by the sea, but they do not say where Tyno Helig was. A poem in an early 15th century MS (see p. 69) may be taken as implying an association with the northern coast of Wales, but the 13th century translation of a Triad in an Exeter Cathedral MS (p. 68) unequivocally locates the submerged lands of Helig ap Glannog in Cardigan Bay—a region to which other early manuscripts assign Maes Gwyddno (the Cantre'r Gwaelod or Lowland Hundred of later writers), the ruler of which was Gwyddno Garanhir according to some, Seithennin according to others. The latter's name is also spelt Seithenin, Seithenyn, Seithennyn, Seithinnen and Seithenhin. The last of these and Seithennin occur in the *Black Book of Carmarthen*, the oldest manuscript in which he is mentioned. Except when quoting, Seithennin will be used in these pages, because that is the form the name takes at its first appearance in the Black Book.

One of the earliest of the *Bonedd y Saint*, the early 13th century Peniarth MS No. 16 [103] mentions both Helig and Seithennin and calls the latter King of Maes Gwyddno (Seithennin, Vrenhin o vaes gwydno). It says of them both, in similar words, that their lands were overwhelmed by the sea. St. Tudno, founder of the little church on the Great Orme, is cited as ' one of the sons of Seithennin, King of the Plain of Gwyddno ' [127], and according to the saintly pedigrees it was after their lands had been lost to the sea that the sons of Seithennin embraced the religious life.

Another link with Seithennin occurs in the Exeter Triad, with its reference to Tewthi Hen, for (and I am indebted to the late Prof. W. J. Gruffydd for the suggestion) the Triad is most likely founded upon a reference in the source of the Mabinogi of Culhwch and Olwen (the oldest of the Arthurian tales in Welsh) to Teithi Hen, ' son of Gwynnan, whose dominion the sea overran, and with difficulty he himself escaped.' [74a] Teithi Hen is more than likely a copyist's mistaken rendering of Seithinnen. It is not uncommon for *s* to be miscopied as *t*, and *n* as *h*.

The writer of the *Notes to bee observed* also described Helig as ' Lord of Cantre Gwaelod ' and as having a palace at ' Pwll Helig,' thus associating him with Cardigan Bay, although he located Tyno Helig in the region between the Great Orme and Anglesey, and was, as far as I have been able to ascertain, the first to define its supposed limits.

The references connecting Helig with Cardigan Bay are few in number and of doubtful authenticity, but Gwyddno Garanhir and Seithennin have been associated with the region ever since it has been referred to in writing, and it is they who now demand our attention.

The modern version of the story of Gwyddno Garanhir, Seithennin, and the submerged kingdom in Cardigan Bay was summarised by T. Gwynn Jones in *Welsh Folklore and Folk Customs*. It is as follows :

> ... Cantre'r Gwaelod was a fertile territory extending from the Teifi to Bardsey Island, forty miles in length and twenty in breadth. In it there were sixteen noble cities. It was defended from the sea by an embankment and sluices. In the time when Gwyddno Garanhir was lord of the Cantref, Seithennin was keeper of the Embankment, and he was a drunkard.

One evening when there was a great banquet, Seithennin, having drunk much wine, left open the sluices. The sea broke through and only a few of the inhabitants escaped. When the sea is very still and the water clear, the great walls and other buildings can be seen ; and the faint music of the church bells, as they are gently moved to and fro by the water in the depth, can be heard coming up in very quiet weather. [81b]

This story, like modern versions of the one relating to Llys Helig, is very different from the much simpler one in which it originated, but the stages in its embellishment are more easily traced than in the case of its north Wales parallel. Before proceeding to do so, however, we must note that the story, as now told, illustrates very well the disregard for the older forms that characterises the modern popular versions of many legends and greatly increases the difficulty of evaluating the various elements that go to make up a story.

It is stated that ' Cantre'r Gwaelod was a fertile territory extending from the Teifi to Bardsey Island, forty miles in length and twenty in breadth ' ; but this implies almost the whole of Cardigan Bay, the area of which is about 1,200 square miles,—half as much again as the product of 40 and 20. Now the 20-fathom submarine contour line—that is, a line connecting points on the sea floor covered by 20 fathoms of water at ordinary high tides—runs more or less directly from Bardsey Island to the mouth of the Teifi, so that for the whole of Cantre'r Gwaelod, as so defined, to have been inundated by a single catastrophe, there must have been a sudden rising of the sea or a sinking of the land to the extent of about 120 feet.

Had this actually occurred it would have affected a much larger area than Cardigan Bay—certainly the whole of the coastal regions of the British Isles and probably the adjacent parts of the continent as well—and apart from recognizable material traces that it would have left it is inconceivable that the only ' record ' we should have had of it is an obscure reference in 13th century manuscript to a man whose lands were overwhelmed. We are, however, not called upon to consider the probability of a catastrophe of that magnitude, for not only is such a pheomenon unknown in geological history, but the indication of its geographical extent is an addition made by modern writers.

The region affected by the inundation is described as a Cantref, a Hundred, and although the size of the old territorial unit called a Cantref varied considerably in different parts of Wales, an average size for those in the regions now represented by Cardiganshire and Merionethshire was in the neighbourhood of 180 square miles and there were usually at least three within the limits of what is now a modern county. The story, then, only calls for the submergence of an area equal to about one third of a county like Cardigan, not an area more than twice its size. Such a tract, in Cardigan Bay, would lie entirely within the area bounded on the east by the present coast, on the west by the 10-fathom submarine contour, and stretching from the neighbourhood of the submerged stony ridge called Sarn Badrig, north of the Barmouth Estuary, to a little south of Aberystwyth.

The sudden submergence of even this relatively limited tract would involve subsidence to the extent of 60 feet, and as we shall have to consider later on whether or not the requirements of the story demand the subsidence of all this area at one time, it is sufficient for our present purpose to note that our credulity need not be taxed quite to the extent that the modern version of the story appears to require.

The earliest known references to Seithennin, the hero (or villain) of the story, date from about the middle of the 13th century and are found in the Black Book of Carmarthen. One includes eight triplets, but the scribe added a ninth, copied from the *Verses of the Graves* which occupy earlier folios in the manuscript. It probably seemed to constitute a desirable ending to the story because it refers to Seithennin's grave.

It will be sufficient here to quote four of the triplets (the first, second, seventh, and ninth) in translation, for they include all the details that we shall need to discuss. They are as follows :

Seithennin, stand thou forth,
And look upon the fury of the sea,
Gwyddno's plain it has covered.

Accursed be the maiden
Who let it loose after feasting,
The well-servant of the fierce sea.

The cry of Mererid upon the fine bay steed
The bountiful God has wrought it,
After excess want is wont to come.

The grave of Seithennin of feeble sense
(is) Between the fort of Kenedir and the shore,
(with that of) Môr the Grand and Kynran.

The poem has proved as difficult to translate into modern Welsh as into English and there are several versions. For the one used here I am indebted to Professor Henry Lewis. It differs in one important respect from that given by Rhŷs in *Celtic Folklore* in referring to Mererid upon the fine bay steed whereas Rhŷs translates the line as ' Mererid's cry over generous wines.' This or something to that effect seems to have been the generally accepted translation in the past, and although, as will appear later, the fine bay steed associates the story with similar ones told of other areas, the notion that there was a reference to generous wines played an important part in the subsequent embellishments of the story, even though it may have been without foundation.

In the poem Seithennin is invited to see what had happened to the Plain of Gwyddno and the disaster is attributed to a maiden who let loose the waters of a well, so that in its earliest form the story is related to the folklore of wells rather than to that of the sea ; we are reminded of stories like these associated with Llyn Llech Owen, the little lake on Mynydd Mawr in Carmarthenshire in which the Gwendraeth Fawr river has its origin. A former resident on Mynydd Mawr, it is said, had a well, and one day, forgetting to put back the large flat stone that served as a lid, he found that in his absence the water had overflowed and made the lake. [145p] Bala Lake and Lough Neagh in Ireland also have legends telling how they were formed by the overflowing of wells.

The Irish version of this widely distributed well-lake legend occurs in the story of the Death of Eochaid, son of Mairid (and it cannot be without significance that the maiden in the ' Black Book ' poem was Mererid). It tells of a magic well that was in charge of a daughter of Eochaid, and of how, one day, she failed to replace the cover, with the result that the water continued to flow unhindered, and so Lough Neagh was formed. [122].

These well-stories relate to lakes and not to the sea, and the association of one of them with the earliest known references to Seithennin introduces an interesting problem. Are we to see in it a story associated with a spring that flowed from the sandy shore when the tide was out, and was thought to be concerned in supplying the sea with water ? Such springs are not unknown where water-bearing strata crop out on the foreshore, but they are not usually seen owing to the beach deposits that have been spread over them ; there is one such near New Quay on the shores of Cardigan Bay and another near Porthcawl.

In the *Black Book* poem it was Gwyddno's land that was overwhelmed and Seithennin was invited to see the damage which had been done ; similarly in an elegy to Rhŷs, Abbot of Ystrad Fflur (Strata Florida), Guto'r Glyn, who was domestic bard to an abbot of Llanegwestl (Valle Crucis near Llangollen) and flourished between 1430 and 1460, wrote of ' the lament of Gwyddno Garanhir, over whose land God turned the sea.' [18a]

Quite early in its history the story was complicated by a reference, in one of the pedigrees of the saints, to five saints who were the sons of King Seithennin of the Plain of Gwyddno, whose realm was swallowed by the sea. [75a] In the *Black Book* reference to his grave, however, Seithennin was described as feeble-minded, and in the Third Series of Triads he figures as one of the Three Arrant Drunkards of Britain—' Seithennin the Drunken, King of Dyfed, who in his cups allowed the sea to overflow the Lowland Hundred, the territory of Gwyddno Garanhir, King of Ceredigion, in which there were sixteen fair cities.' [75b]   Now although the genuine Triads are very ancient, the so-called Third Series is regarded as one of Iolo Morganwg's fabrications, and it is not at all unlikely that he got his idea from the *Celtic Remains* of Lewis Morris (written in 1757), where it is suggested that ' it seems there were dams between it (the Lowland Hundred) and the sea, and that by drunkenness the floodgates were left open, as that ancient poem hints.' [110b]

The 'ancient poem' was the one in the *Black Book of Carmarthen*, but in his reference to it Morris combined a notion that might have originated in the allusions to the feasting and the privations that follow excess, with a suggestion made by Robert Vaughan, the antiquary, of Hengwrt. The latter, writing in the middle of the 17th century, connected the story with the submerged pebble ridge called Sarn Badrig which extends for some miles out into Cardigan Bay from the coast north of the Barmouth Estuary. He regarded it ' as a stone wall made as a fence against the sea ' and referred to the inundation as if it were an unquestioned historic fact. In a *Sketch of the History of Merionethshire* printed in the *Cambrian Register* for 1795 he is quoted as saying :

'A whole cantred or hundred called Cantre'r Gwaelod, stretching itself west and south west above 12 miles in length . . . hath been overwhelmed by the sea and drowned, and still a great stone wall, made as a fence against the sea may be clearly seen . . . to extend from Harddlech towards St. Davids land, a great way, and is called, Sarn Badrig, i.e., St. Patrick's Street, or Bad-rwyg, i.e., the boat or ship-breaking causeway.'

Pennant favoured the second of these interpretations and wrote of ' Sarn Badrig, more properly called Sarn Badrhwyg or Ship-breaking Causeway from the number of ships lost on it.' [131d]

The reference to Bad-rwyg provides an interesting example of the dangers of accepting quotations at their face value, and of the way in which incorrect statements acquire the status of established facts. Vaughan's original manuscript, which is now in the National Library of Wales (MS 472) and had not been printed until recently, does not mention Bad-rwyg but refers simply to ' a great stone wale . . . caled Sarn Badric, yt is Patrike's Streete.' Mr. E. D. Jones, who drew attention to the holograph (in the Journal of the Merioneth Historical and Record Society, 1955), suggests that the ' Cambrian Register ' version was most likely derived from a copy made and amended by Edward Jones (Bardd y Brenin) from an earlier copy by Evan Evans (Ieuan Brydydd Hir).

Morris added the dams and the flood gates, and William Owen, in his *Cambrian Biography* (1803) completed the synthesis by making Seithennin their Keeper. [127a]

It is not difficult to see how the dykes and the dams came into the story, for in the 16th and 17th centuries travellers were coming home with stories of submerged lands in Holland and of the methods employed by the inhabitants in their efforts to prevent the sea from overwhelming a considerable part of their country. News of such operations could have been brought to Wales by Richard Clough, friend of Humphrey Llwyd, who looked after the business interests of Sir Thomas Gresham in Antwerp.

Thus, with the passage of time, the well and the well-maiden disappeared from the story, and Seithennin, who in the *Black Book of Carmarthen* was an observer and a person of feeble intellect, became, in turn, King of Maes Gwyddno, and Keeper of the sluice gates in embankments that had been built to limit the incursions of the sea ; in this last capacity, he was, by his failure to attend to his duties after a drunken carousal, made responsible for the disaster instead of merely an observer of its effects.

By the end of the eighteenth century the story had assumed its modern form and was being recorded, not as tradition, but as history. In the description his *Tour round north Wales* in 1798, William Bingley wrote :

‘ West of Harlech there was formerly another habitable hundred belonging to Merionethshire, called Cantre’r Gwaelod, *the lowland hundred*, on the edge of which this great stone wall [Sarn Badrwyg] was built, as a fence against the sea. But about the year 500 when Gwyddno Garan-Hîr was lord of it, one of the persons who looked after the dams was so careless as to let the sea break through them, and ever since that time it has been always completely flooded.’

This was, of course, merely an amplification of the passage in Robert Vaughan’s *Sketch of the History of Merionethshire*.

Although rarely mentioned by those who have written about Cantre'r Gwaelod and now almost forgotten, what probably did more than anything else to lay the foundation of modern interest in the story was a poem in a book called *Welsh Minstrelsy containing the Land beneath the Sea, or Cantrev y Gwaelod, a poem in three Cantos, with various other poems*, by T. Jeffrey Llewelyn Prichard. It was published in 1826.

Having announced his intention to publish a poem about 'Cantrev-y-Gwaelod' the author soon found that he had very little material upon which to work. In his Preface he wrote, ' I began to be alarmed for the scantiness of the authenticated materials . . . the universal tradition respecting that calamitous inundation composed my sum total . . . [but] with an anxious desire that no part of my subscribers should experience disappointment, I assiduously sought for documents on my subject.'

He searched to such good effect that he was able to produce a poem of about 3,600 lines, supplemented by ten pages of what he called ' Historical authorities ' to prove that the inundation actually took place, and a further 26 pages of explanatory notes and quotations from poetry and prose.

He thought it necessary thus to set forth his evidence because, he wrote,

' The author has met with some wiseacres who ground their claim to extraordinary knowledge on an affection of stubborn incredulity as to the extent of this calamitous and well authenticated event, in the face of the most absolute proofs. . . . Whatever may be the merit or demerit of the poem it is hoped that the documents here inserted will at least set the question at rest for ever and establish the indubitable fact of the inundation to the satisfaction of all parties, except those who love cavilling and hate the conviction which would destroy a preconceived notion, however at variance with truth.'

Unfortunately, however, although considerable in quantity, the evidence was extremely poor in quality. It consisted of extracts from works like Camden's *Britannia*, Meyrick's *History of Cardiganshire*, Carlisle's *Topographical Dictionary*, Bingley's *Tour in North Wales*, Lewis Morris' *Survey*, Owen's *Cambrian Biography*, Fenton's *Pembrokeshire*, and Fuller's *Worthies*, none of which can be regarded as a good 'authority' for accounts of what is supposed to have happened in the 6th century, A.D., but, as Francis Bacon wrote in his *Novum Organum*, 'What a man were rather true, he more readily believes.'

Prichard seems to have overlooked the fact that none of the authors whose books he had consulted could have had other than hearsay information and that the more recent ones had derived their information from the earlier ones, but, even accepting them at face value he was still not satisfied with the meagre results of his research and introduced into the story an entirely new conception of his own.

Wishing to impress the reader with the importance of the region that had been submerged he wrote :

> For bright in Cambria's history,
> Shines that beauteous level land,
> Now changed to water, stone, and sand,
> The Land beneath the Sea—
> The lawns, at which all strangers wonder'd
> E'en Europe's gem, the Lowland Hundred.

He described the story as being told by an old blind man whom he saw ' By Aberystwyth's castle's ruin.' The Lowland Hundred was replete with smiling farms and neat villages, and had sixteen fair and fortified towns, surpassing all the rest in Wales excepting only Caerleon. The sixteen fair cities, were derived from the translation in Meyrick's *Cardiganshire* of the Triad of the famous drunkards. [98]

In Prichard's poem the ruler of this favoured land was Gwyddno, King of Ceredigion, while ' Seithenyn, the worthless son of Dyfed's brenin,' wished to marry Rona, a princess of the land, but the lady preferred Elfin, Gwyddno's son. It was a neat touch to use the Welsh equivalent of king in order to get a rhyme with Seithennin !

Angered at her refusal, Seithennin determined to find some means of punishing her. Eventually he thought of a plan, that was

. . . awfully terrific, great
As master-fiend could machinate.
While stalking once with steps unhallowed
Through Gwyddno's pride, Cantrev-y-Gwaelod,
His eye the embankment caught
That parted from that vale the sea ;
He glutted on it joyously,
And hatch'd a damn'd thought—

he would undermine the embankment so that the sea might
break it down and overwhelm the land ; then, from his own
country he brought

Those ruffians, who'd impignorate,
Their souls for pay,

and night after night,

Th' embankments deep they undermined,
Jagged all their length with channels wide,
To invite the entrance of the tide.

The nefarious work accomplished, Seithennin sat on a hill
and watched for the sea to break in and overwhelm the land.
At last came a time when,

Impelled by blust'ring tempest wrath,
Old Ocean forced herself a path,

and

Of th' embankments there were none—
But all dissolved and ceased to be.
The vale's incanton'd with the sea.

The land was devastated, the buildings destroyed, and the
people for the most part drowned, but,

Some by the ebbing tide were driven,
To many a distant bay or haven,
Where then perforce they made a stop.
Some settled on Eryri's top . . .
Where tarrience ne'er made man before.

Gwyddno is made to stand

In armour pond'ring o'er the flood,

in which he saw,

> . . . distracted, disappear,
> Many a village, many a town,
> Fair mart and city of renown,
> The gems of all his proud domain.

These are the essential features of Prichard's story, but by the inclusion of much irrelevant detail and many moral reflections he made it take 130 pages of his book.

That this story, with Seithennin in a new role, does not represent a stage in the development of a folk tale, is indicated by a passage in the author's own words. In his preface he said :

' For the purpose of Poetry, an atrocious motive is here given Seithenyn for what is traditionally imputed to him merely as neglect . . . and indeed it would otherwise be difficult to reconcile why a prince, and of another country too, should be a kind of sentinel over the sluices.'

It is, I think, not without significance that Thomas Love Peacock's *Headlong Hall* had recently been published (1816) when Prichard began his search for material upon which to base the poem he had promised to his subscribers. *Headlong Hall*, it will be remembered, gave prominence to the embankment which W. A. Madocks (sometime M.P. for Boston, Lincs) had built across the entrance to Traeth Mawr with a view to re-claiming part of the Glaslyn estuary.

In 1812, only a few months after the embankment had been completed at the cost of much labour and expense during more than 10 years, it was partially destroyed by gales and heavy seas. It was regarded as one of the wonders of Wales, and had received so much publicity that it is impossible to suppose that Prichard did not know all about it.

A few years later, Peacock himself further elaborated the story of Cantre'r Gwaelod in *The Misfortunes of Elphin*, published in 1829. In that book he pictured ' an embankment of massy stone that protected the lowland country from the sea, and wrote of watch towers and watchmen under the control of ' Prince Seithenyn who held the office of . . . Lord High Commissioner of the Royal Embankment.'

Seithennin was portrayed as being more interested in

convivial living than in duty, and he refused to heed the warn-
ings of Teithrin, who was in charge of the embankment at its
northern end near Mochras in Ardudwy and visited Seithennin
in company with Elphin the son of Gwyddno.   When Seithennin had fallen into a drunken sleep his daughter Angharad
(not as in Prichard's poem, Gwyddno's daughter) came in to
entertain the visitor, but the sea overflowed the embankment
and caused the collapse of the castle tower.   Seithennin,
awakened by the noise, drew his sword and threatening the
unknown enemy, jumped into the sea.

    Angharad, Elphin, Teithrin and some others made their way
along the embankment, thrusting the points of their spears into
the earth to save themselves from being blown away.   As the
tide receded and the moon came out they saw their path before
them—an irregular line like a ribbon on the deep.   They
eventually reached Gwyddno's castle to tell him of the loss of
his land, and while Elphin married Angharad and built a
fishing weir on the river Mawddach, Gwyddno sat on the rocks
' pouring forth his soul in pathetic song on the change in his
own condition.'

    In Peacock's story, Seithennin survives the disaster and tells
how he escaped by throwing his arms over two empty barrels as
they floated out through a breach in the cellar wall, ' It was
well for me,' he said, ' that I had been so provident as to
empty so many barrels, and that somebody, I don't know who,
had been so provident as to put the bungs into them to keep
them sweet.'   No one is likely to have taken this part of the
story seriously because it is so extravagant ; it has been mentioned here only as a reminder of the tendency to accept less
extravagant embellishments without question.

    In due dourse, the bells of sunken churches were introduced
into the story.   In *The Monthly Packet* for 1859 [145r] a story
about Aberdyfi tells of a great tract of land which formerly
occupied the site of Cardigan Bay and was inundated when a
wicked prince left open the sluices of the sea-wall that protected
the country.   There were, the writer, added,

    'Cities with marble wharfs, busy factories, and churches
whose towers resounded with beautiful peals and chimes of

bells. . . . Even now, though very rarely, eyes gazing down through the green waters can see not only the glistening sand dotted here and there with shells and tufts of waving sea-weed, but the wide streets and costly buildings of that now silent city. Yet not always silent, for now and then will come chimes and peals of bells, sometimes near, sometimes distant, often in the long twilight or by night.'

Under the title ' The Drowning of the Bottom Hundred,' *The Welsh Fairy Book*, to which we have already had occasion to refer, gives a story which commences like this :

'In the beginning of the sixth century Gwyddno Garanhir was King of Ceredigion . . . [his land] contained one of the three privileged ports of the Isle of Britain which was called the Port of Gwyddno, and had been known to the Phoenicians and Carthagenians, when they visited the island for metal in the dim dawn of history.'

The remainder of the story, as the author indicated, closely followed T. L. Peacock, and concluded

' The nearest town to the submerged realm of Gwyddno is Aberdovey. If you stand on the beach there you will sometimes hear . . . evening chimes and peals of bells . . . The sounds come from one of Gwyddno's drowned church-es.' [163d]

In his preface the author explained that he was dealing with ' the Welsh variants of the universal folk-tales,' and said, ' it may be as well to add that while in some stories it has been necessary to piece things together, nothing has been inserted that is not genuinely traditional ' ; but in this story of *The Drowning of the Bottom Hundred* the ' genuinely traditional ' character of much of the material is, to say the least of it, doubtful, and the result of the ' piecing together ' is not the Welsh variant of an universal folk tale but the author's own variant.

The most recent version of the story (1947), in a little book entitled *Folk Tales of Wales*, also follows Peacock's. Like the one last mentioned, it introduces additional ' historical ' detail, some of which, because it purports to be factual and not (like Peacock's effusion) a fantasy supplying what history fails to record, makes nonsense. It begins :

'Many centuries ago—in the sixth century to be exact—the King of Ceredigion was Gwyddno. He . . . ruled over vast lands, but none was more fruitful than that part called Cantre'r Gwaelod.

More people lived in that district than in any other part of Wales. Twenty fortified towns had been built on it, and the busiest ports of Britain were on its shore. . . . In the very early days the Phoenicians visited them when they came to our island in search of tin, calling our country Bri-tin, the island of tin.'

In this story, which surely enters the realm of sheer nonsense, the sixteen fortified cities of Maes Gwyddno have become twenty, Seithennin's daughter is Rhonwen, and when the survivors reached Gwyddno he stood with them on the hills of Ardudwy and drew their attention to the fact that Aberdyfi, which formerly stood far inland, was by the side of the sea. Those who doubt the story are advised to walk on the shore at Aberdyfi at midnight, when they will hear the bells ringing a tune knwon as ' The Bells of Aberdovey.'   The ' Bells of Aberdovey ' had not been thought of in Peacock's time and in her reference to them the authoress improved upon the version of the story given in *The Welsh Fairy Book*, but seems to have overlooked the fact that the ' hills of Ardudwy ' lie northwards of the Mawddach estuary, not that of the Dyfi !

Poetry and novels were freely read during the time when these stories were assuming their modern forms, but little attention was paid to more serious studies, such, for example, as a paper communicated to the Geological Society of London in 1832 by the Rev. James Yates [184]. In it, reference was made to peat beds near the shores of Cardigan Bay, in which the wood of *Pinus Sylvestris* (the Scotch Fir) was present, and the report concludes, ' the author refers to the Triads of Britain and other ancient Welch testimonies which prove that it was submerged about 520 A.D., and ascribes the disaster to the folly of Seitheryn the Drunkard, who in his drink let the sea over the Cantrev Gwaelod.'

L

As far as the peat beds were concerned, Yates suggested that it was ' not necessary to suppose a subsidence affected by submarine agency,' on the grounds that the tract of bog and marsh under which the remains of the forest occur (covered by a bed of peat) was formed by streams of water partially discharged by oozing through sand and shingle. He attributed the peat of the forest to impeded drainage from the land, due, he supposed, to a wall of shingle like one that was then to be seen on the landward side of the marsh, but subsequently washed away. He was, indeed, referring to the peat bog at Borth, the surface of which lies above high water mark, and not to the so-called submerged forest. This paper was cited by Rice Rees in his *Essay on the Welsh Saints* (1836), in a reference to ' a calamity on the coast of Wales, of which the most exaggerated and mystified accounts have reached posterity,' but, he added, ' It is not necessary to dwell upon the proofs that such a calamity could not have occurred to the extent related.'

In a paper read to the Cambrian Archaeological Association in 1849 [26] and enlarged to form a separate publication [27], the Rev. G. Edwards of Llangollen gave an outline of the story as commonly told in those days and a poem ' translated from the works of the Welsh Bards,' which included the following stanzas :

> Then, in a moment came a roar
>   Like thunder on the laughing throng ;
> The rushing torrent from the shore
>   Broke up the dance, and mocked the song.
>
> Seithenyn, buried now in sleep,
>   The floodgates opened in his wine ;
> And on them rushed the angry deep,
>   Commissioned by the wrath divine.
>
> The torrent deluged wide the land,
>   And to the cities forced its way ;
> The palaces were filled with sand,
>   And thousands in the ruins lay.

From Bardsey, famed in ancient lore,
    To Ramsey and its coast, they say,
The Lowland reached, along the shore,
    Now guarded by the fatal Bay.

And here Gwyddno's noble estate,
    Now lies beneath the raging main.
He long survived his cruel fate,
    And of his loss did not complain.

Mr. Edwards seems to have been willing to accept the fact of the sudden inundation, but expressed doubts concerning the period in which it was supposed to have taken place. This is what he wrote :

' Many circumstances lead me also to think it must have happened at a much earlier period than in the fifth century for if it had taken place as late as that time there would have been found a better and more circumstantial account of it, connected with the history of Wales during that period : and we find nothing in the geographical description of the country in the time of the Romans likely to lead us to form an opinion that any great extent of land, or any towns of importance existed in their time where Cardigan Bay now lies. We find no trace of any extensive territory situated there in the Itinerary of Antonius, in Ptolemaeus, or in the works of Richard Cirencester. And it is not likely, if such an extensive territory and so many towns existed there during the Roman period, that they would have left them unnoticed ; therefore, we may reasonably conclude, that the inundation happened at some period before the Christian era.'

If attention had been paid to that clear and simple statement at the time it was penned, it would have led to a much earlier appreciation of the real significance of our ' sunken city ' stories.

(b) The Sarnau, Caer Gwyddno, and the estuaries on Ptolemy's map

Our inquiries up to now show that it is a modern story and not an ancient legend that postulates the sudden submergence of a large area in what is now Cardigan Bay, and we have

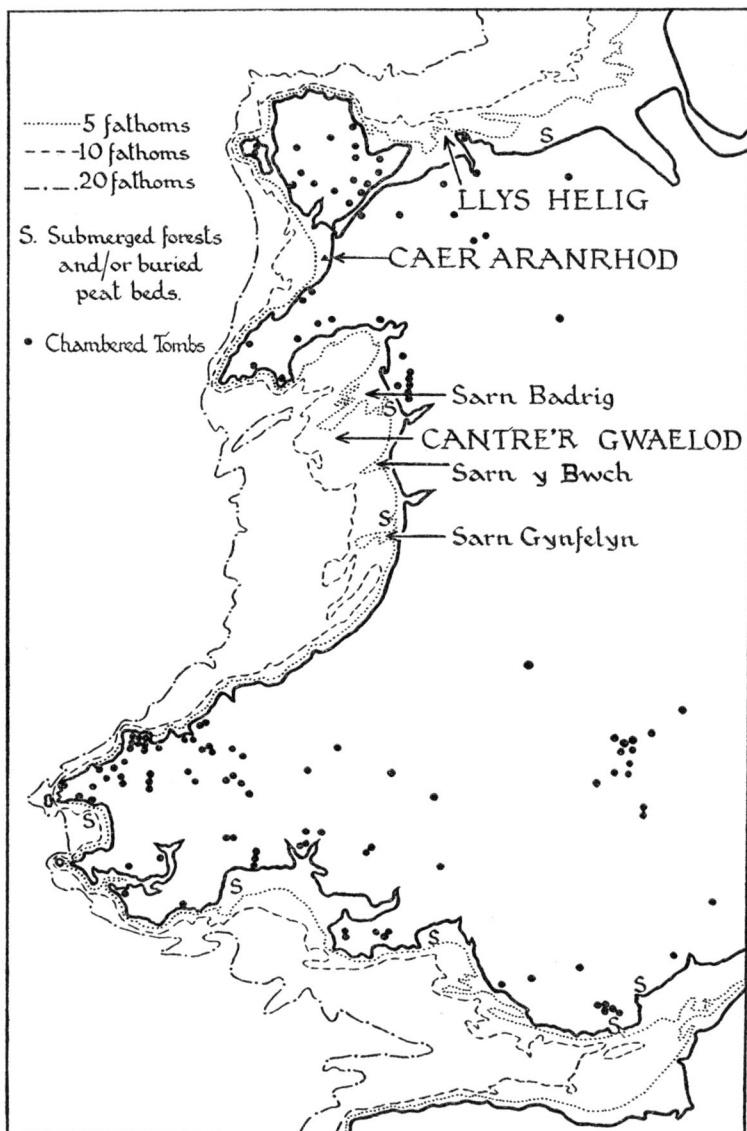

Fig. 8.   The drowned lands around the Welsh coast
and the distribution of chambered tombs

The Welsh coast with its sarnau, submerged forests and submarine contours.
The distribution of chambered tombs after W. F. Grimes [56].

adopted, in advance of evidence, the view that the occurrence of a catastrophe of that nature is contrary to what we know of the geological history of the region. The evidence will be given in a later chapter and in the meantime it will be convenient to consider some of the local features which have been introduced into the story and some of the obscurities in which it is involved.

The principal submerged ridges or sarns (Welsh plural, *sarnau*) which those who follow Robert Vaughan see as embankments erected to keep the sea within its bounds are three in number. They are called Sarn Badrig, Sarn y Bwch, and Sarn Gynfelyn ; the first two trend in a generally west-south-westerly direction, whilst the third trends more nearly east and west (Fig. 8). The third is often given as Sarn Cynfelyn or Sarn Cynfelin, a form which fails to use the required mutation of the initial letter. Cynfelyn is the modern Welsh equivalent of Cunobelinus, Shakespeare's Cymbeline.

Sarn Badrig is the largest of the ridges and it extends for about 11 miles from the shore south of Mochras Peninsula (between Harlech and Barmouth). It consists mostly of more or less rounded pebbles and boulders from an inch to more than a foot in diameter, and at the lowest of tides parts of it are exposed to a width of from 20 to 80 yards.

On Mackenzie's chart of *The North Part of Cardigan Bay in Wales* (1775) ' Sarn Badrach, or the Causeway ' appears as a long narrow bank, not actually connected with the shore and slightly expanded at its seaward end where there are some symbols indicating the presence of large stones. On the Lewis Morris Chart of *St. George's Channel* (1800) ' Sarn Badrig, Patrick's Causeway ' is a snake-like sinuous band expanding at the end to an oval head with symbols for stones described as ' Sixteen large stones, dry at low water, one 4 yards in Diameter.' Neither map suggests that the Sarn is a dam, if by that we understand an erection that could keep water either in or out of an enclosed region. The other ridges are farther south, Sarn y Bwch commencing near the mouth of the Dysynni River and Sarn Gynfelyn commencing between Borth and Aberystwyth.

Some writers have located ' Caer Gwyddno,' one of the six-

teen fair cities of Maes Gwyddno, at the seaward end of Sarn
Gynfelyn, seven or eight miles out to sea, [4k] and the eighteenth century Mackenzie chart already mentioned seems to
have contributed to the crystallization of the idea. On this
chart *Sarn ginvelin* appears as a beach-like strip, at first narrow,
but expanding beyond a short interruption into a pear-shaped
seaward extremity, with some symbols indicating stones and the
name *The Patches*. Morris's *Chart of St. George's Channel* also
indicates ' Sarn Gynfelin, or Gwallog ' as a beach-like strip
expanding considerably at the seaward end, but calls it *Caer
Wyddnw or Patches*.

Except in being somewhat diagrammatic the delineations of
Sarn Gynfelyn in the Mackenzie and Morris charts do not differ
materially from the outlines given in a modern Admiralty
Chart. On this, a narrow slightly sinuous bank, interrupted
near the middle, has an expanded extremity, but on Singer's
map of Cardiganshire, 1803 (one of the few early large-scale
maps of parts of the Principality) the ridge is described as
' Sarn Gynfelyn, extending about 7 miles at Sea, at the end of
which is that Rocky Ground called Caernyddno ' ; it is depicted
as being very narrow and perfectly straight. Had it been drawn
on the land instead of in the sea it might be mistaken for a
railway embankment, and if the early 19th century writers
who made use of the story of Cantre'r Gwaelod were familiar
with this map, as they may well have been, their belief that the
Sarn was something made by man must have been considerably
strengthened by it. (Fig. 9).

The impression given by the maps just mentioned would have
become more widely spread when atlases of county maps
began to be published early in the 19th century. The map of
Cardiganshire in *Langley's New County Atlas* (1808) shows a long
parallel-sided sand bank in the position of Sarn Gynfelyn with,
at the seaward end, a group of symbols to indicate rocks and the
name Caernyddw. This map may well have been originally
responsible for the increase from sixteen to twenty fair cities in
one of the modern versions of the Lowland Hundred story, for
there are twenty symbols (like plus signs) at the end of the
embankment.

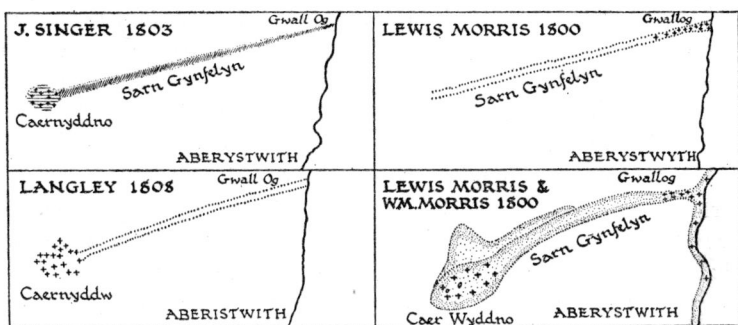

Fig. 9.   Map-representations of Sarn Gynfelyn

To illustrate variations in interpretation and the influence of maps upon writers
who retold the story of Cantre'r Gwaelod.

Whatever people may have thought about Caer Wyddno
(or Gwyddno) and the fair cities, it is difficult to see how
anyone, not obsessed with the dam (or wall) idea, can actually
have seen the sarnau without realizing that they were natural
and not artificial features.   In the Admiralty's *West Coast of
England Pilot* it is recorded that :

' Sarn Cynfelin and Cynfelin Patches constitute a dangerous shoal with depth of less than 3 fathoms over it, which
extends about $6\frac{1}{2}$ miles in a west-south-westerly direction
from a position near Wallog.

The inner portion of Sarn Cynfelin is formed by a narrow
spit of shingle and gravel, interspersed with large stones. . . .
Cynfelin Patches lie westward of Sarn Cynfelin from which
they are separated by Main Channel, which is half a mile
wide. . . . The western end of Cynfelin Patches is named
Outer Patch and on its eastern side are three large stones,
which were formerly uncovered, but now are always
covered.' [1]

From the same source we learn that :

' Sarn Badrig or St. Patrick's Causeway is a remarkable
shoal with depth of less than 3 fathoms over it, and with
depths of less than one fathom over the greater part, which
extends for about 11 miles in a south-westerly direction from
the coast just southward of Mochras Point . . . [it] appears to

be mainly composed of large loose stones. . . . Near the outer end is an extensive patch of rocks and stones, one of which dries 1½ feet.'

These do not read like descriptions of ruined embankments, and although the name Caer Gwyddno is well-established for the extremity of Sarn Gynfelyn, no one in recent years has seriously suggested that the remains of a city or fort can be seen here. More than a century ago, however, Wm. Owen Pughe claimed to have seen them ' three or four miles in the sea, between the outlets of the rivers Ystwyth and Teivi. Here,' he wrote, ' are the remains of the fort of Gwyddno. . . . In the summer of 1770 I sailed over the ruins, on a very calm day, and thus for about three minutes I had a clear view of them, and many of the stones seemed to be large slabs, and lying to confusion on the heap.' [138]

The seaward end of Sarn Gynfelyn, is, indeed, characterized by boulders considerably larger than those to be seen nearer the shore, and although the Sarn lies north of the mouth of the Ystwyth and not south of it, it is more than likely that they are what Wm. Owen Pughe saw from his boat : but his recollections of their appearance and his suggestion concerning their significance lose much of their value when we realize that he was writing 63 years after a visit made when he was 11 years old !

There are a few references to worked stones having been seen on the sarnau and to stones with mortar adhering to them [4e], but nothing of this sort has been either photographed or collected, and in the absence of tangible evidence we cannot regard the claims as in any way militating against the view that the ridges are, like Llys Helig, accumulations of pebbles and boulders derived from glacial deposits (Boulder Clay). The glacial deposits are widely distributed in the adjacent parts of Wales and their former seawards extension is indicated by their appearance in the local cliffs.

A very likely explanation for the occurrence of the sarnau as long narrow ridges is forthcoming when we note that Sarn Badrig begins about midway between Traeth Mawr and the estuary of the Mawddach, Sarn y Bwch between the latter and

the estuary of the Dyfi, and Sarn Gynfelyn between the Dyfi
and the combined estuary of the Rheidol and the Ystwyth.

This suggests that they represent continuations of the water-
sheds between these rivers on the now submerged coastal plain,
and that, consisting largely of Boulder Clay, they left accumulations of stones when the finer materials of the deposits were
washed away. The linear arrangement of the stones may well
have been emphasized by wave action which piled them up
after the fashion of storm beaches. The positions of the sarnau
may have been influenced by continuations beneath the
Boulder Clay of the outcrops of the rocks of the mainland, and
the larger blocks to be seen at the extremities of some of them
may have been derived from submarine exposures of those
rocks.

That they extend out to sea instead of lying more or less
parallel to the coast is sufficient to suggest that the sarnau are
not likely to be parts of any protection scheme, even if it were
possible to admit that the local inhabitants were numerous
enough at the time in question and had sufficient skill to undertake a work of this magnitude and complexity. It must be
remembered that the reference to Seithennin's control over
sluices implies a system in which measures had been taken not
only to keep out the sea, but also to ensure the discharge of land
waters that accumulated when the rising tide brought the level
of the sea to or above that of the channels which drained the
land.

It will be interesting to close these notes on the sarnau by
quoting from the *General view of the Agricultural and Domestic
Economy of North Wales* (1810) by Walter Davies (Gwallter
Mechain), who in many ways was much in advance of his
contemporaries.

' *Sarn y Bwch*,' he wrote ' is a ridge of huge stones, . . .
appearing at low water, near the mouth of the Dysynni.
Sarn signifies a causeway or pavement ; and this, as well as
another near Harlech, called *Sarn Badrig*, are supposed by
some to be the work of art : others take them to be skeletons
of hills, reduced into their present state by the repeated
operations of the tides. The oracles of the cloister would fain

have persuaded the credulous of those days, when superstition was in its zenith, that the latter *Sarn* was a footpath
miraculously formed by St. Patrick, to expedite his passage
to and from Ireland. It is moreover said, with much greater
probability, by the assertors of its being the work of art, that
it formerly was the north-western barrier of *Cantre'r gwaelod*,
or the hundred townships of the plain ; which extended from
thence over a vast tract of Cardigan Bay towards Aberystwyth. That this part of the sea was formerly dry land,
seems to be well attested by immemorial tradition : the
catastrophe of its being deluged is recorded in ancient verse.'
Unfortunately for those who subscribed to the view that the
Sarn is part of St. Patrick's causeway to Ireland, it points, not
to Ireland but to South America !

We saw, when considering Llys Helig, that Ptolemy's map of
Britain could not be cited as evidence of changes in the northern
coast of Wales, but since it has from time to time been mentioned in connection with Cantre'r Gwaelod, it is necessary to see
whether it is any more informative concerning Cardigan Bay.

'It is significant that the map attributed to Ptolemy that
is reproduced in the frontispiece plate to Rhŷs' *Celtic Britain*
shows the Cardigan Bay coast as extending much further west
than it does today.' That passage, from *The Evolution of a
Coastline* shows how easily reference to a standard work may
invest a statement with an appearance of authority to which it
is not entitled.

The map reproduced in *Celtic Britain* [146] is a little outline
($1\frac{3}{4}''$ x $1\frac{3}{4}''$), obviously intended to illustrate the shape of
Ptolemy's Albion and Ivernia (Great Britain and Ireland) and
their relation to continental Europe. So small a map, based as
it is upon one of the late 16th century versions of Ptolemy's,
and not upon one that Ptolemy could have made from the
data in his tables, is of no value whatever as an indication of the
geography of Cardigan Bay in the 2nd century, A.D., and was
never intended to be cited as if it were ; but since it is customary either to speak of Ptolemy's maps as if they are necessarily
reliable criteria, or else to dismiss them as being so inaccurate
as to be no more than cartographical curiosities, their intro-

duction into our discussion for the second time provides an opportunity for showing that neither of these extreme views is reasonable : the one puts the maps to a use for which, in view of the way in which they were prepared, they are obviously unsuitable, and the other blames them for not being what we have no right to expect them to be.

For the Cardigan Bay area, Ptolemy mentioned and gave the supposed positions of four localities ; *Canganorum promontorium*, which is universally believed to mean the Lleyn Peninsula, and most probably its extremity, Braich y Pwll ; *Stucciae fluvii ostia* and *Tuerobis fluvii ostia*, for which the usually accepted modern synonyms are the mouths of the rivers Ystwyth and Teifi ; and *Octapitarum promontorium* which, if not actually St. David's Head as many suppose, must have signified one of the western extremities of Pembrokeshire. The above names are as given in the Latin editions of Ptolemy's work ; in one of the oldest of the Greek manuscripts (a treasure of the Mont Athos Monastery) the names appear as Gangani, Stoukia, Touerobis and Oktapittaron.

It is not necessary here to complicate the matter by considering the problem raised by the fact that in some of the early copies of Ptolemy's tables the estuary of another river—*Toesobis*—is listed between *Canganorum promontorium* and *Stucciae fluvii ostia*, whereas in others it is listed as though it belonged to the north-western coast of Caernarvonshire, for we are primarily concerned with the position assigned to the *Stucciae* estuary.

If we plot the Welsh localities on the basis of the latitudes and longitudes assigned to them by Ptolemy the result is indicated by the broken line in Fig. 10, taking *Canganorum promontorium* as the common point in order to make comparison with a modern map possible. This comparison lends support to the view that the map need not be taken seriously. It is, however, far from being a fair comparison, because, by adopting the estimate of the earth's circumference made by Posidonius in the first century B.C., Ptolemy's globe was about one-fourth too small, so that to him, a degree of latitude in the neighbourhood of Wales was only about 51 of our miles instead of approximately 69.

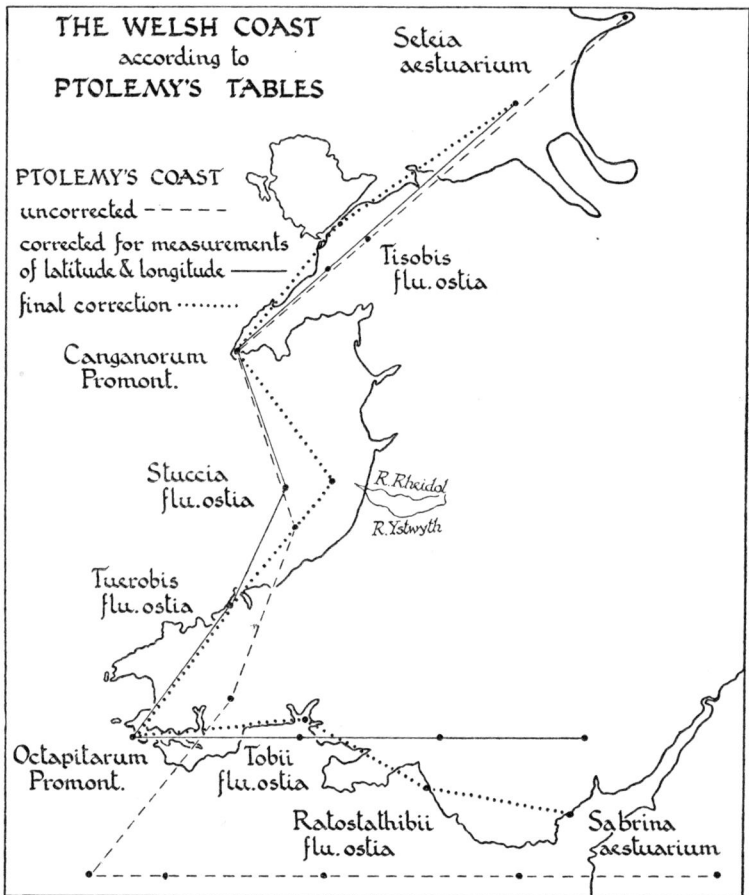

Fig. 10.   The Welsh coast according to Ptolemy's Tables

The positions of capes and estuaries are taken from a manuscript of the *Geographia* of about A.D. 1400 (Burney MS No. 111 in the British Museum). The corrections are explained on page o.

The degree of longitude was, of course, also one-fourth too small, but an additional error was introduced into the map of Albion because the island was placed about 3° too far north, and the length of a degree of longitude decreases with distance from the equator. Making allowances for both these errors,

Ptolemy's degree of longitude in Wales was about 29.5 miles instead of as it should be, approximately 42.

As a result, by assigning latitude and longitude to places on the basis of his information regarding the distances between them, he made them appear to be too far apart ; for example, a place he thought to be 51 miles north of another would be separated from it on his map by 1° and so would appear, in terms of a modern map to be 69 miles away.

By replotting the places in terms of the smaller network of parallels and meridians we get a more accurate impression of the distances by which Ptolemy thought they were separated. The result is indicated by the continuous line in Fig. 10. A further correction that might be applied is based upon the assumption, reasonable in the light of what is known about the information on which Ptolemy's tables were compiled, that the estuaries he included represented stages in coastal journeys, and were, in fact, roughly equally spaced. If then, we place the *Stucciae* estuary as far from the *Canganorum* promontory as from the *Tuerobis* estuary, which is as far as the latter place is from the *Octapitarum* promontory, and that, in turn, from the *Tobii* estuary, we find it occupying a situation only about eight miles from Aberystwyth.

The apparently inland position assigned by the tables to some of the Bristol Channel estuaries probably resulted from the fact that they were recorded as being encountered during the course of a journey from West to East, and in the absence of further information were assumed to be on the same latitude. Placing them in their relative positions on the coast completes the outline of the map, which shows that Ptolemy's information was not so inaccurate as might at first appear. This, of course, does not affect the conclusions previously arrived at (see page 57) concerning the use of his map in discussions about changes in the coast of North Wales. The determining factor in that region is the lack of information, not the accuracy or otherwise of the little he had.

If *Tuerobis* is really the Teifi, its mouth on our corrected map is in nearly the right position ; indeed, its position might reasonably be regarded as helping to confirm the identification.

Octapitarum promotorium now comes near the south-western extremity of Pembrokeshire. This confirms the view that the promontory to which the name originally referred may not have been St. Davids Head, as is now usually supposed and as the Ordnance Survey map of Roman Britain suggests. None of the Roman authors who discussed Britain mentioned *Octapitarum*, nor does it appear in any of the topographical works up to and including Leland's *Itinerary*, which was written in the fifteen-thirties. When Humphrey Llwyd wrote of ' a region . . . termed of our countrymen, Dyfed . . . the farther promontorie where of Ptolemaeus called Octopitarum,' [167] it was, as his map of Wales clearly indicates, the southern of the two limbs that enclose St. Bride's Bay that he had in mind. The identification with St. Davids Head may have been suggested by Camden's reference, in *Britannia* to ' A spacious promontory called by Ptolemy Octopitarum . . . and in English Saint Davids Land.' [10d]

This digression has taken us away from our proper theme, but it serves to remind us that whilst much that has been taken for granted in maps based upon Ptolemy's tables will not bear close investigation, he often came nearer to the truth than we suppose.

Returning to the Stucciae estuary, we find that when all possible corrections have been applied, the position assigned to it by Ptolemy is about 8 miles out in the sea—westwards of any line likely to have been followed by the sea coast since the beginning of the Christian Era. Whether Ptolemy's information was inaccurate, or whether, during centuries of copying, an error was introduced into the tables—and such errors are by no means uncommon—cannot now be determined, but we can at least assume that an estuary, important enough to have been reported to Ptolemy in Alexandria, existed somewhere along the central part of the Cardigan Bay coast. If, in those days, the coast lay a little farther out than it does now, a very likely possibility, the rivers Ystwyth and Rheidol would have joined before reaching the sea and Ptolemy's *Stucciae fluvii ostia* may well have been the combined estuary of those two streams. Its latitude is nearly correct.

The position that Ptolemy assigned to the estuary places it almost exactly on the 10-fathom submarine contour, and that corresponds roughly with the coastline of an early part of the human era when the sea was still gaining upon the land, but the map cannot be cited as evidence for the inundation in the sixth century A.D. that is required by the story of the Lowland Hundred.

(c) Some obscurities

Although modern versions of his story always refer to Gwyddno Garanhir as lord of the Lowland Hundred which now lies at the bottom of Cardigan Bay, early references to his identity and place of residence are both vague and contradictory. In the *Black Book* poem it was Gwyddno's land that was overwhelmed, but in the almost contemporary Peniarth MS. No. 16 the King of Maes Gwyddno is Seithennin whilst other early manuscripts associate Gwyddno with the region in which Helig ap Glannog had his home.

In *Bonedd Gwŷr y Gogledd*, Genealogies of the men of the North, said to have been transcribed in 1300, Gwyddno appears as one of the kings of the north, and the first series of Triads speak of a *Porth Wyddno yn y Gogledd* (in the North). This seems to point to another Gwyddno, for Gogledd or the north in the contemporary sense of the term was roughly the country west of a line from Chester to Edinburgh and south of a line from the Clyde to the Firth of Forth.

The Third Series of Triads speaks of *Porth Wyddnaw yng Ngheredigiawn* as one of the three royal ports of the Island of Britain. Although worthless as evidence the allusion has been cited as associating Gwyddno with Cardigan Bay, for Porth Wyddno in Ceredigion is regarded as meaning Borth, a few miles north of Aberystwyth [145f], or else the Caer Gwyddno supposed to have been situated at the end of Sarn Gynfelyn [4k]. In the First Series the other two great ports were *Porth ysgewin yngwent*, and *Porth Wygyr ym Mon* [75c] and, however they may be specifically identified, one was in Gwent (roughly, Monmouthshire) and the other in Mona or Anglesey : if, then, the third of the series was *yn y Gogledd*—in the north—it is hardly likely to have been in Cardigan Bay.

Remembering the doubtful authenticity of many of the Triads in the Third Series we are tempted to ask whether Iolo's Porth Wyddnaw is any more than a product of his fertile imagination—a place conceived in order to give greater plausibility to the story of the Lowland Hundred.

We find, then, that these early documentary associations between Gwyddno and the realm of Helig are more apparent than real, and also that Porth Wyddnaw in Cardigan Bay is more likely to have been invented than to have been named by or after a former lord of the Lowland Hundred.

In his *Arthurian Legend*, Rhŷs mentions a small river called Gwenwyn Meirch Gwyddno—the Poison of Gwyddno's horses—near Bangor [143a]. This also takes us away from Cardigan Bay and introduces the cauldron of Ceridwen which comes in the story of Taliesin.

The cauldron, which plays an important part in Celtic mythology was regarded as the source of inspiration and the origin of poetry and the arts. It was usually associated with water, as in the Mabinogi of Branwen the daughter of Llŷr (see page 239) where Brân saw a man coming out of a lake with a cauldron on his back. In *Hanes Taliesin* Ceridwen was the wife of Tegid Voel who lived in Llyn Tegid (Lake Bala), and we may note, without attempting to read anything into the fact, that some of the genealogies speak of *Helig Foel* (i.e., the Bald). Ceridwen caused the cauldron to be boiled in order to get inspiration for her ill-favoured son. The vessel burst, and since the contents, all but three charm-bearing drops, were poisonous, they polluted the stream into which they ran and the water poisoned Gwyddno Garanhir's horses.

If the stream in question was really near Bangor, the story associates the Gwyddno who lost his lands with something which happened in North Wales. The matter is not, however, as straightforward as might at first appear. In the first place, Ceridwen is described as the wife of Tegid Foel whose dwelling was in the midst of Lake Tegid, i.e., Bala, and the scene of her unfortunate experiment with the cauldron was situated in Powys, which indicates a place in the southern part of North Wales, not in the north-west, near Bangor, in the old division called Gwynedd. In the second place, there are other streams said to have been called Gwenwyn Meirch Gwyddno, whilst early references to the one near Bangor are to a stream called Gwenwyn Meirch; Rhŷs appears to be the sole written authority for adding Gwyddno to the name of this one.

Wm. Owen Pughe, in a footnote to his copy and translation of the *Story of Taliesin* in the Cambrian Quarterly Magazine (1833) [138] said that the river called Gwenwyn Meirch Gwyddno ' in the old story ' was near Towyn and was (at the time he wrote) called Avon Llyn y Pair or the river of the pool of the cauldron. There is indeed a mill called Llyn Pair Mill (Melin Llyn Pair) on the north side of Afon Dyffryn Gwyn, about two miles ESE of Towyn, and another Mr. Pughe, writing in 1853 [136] mentioned it in connexion with a story told of Llyn Barfog, which lies at the foot of Mynydd y Llyn, about four miles ESE of Towyn and on the south side of Afon Dyffryn Gwyn.

The story concerns a ' mystic Afanc y Llyn, monster of the lake,' which seems to have been concerned in creating a deluge by breaking down the banks of a lake—Llyn Barfog according to local tradition. The rest of the story, which does not concern us, will be found in *Celtic Folklore* [145q], but Pughe recorded that it was locally believed to be perilous to let the waters out of the lake, and mentioned an aged inhabitant who could remember that, when this was done to provide water for Llyn Pair Mill during a period of drought, the neighbourhood was inconvenienced by long and continuous rains. We are reminded of the threat as to what was to happen if Llyn Cwm Llwch should be tampered with.

We must, however, remember that Ceridwen was associated with Bala Lake, and if the story is, in fact, responsible for the name of a stream, it is in the neighbourhood of Bala that we should expect to find it. In *Clych Adgof* [28] Sir Owen Edwards stated that the stream running into Bala Lake near Llanycil was called Aber Gwenwynfeirch Gwyddno, from its association with the pagan tradition of Ceridwen, but here again no authority was cited for the addition of Gwyddno to the name, which appears on the Ordnance Survey map as Aber Gwen-

M

wynfeirch. The Aber part of the name seems to have been derived from the story as published in the *Myvyrian Archaiology* and by Wm. Owen Pughe in the *Cambrian Quarterly Magazine* (Vol. 5, 1833). In these, Aber is used to indicate the stream or the brook and not in its more familiar modern sense as meaning the fall of one river into another or into the sea.

If any stream received its name on account of the legend, it would seem to be this one near Llanycil. The stream near Bangor is mentioned in Leland's *Itinerary* where it is called *Guenwynmyreth*, and since Leland gave its meaning as ' Horsis Broke ' the word he used was evidently intended for meirch.

The Hemlock Water Dropwort grows by the side of many streams in Wales, including those near Bangor, and, as it is known to be poisonous to cattle and horses which eat it willingly, it is easy to see why a stream might have been called ' Horses' poison,' quite apart from any association with a legend—and, as already indicated, Rhŷs did not cite any authority for adding Gwyddno to the name of the Bangor stream.

It is clear that individuals, times, and localities are mixed with curious inconsistency in most of the early stories and genealogies. It is to this that we must attribute some of the statements associating Helig with Cantre'r Gwaelod, and others associating Gwyddno Garanhir with localities in the north. The modern forms of the two stories are distinct, but there is always, in the background, the vague allusion to an inundation or to a person whom tradition associates with an inundation, and if we could get back to ultimate origins we should probably find that both stories have sprung from a common source. We are reminded of the streams which emerge from subterranean channels in limestone regions, leaving us to guess whence and by what route the water has travelled unseen.

As with Tyno Helig, so with Cantre'r Gwaelod ; it is not an encroachment of the sea that has to be questioned, but the suddenness with which it is supposed to have occurred and the period at which it is supposed to have taken place. In neither case did floods like those demanded by the legends occur in the early days of the Christian era, so that if the stories originated in actual happenings, the events took place so long ago that when they came to be reduced to writing, by those who laid the foundation of Welsh written literature, only their basic facts remained ; but, once recorded, those facts became the nuclei of stories so full of circumstantial detail as almost to pass for eye-witness accounts of events that occurred in the Dark Ages or in Medieval times.

Before setting out to inquire into the circumstances in which legends like these we have been discussing may have had their origins, we should recall that similar stories are told of other regions. There is, for example, a tradition that a fertile land once existed between Cornwall and the Scilly Isles. It is supposed to have been called Lyonesse and to have had no fewer than 140 churches. In the distant past, so the tradition says, it was overwhelmed by the sea so suddenly that only one person escaped, a man named Trevilian, who got away by riding on a swift horse towards the mainland—reminding us of the Tewthi Hen of the Exeter Triad and Teithi Hen in the story of Culhwch. [15]   Here, as in the areas we have discussed, there is plenty of evidence that the sea has encroached upon the land, but none that the encroachment took place in the way the legend describes or that it affected much more than the area now embraced by the Scilly Isles.

Brittany also has its story of a city below the sea, in a bay that was once a green meadow. The City (Cer a Iz or Kaer a Iz) appears to have been situated near Pointe du Raz, west of Quimper. The inhabitants were drunkards, given to every excess, and the ruler was Gradlon. An enemy persuaded his daughter (Dahut) to hand over the keys of the sluice gates in the dyke which kept out the sea. The enemy unlocked the gates and the sea rushed in, but, just as the torrent was reaching his palace, the king tried to escape with his daughter on a horse. The ghost of a saint (St. Gwenole) appeared and told Gradlon to throw his daughter into the water because she had been the cause of the catastrophe.

It is interesting to note that this story resembles the earliest known one about the Lowland Hundred in attributing the disaster to a girl, and the somewhat later ones in referring

to drunkenness. There is also another common factor. Gradlon
and his daughter tried to escape on a horse, Trevilian got away
on a swift one, and we saw Mererid upon a fine bay steed.
That all these stories are related is evident, but whether
because of independent derivation from a common source or
because a story told in one region was carried to others is
difficult to say.

The coast of Britanny like that of Cardigan Bay shows un
mistakable signs of subsidence since Megalithic times, for, on
the shore of the island of Er Lanic there is a stone circle, now
half submerged, with some of its stones standing up in the
sea, [15] and it cannot be altogether without significance that
the route by which the megalithic cultures reached Britain
from the Mediterranean lay past Britanny and the Scilly Isles on
its way to the channel between Wales and Ireland. [40a]

However and wherever the story of Cer a Iz began, the
reference to sluice gates shows that, as now told, it is, like the
modern story of Cantre'r Gwaelod, a product of comparatively
modern times.

X

INUNDATIONS BY WHICH THE LEGENDS
MAY HAVE BEEN INSPIRED

SUBMERGED ' forests '—stumps of trees *in situ* and beds of peat—
seen on the foreshore at low spring tides or met with in excavations around many parts of the Welsh coast are indications of
encroachment by the sea before and during Bronze Age times.

Comparison between the assemblages of terrestrial animals
characteristic of Ireland, Great Britain, and the Continent shows
that those of the two former regions arrived by land from the
third, from which it follows that there has been extensive submergence since the animals arrived in Great Britain and Ireland.

Conditions associated with the accumulation of ice during the
Glacial Period would have resulted in a temporary lowering of
the sea level, whilst the subsequent melting of the ice (within the
limits of the human era) would have replenished the sea, allowing
it to re-cover the coastal regions that had temporarily been land.

Whether due to a lowering of the land or a rise in sea level,
submergences like those that have affected the Welsh coast take
place slowly, but tides and storms could, from time to time, have
created conditions leading to the sudden inundation of limited
areas.

(a) The evidence of submerged land surfaces and sand dunes

THE stories of Helig, Seithennin, Gwyddno Garanhir, and
Seiriol all involve reference to sudden encroachment of the
sea, but history preserves no record of such floods in the regions
concerned and the available evidence shows that none such
could have occurred in the periods to which the legends are
supposed to relate.

We have now to ask whether it is likely that such changes in
the relation between land and sea may have taken place
around the Welsh coast at earlier periods but still within the
limits of human memory, and if so, when, and to what extent
man is likely to have been affected by them.

It must, of course, be remembered that in confining our
attention to the Welsh coast we do not overlook the fact that
flood-phenomena of this nature involve differential movement
between land and sea and would therefore have been wide-

spread, so that evidence could be sought for in other parts of our island as well. Our concentration upon Wales does not mean that the region is thought to be peculiar in the latest stages of its physical history.

The compiler of the *Notes to bee observed* possessed information which he rightly interpreted as pointing to an encroachment of the sea, but he was not in a position to realize that it was associated with a period much earlier than any of those in which Helig is supposed to have lived. Referring to the Lavan Sands he wrote :

> ' In this greate washe uppon a lowe grownd ebbe, when ytt ebbes farthest, are to be seene the rootes of great oake and asshe . . . this I speak as an eye witnes, havynge seene the rootes mysealf and taken them upp soe that ytt shoulde seeme that this vale before the inundacōn was a woodland countrey.'

He had evidently seen one of the submerged land surfaces which, occurring here and there around our coast, indicate an encroachment of the sea over what was at one time a continuation of the present land. [Pl. II].

These material records of the geography of the past are often called ' submerged forests,' as indeed they sometimes are, because erect stumps of trees are to be seen still rooted in dark coloured clays that are exposed here and there on the foreshore at low spring tides ; often, however, they are beds of peat— partially decayed vegetable debris—associated with clays that, like those in which the stumps occur, represent ancient soil, or with silt that accumulated as mud in ancient marshes, so that ' submerged land surface ' is, on the whole, a better general term to apply to them.

The submerged forests seem to have caught the popular imagination at about the time the *Notes* were compiled ; one off the shores of Wirral, near Leasowe, was referred to by Richard James (sometime librarian to that great antiquarian, Sir Robert Bruce Cotton) in his *Iter Lancastrense*. This poem, written when the author was on a visit to Lancashire and the neighbouring counties, includes the following passage : [72]

And in summe places, when ye sea doth bate
Down from ye shoare, tis wonder to relate
How many thowsands of thies trees now stand
Black broken on their rootes, which once drie land
Did cover ; whence turfs Neptune yeelds to showe
He did not allways to theis borders flowe.

Another writer of the time, William Webb (1622) recorded
that ' some are of opinion that they [the trees] have been there
since Noah's flood,' whilst the eighteenth century naturalist,
Thomas Pennant, when dealing with the coast near Abergele,
mentioned, as proof that the sea had encroached upon the land,
that he had ' observed far from the clayey banks, a long tract
of hard loam, filled with the bodies of oak trees, tolerably
entire. . . . The wood is collected by the poorer people and
carried home and used as fuel.' [131b] In circumstances like
these, faced with evidence that the sea had encroached upon
the land, local residents would naturally find no difficulty in
accepting the story of Helig's misfortune.

It is necessary at this juncture to interpolate a brief reference
to the terms used to indicate the successive periods into which
the prehistoric ages of the human era have been divided for
purposes of description and comparative study. [40, 55]

Three principal sub-divisions were originally recognized, and
named—according to the materials that were dominantly used
at the time for the manufacture of weapons and implements—
Stone Age, Bronze Age, and Iron Age, respectively. The Stone
Age, by far the longest of the three, may have begun in Britain
as far back as 500,000 years B.C., the Bronze Age about
2,000 B.C., and the Iron Age, which merged into the Roman
period, about 500 B.C.

The Stone Age, which obviously embraced more than one
distinct phase of human advancement, was subdivided into an
earlier Old Stone (Palaeolithic) Age and a later New Stone
(Neolithic) Age ; the former was characterized by implements
that were brought to the required shape by the removal of
chips or flakes from a larger fragment, using another stone as a
hammer or as a means of applying pressure, and the latter by

implements made smooth and sometimes polished by rubbing or grinding.

Further study made it desirable to introduce a third sub-division of the Stone Age—a Middle Stone (Mesolithic) Age. The Old Stone Age, especially during its later portion, was a period of cold in Britain and northern Europe, and men favoured caves for their habitations ; after its close the climate became warmer and forests established themselves wherever suitable conditions obtained, but the cultural traditions of the ' Cave ' period, modified to meet the changed climatic conditions, continued to influence human activities in our area for a very long time before they gave place to new modes of life that, introduced by new arrivals, marked the beginning of the Neolithic Age. It is this transitional period that constitutes the Mesolithic Age, one characteristic of which was the manu-facture of small flint implements (microliths) intended for making such things as arrowheads and harpoons.

The Mesolithic Age is considered to have commenced about 8000 B.C. and the term began to be generally adopted about 1932. In the circumstances many of the objects and events referred to in earlier publications as of Neolithic Age may have been older than that name now implies. The chronological basis of our present discussion may be summarized as follows :—

Palaeolithic (or Old Stone) *Age*, the latest sub-division of which, the Cave period, is believed to have commenced in Wales before 100,000 B.C.

Mesolithic (or Middle Stone) *Age*, beginning about 8000 B.C.

Neolithic (or New Stone) *Age*, beginning about 2500 B.C.

Bronze Age, beginning about 2000 B.C.

Iron Age, beginning about 500 B.C., and continuing (in Britain) into the Roman period.

The dates are, of course, approximate, those for the earlier ages, in particular, being under constant review by archaeol-ogists. They are not necessarily applicable in other countries where improvements in the methods of making stone imple-ments, or the substitution of metal for stone, may have been effected more rapidly or may have been longer delayed. When Captain Cook landed in New Zealand in 1769, for example, the Maori were still using polished stone tools like those associated with the Neolithic Age in Britain, and even in the present century some of the native peoples of Australia have been living in what to all intents and purposes is a Stone Age.

Geological and archaeological evidence, to be cited later, combine to show that the change of relative level between land and sea, which caused the forests and land surfaces of our coastal regions to become submerged (and the accumulations of vegetable debris to become layers of peat interbedded with layers of clay), was in progress during the Mesolithic and Neolithic periods ; they also show that it was, as far as Wales and the west of England are concerned, almost completed before the commencement of the present era. [115]   There have, of course, been local and in some cases quite extensive encroachments of the sea during historic times, but this has for the most part been due to the destructive action of the waves which have washed away beaches and even cliffs, rather than to conditions which have caused the land to sink or the level of the sea to rise.

To deal first with the closing phase of the submergence ; evidence relating to periods during which the subsidence came to an end derives mostly from the beds of peat or other in-dications of land surfaces that are exposed on foreshores, or met with in excavations on or near the coast like those made for docks or in connection with drainage schemes.

During the construction of Barry Dock in Glamorgan, clays with beds of peat were met with at a depth of about 36 feet below O.D. (Fig. 11). Allowing for the fact that the land must have been out of reach of the sea at high tide in order that oaks could grow—and the remains of oaks were abundant in the peat—these sections through the superficial strata indicate a relative downward movement of at least from 54 to 56 feet since the material that is now peat began to accumulate, and those figures remind us of the 10 fathoms already mentioned in connection with Cardigan Bay.

The only evidence of human occupation in the Barry peats was provided by some bone needles and a polished axe found in the topmost beds, barely four feet below O.D. [161]   They

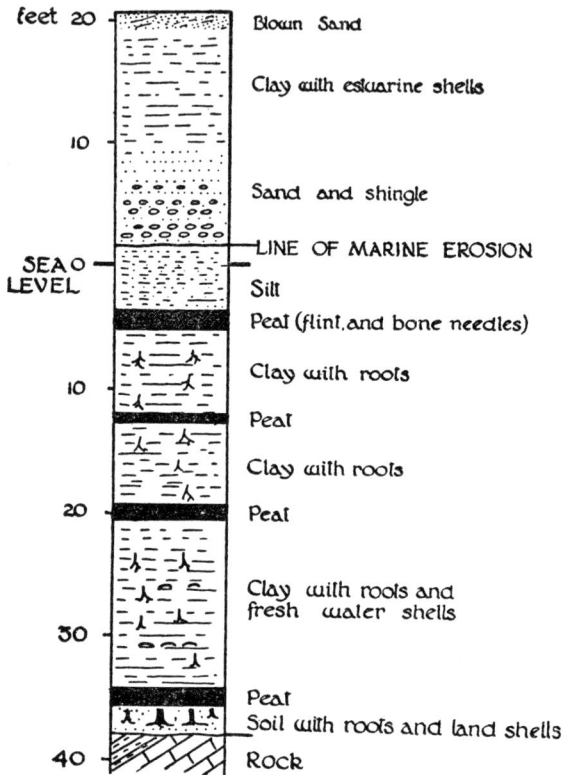

Fig. 11. Section illustrating the submerged land surfaces at Barry, Glamorgan

Based on records made during excavations for the Dock [161] and indicating the level of the peat beds in which human artefacts were found.

were regarded at the time of their discovery as of Neolithic Age, but are now considered to have belonged to a somewhat more recent period—some part of the Bronze Age. In that case they indicate that men living nearer to our own time than Neolithic days were affected by the closing stages of the encroachment of the sea.

Modern methods of peat-study (based upon pollen-analysis to which we have already referred) were applied by H. A. Hyde to a section exposed during the course of constructional work at Cardiff Docks in 1937 ; they permit of a more precise indication of the time at which the present sea level was established in the Bristol Channel area, and therefore of the time by which the subsidence had ceased.

Borings revealed layers of peat, resting upon and covered by clay, at depths varying from about 12 feet above O.D. to 6 ins. below O.D. One of the peat beds, subsequently exposed more fully in an excavation, was about 2′ 6″ in thickness and had its base about 8 feet above O.D. It contained the trunk of an oak tree and an examination of the pollen grains revealed the presence of pine, birch, elm, oak and alder. This association of plants indicates a period considerably more recent than the Mesolithic Age, and there was also, especially near the base of the deposit, a significantly high proportion of the pollen of lime which points to the Late Bronze and Early Iron Ages. The presence of pollen derived from members of the pink family, which includes several maritime species, suggests that when the peat was formed, the sea was not far away. [70]

From this evidence we are entitled to infer that here, at least, the present coastline is not far removed, either horizontally or vertically, from that which existed when the constituents of the peat were parts of living plants—that is, at a period not very far removed from the beginning of the Christian era. There has been a small amount of submergence, because oaks are not likely to have thrived on a site liable to marine flooding, as, in the absence of protecting banks, one in this region no more than 8 feet above O.D. would have been.

Supporting evidence of a different kind was obtained from another part of the Glamorgan coast when a site in the dunes at Merthyr Mawr, examined by Sir Cyril Fox, proved to have been occupied early in the Iron Age. [38] The ' finds ' included objects of bronze and iron, fragments of crucibles in which bronze had been melted, the bones of domestic animals, and the shells of edible mollusca. The distribution of the objects made it clear that the people with whom they had been associated actually lived in, or at least visited the dunes whilst the sand was accumulating. The dunes were, therefore, forming during the early part of the Iron Age, from which it follows that the relation between the levels of land and sea in this region has not materially changed for more than two millenia ; sand dunes cannot form on a sinking shoreline, for in such circumstances any sand that might be blown on to the shore would soon be levelled off by the incoming water.

A similar story is told by the submerged peat beds and land surfaces in Swansea Bay and around the coast of Gower studied by T. Neville George [44]. In this region a whetstone and fragments of iron ore were found in circumstances which suggest that Early Iron Age man may have lived in the forests before they were finally submerged. This implies a late but probably local continuation of the movement which permitted the encroachment of the sea.

Farther west, prehistoric land surfaces, now submerged, are from time to time exposed along the shores of Carmarthen Bay and Pembrokeshire. In one such laid bare in 1917 at Lydstep Haven, A. L. Leach, Honorary Curator of the Museum at Tenby, discovered the skeleton of a pig ; across its neck lay the trunk of a fallen tree, between which and the skeleton two microliths were found.

This interesting discovery, recorded and photographed under conditions of extreme difficulty, since the spot was only un-covered in the intervals between successive waves, shows that the downward movement of the land was in progress when early man hunted in a forest that had become so waterlogged that trunks of fallen trees were buried in masses of sodden vegetation and subsequently became peat. [85] The site probably relates to a somewhat earlier phase of the sub-mergence than is indicated by the human artefacts found in the peats at Barry and Swansea Bay for it is covered by at least 22 feet of water at high spring tides—how much earlier is doubtful, because although microliths are typical of the Mesolithic Age, they are known to have survived into the Bronze Age.

Other indications of the presence of man in our coastal regions whilst the encroachment of the sea was still in progress come from the southern side of the Bristol Channel, where an early Bronze Age burial was found a few years ago just below high water mark at Brean Down in Somerset. [21] The cist contained a beaker that was probably one of the oldest yet discovered in this country.

Cardigan Bay, too, has its submerged forests (Pl. 11B). Walter Davies mentioned them in 1810 :

'There are also physical appearances now existing, which seem to corroborate what is asserted by tradition and history respecting this inundation. Trees are observed to lie prostrate in the bay. Between Tywyn Meirionydd and Aberdyvi, a turbary, of excellent peat, extends under the sea to an unknown distance. The people dig through several feet of the sand, which the sea has deposited upon the surface of the turbary, in order to get at the peat. The flame of this saline fuel is so pungent that it corrodes vessels hung over it in a short time. The sea, over the whole extent of the bay, is not deep,' [20]

Near Llanaber, silts with rootlets indicating an ancient soil occur at from six to eight feet below high water mark, passing seawards to greater depths, and there are indications of a submerged forest on the coast a little north of Borth. [4,48]

The evidence from North Wales and its neighbourhood confirms the conclusions arrived at in respect of South Wales and Cardigan Bay. The rooted tree stumps and the beds of peat exposed on the foreshore at Rhyl are, like those at Barry, indicative of submergence for they are the remains of plants that grew upon a land surface. The peat beds are not the remains of forests that established themselves on the land surface originally exposed after the retreat of the ice at the end of the Glacial Period ; they represent trees and other plants that grew on clay containing the shells of freshwater and estuarine mollusca, and this must have been laid down in an estuary. [47] The clay with its intercalated beds of peat rests upon the glacial deposits and may be as much as 10 or 12 feet in thickness. It must have been deposited in a region where a slow encroachment of the sea was occasionally interrupted for periods long enough to permit the establishment of land surfaces upon which trees could grow.

The change of sea level in this region was in progress in prehistoric times because artefacts found by T. A. Glenn in

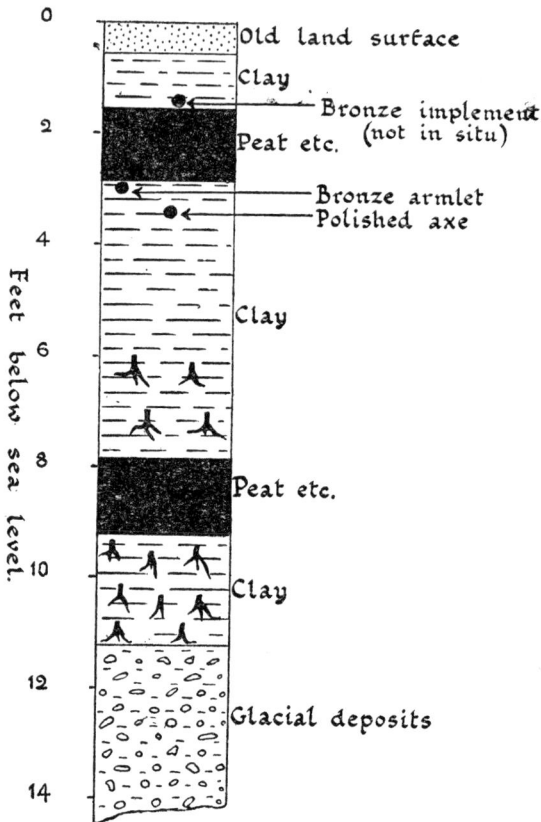

Fig. 12. Section illustrating the submerged land surfaces
near Rhyl

Based upon information provided by the late T. A. Glenn, and illustrating the
levels of the peat beds in which human artefacts were found.

association with the peat beds are indicative of the presence of
Bronze Age man (Fig. 12), but they show that since his time
the downward movement cannot have been more than 5 or
6 feet. It may have been appreciably less for some of the ' finds '
were not seen *in situ* ; they appear to have been derived from
peat beds that have since been washed away and to indicate an
ancient land surface that may, before its comparatively recent
destruction by the normal processes of coast erosion, still have
been above mean sea level.

The relation between the sand dunes near Liverpool and the ancient land surfaces on which they rest confirms the conclusions arrived at after the study of those on the Glamorgan coast because it indicates that the sand has been accumulating at intervals for at least 2,000 years, during which period there can have been no marked relative downward movement of the land. [140]

In these circumstances it is certain that there can have been no extensive loss of land in North Wales during historic times due to subsidence of the land (or rise in sea level) of the order of over forty feet—the amount that would be involved in bringing an inhabited land surface, drained by natural agencies, to the present depth below high watermark of the site called Llys Helig. Similarly, there cannot have been, in the sixth century, a subsidence of part or of the whole of Cardigan Bay to the extent of 60 feet, which is what would have been necessary to bring about the inundation of an area as large as the legendary Cantre'r Gwaelod.

There are, however, ample grounds for believing that, whilst there has been little if any change in level in historic times *the inhabitants of the coastal regions of Wales were affected by at least the later stages of the development of the present relation between land and sea.* In this connexion we may recall the anthropological investigations of H. J. Fleure and T. C. James. [36] These, based upon skull measurements, suggest that there still remain in Wales (especially in the remoter hill districts) groups of people that are descended from the Neolithic inhabitants of the land, and as the submergence was in progress in Neolithic times it is not unreasonable to suggest that ' the ancestors of the present population of Wales and the adjoining countries of Ireland and the Isle of Man to have witnessed its effects ' [76], but what they witnessed was slow encroachment due to a series of minor inundations, not a single wide-spread catastrophe.

From the eastern shores of England, also, there is evidence that early man was consciously affected by the encroaching sea. [185] Fisher folk of Neolithic and Bronze Age times had villages in the marshes along the Essex coast, and sections that have been exposed near Walton-on-the-Naze indicate a rise in mean sea-level during the time in question. It reached as much as 3 feet in a century and was probably considerably more, so that it may well have produced quite serious results during the span of a human life time. It is significant that practically all the archaeological material found in the neighbourhood is waste and refuse, good specimens being very scarce. This seems to suggest that the Bronze Age people, aware of impending danger due to a rising sea, removed in time and in an orderly manner to other sites. Even in the absence of material evidence from the shores of Cardigan Bay it is not unreasonable to picture former inhabitants of the region taking similar evasive action as they became conscious of the menace of the sea—a slowly progressive menace, not a sudden overwhelming catastrophe.

It is interesting to recall that the submerged ' forests ' had been noticed even before the date of the earliest known written references to Seithennin and Helig and their lost lands. Giraldus Cambrensis recorded that at ' Niewgal ' (Newgale in St. Bride's Bay) a storm in the winter of 1171-2

' laid bare the surface of the earth . . . and discovered the trunks of trees cut off, standing in the very sea itself, the strokes of the hatchet appearing as if only made yesterday. The soil was very black and the wood like ebony. By a wonderful revolution the road for the ships became impassable and looked, not like a shore, but like a grove cut down, perhaps at the time of the Deluge or not long after, but certainly in very remote ages, being by degrees consumed and swallowed up by the violence and encroachment of the sea.' [46c]

This region, we may note, corresponds in part to one of the three Kingdoms submerged beneath the sea—the one between St. David's and Ireland—mentioned in the Triad in a thirteenth century manuscript in Exeter Cathedral (see p. 68).

Although it may not have quite the significance that Giraldus intended, the reference to the hatchet marks on the stumps is not so far-fetched as might at first appear. In the first book of his *Description of Penbrokshire*, completed in 1603, George Owen recorded that ' an other want wch pincheth this countrye

Pl. 11A. Part of a ' Submerged forest ' *Photo : A. L. Leach*

Stump of a tree at Marros, Pembrokeshire, exposed only at low tide. Its roots are embedded in the soil on which it grew.

Pl. 11B. Submerged forest in Cardigan Bay *Photo : J. Challinor*

Tree stumps between tide marks at Ynys-las, south of the Dyfi estuary.

Pl. 12A. Glacial deposits at Degannwy   *Photo : F.J.N.*

A low cliff of boulder clay with (on the beach) boulders left behind after the clay
has been washed away.

Pl. 12B. Boulders on the beach at Degannwy   *Photo : F.J.N.*

Looking towards the cliff, with an apparently straight band of boulders resulting
from the denudation of a ridge of boulder clay.

[i.e., Pembrokeshire] is scarcitie of timber,' and it is by no means unlikely that when the tree stumps were exposed on the shore the local inhabitants may have tried to hack away some of the wood which the sea had so conveniently laid bare for them, just as the people of Abergele did in Pennant's time. The statement that the marks appeared ' as if made only yesterday ' may, therefore, have been a record of fact, whilst the reference to the Deluge was a not unreasonable inference at a time when men knew the Bible but not the Geological Record.

The remains of the submerged forest at Newgale seem to have been temporarily exposed on several occasions. George Owen mentioned them as having been seen in the last decade of the 16th century. He, too, referred to the ' verye strookes of the hatchet at the fellinge of these tymbers,' probably repeating (although he did not say so) what he had read in Giraldus, with whose *Description of Wales* he was familiar.

In due course the story was taken up by Richard Fenton in the account of his *Historical Tour through Pembrokeshire* (1811), where he tells us, in his characteristically involved style, that ' on all the sand round the coast of Pembrokeshire in every exposure, trunks of various kinds of trees after storms, when, by the violent retiring of the tide they are bared, several with the marks of the axe on them . . . frequently appear.'

There has been a tendency to dismiss these references to axe marks as the product of a too-vivid imagination, but Pennant's record of the use of the wood as fuel near Abergele suggests that Giraldus was more than likely right in his observation at Newgale, and wrong only in his chronology. There was certainly no justification for the view expressed by an Aberystwyth professor who gave evidence before the Royal Commission on Coast Erosion in 1907. He not only ridiculed the notion that axe marks had been seen on the tree-stumps of the submerged forests, but, in reply to a reminder that the record was originally made by Giraldus Cambrensis said that was tantamount to proving that the statement was incorrect. [153b]

In a subsequent chapter Fenton expressed the opinion that ' there can be no doubt, but at some remote period . . . that a

N

vast tract of low ground extended a great way all around the
coast of Pembrokeshire, and far to the northward of it, as well
as the adjoining maritime counties of the Severn.' He also
recorded ' a tradition that a great part of that immense tract of
sea, Bride's Bay, was land ; and I have been told that amongst
the ancient deeds of the house of Brawdy great possessions are
referred to in this direction, now nowhere to be found, therefore
must be overwhelmed by the sea.' Having got thus far, we are
not surprised to learn that ' at a time after a storm, when by the
sudden retiring of the sea the sand was much washed away
[his informant, Mr. Jones, of Lether, a neighbouring manor]
observed the vestiges of a pitched pavement of considerable
breadth laid bare. This happened about 35 years ago '—that
is, about 1775.

   Since the ' great possessions ' must have been lost before the
visit of Giraldus, the Brawdy record must indeed have been
ancient, and one is inclined to suspect that the pavement was
nothing more than a patch of rock traversed by joints, temporarily exposed at a spot where it was normally covered by the
foreshore sand. It is difficult to regard these notes about
Brawdy and the pavement as anything more than local gossip ;
they have none of the glamour of antiquity which places the
legends of Llys Helig and of Cantre'r Gwaelod on an entirely
different plane, but are more in keeping with the story recorded
by Camden that William Rufus saw a large tract of land
extending from Pembrokeshire so far towards the Irish coast
that he said he could easily make a floating bridge over the sea
in order to pass on foot to Ireland. [10e, 168]

(b) The separation of Ireland from Wales

   Human artefacts associated with the submerged land surfaces
around the Welsh coast show that man was affected by the
changes of sea-level to which they owe their origin, and also that
little if any change due to subsidence has taken place since the
end of the Iron Age, but we have yet to see whether we can
discover anything about the earlier phases of the subsidence and
about its full extent. This is a matter of interest because of its
relation to the origin of the legends we have already considered,

and also because of its bearing upon the geographical references in some of the Mabinogion yet to be discussed.

The amount of subsidence indicated by the submerged land surfaces to which observers have had access is about 60 feet, and the coast line at a time when the land stood 60 feet higher (or sea-level 60 feet lower) than at present would obviously be very different from what it is now. It would have approximated to the present 10-fathom submarine contour. This, as indicated in Fig. 8, is the outer limit of a tract extending seawards of the present coastline, for the most part relatively narrow, but with conspicuous widenings off the part of the Cardigan Bay coast that is associated with Cantre'r Gwaelod and also in the region associated with the Llys Helig legend. These two regions, which would have been the last to be submerged, are just those mentioned in the legends.

The accessible submerged land surfaces, however, record only the closing chapters of the subsidence for they are all near the present coast and we do not know how far they extend beneath the sea. Every mile of seawards extension would carry them deeper, and so indicate a greater amount of subsidence since the time when they were parts of a dry land area ; but direct evidence of their existence beyond tidal limits can only be forth-coming in exceptional and at present unforeseeable circumstances and we must approach the problem in some other way.

Geology can help us here, for it is known that towards the end of the Pliocene Period (the sub-division of geological time immediately preceding the one during which man became established as one of the earth's inhabitants) Great Britain and Ireland were part of a peninsular projection from the continent of Europe. The coastline was approximately in the position of the present 100-fathom submarine contour. [115b]

It will be convenient to take a map depicting this state of affairs (Fig. 13) as the starting point of the present phase of our discussion. The evidence upon which such a map can be drawn and assigned to a particular period of earth-history will be known to those familiar with geology, and others will find it set forth in the appropriate text-books. [82, 172]

Geology, then, tells us that in comparatively recent geological

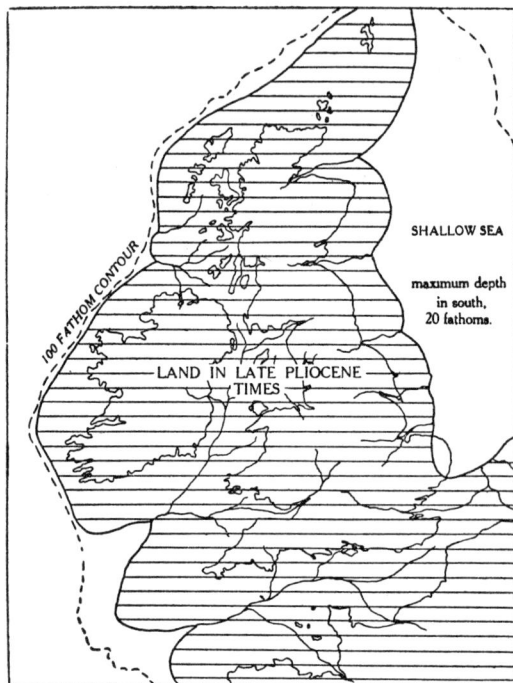

Fig. 13.   Great Britain and Ireland in Pliocene Times

The land-mass from which the present islands have been shaped, partly as the result of a relative rise in sea-level and partly by marine erosion.

times Great Britain and Ireland were united to one another and to continental Europe, and, for reasons that will appear later, it is known that encroachment of the sea resulted in the separation of Ireland from Great Britain before the latter was separated from the Continent. It is also known that the land connexions were not finally broken until after the end of the Glacial Period. As submergence sufficient to isolate Ireland from Wales would have effects more far-reaching than any we have to envisage for the purposes of this book, it is not (as we have already seen) the inundations required by the legends that are in doubt, only their suddenness, and their effect, if any, upon people living in the region.

It is necessary at this stage to interpolate a note about possible causes of a subsidence of the land or a rise of sea-level that would lead to extensive encroachment by the sea.

The fact that many of the rocks of our present lands were formed as deposits laid down on the floor of the sea (indicated, amongst other ways, by the fossil remains of marine creatures which they contain), shows that the earth's crust has been subject to continual movement, which, from time to time and in various places, has allowed land areas to sink beneath the sea. The movement has sometimes continued long enough for deposits many thousands of feet in thickness to have been laid down before any permanent change of conditions was inaugurated.

The complementary facts—that sea-floor deposits now occur in the fabric of our highest mountains, e.g., the rocks, containing the fossil shells of marine creatures, which make up the summit of Snowdon, and that there are, intercalated with marine deposits, many indications of ancient land surfaces, e.g., coal seams derived from the debris of forests—show that the downward movements which allowed the sea to cover the land have alternated with upward movements which have caused the sea-floor deposits of one age to become the rocks of the land in a succeeding age.

It is to these movements that, in large measure, we owe the building of our rocks and the development of the major surface-features and the coastlines of our continents ; but, in addition to these general movements which have been in progress during the whole of geological time, there have been others, due to special causes, which have resulted in emergence or submergence measurable in scores rather than in thousands of feet. These have not necessarily been due to absolute movement on the part of the land, for the level of the surface of the sea has been subject to change.

The comparatively recent submergences in which we are more particularly interested appear to have been associated with one of these special causes and to have been an aftermath of the Ice Age, although small-scale general movements are likely to have taken place as well.

The vast accumulation of snow and ice on land areas during

the Ice Age was effected at the expense of the water in the sea. In normal circumstances water that evaporates from the surface of the sea is deposited as rain or snow, and most of that which falls upon the land eventually—either directly or after an underground passage to feed springs—finds its way into rivers which carry it back to the place whence it came, the sea ; but during immensely long periods in the Ice Age there was one-way movement only, and whilst snow and ice accumulated on the land little or no water returned to the sea.

As a result, the surface of the sea was steadily lowered whilst the area of the land was increased to an extent that varied with the slopes of the newly exposed surfaces ; the more gentle the slope the wider the belt of land that was exposed by any given fall in the level of the surface of the sea. Then, on the melting of the ice, the water returned to re-cover the land that had been temporarily exposed.

The situation is not quite as simple as this brief statement might appear to suggest because the vast quantity of ice that had accumulated at the time of maximum glaciation must have pressed the land regions downwards, involving a corresponding rise when the ice melted. The present depth of water off any part of our coast is a measure of the extent to which the rise of sea level at the end of the Ice Age exceeded the rise of the land, but as it is the overall picture with which we are concerned we need not try to differentiate between the contributions made by the various processes.

It has been calculated that if the Polar ice-caps of today were to melt the resulting water would be sufficient to raise the level of the ocean by at least 150 feet, and it is certain that during the Ice Age a much greater amount of water than that was locked up in the great northern ice cap : indeed, the lowering of the ocean level during the period is likely to have exceeded 400 feet. We need not, then, be alarmed at the prospect of having to envisage submergence since the end of the Ice Age sufficient to isolate Ireland from Wales, although the sea between them is in places over 300 feet deep.

There are two ways in which we can try to fill in the details of the general picture we already have of the changing relations between Ireland and Wales. We can look for evidence which would enable us to picture the conditions which obtained before Ireland was finally isolated from Wales and trace the effects of the isolation, or we can work backwards on the basis of what we know about submergences still in progress until we arrive at a time when conditions were such that the legends we are discussing could have originated. If the conclusions are comparable we shall be entitled to assume that our reasoning has been sound, and, indeed, we might treat the second line of approach as a means for checking the results of the first.

That the coastline of a combined Great Britain and Ireland was situated in regions now covered by the sea is confirmed by the discovery of littoral (or shore line) shells dredged up from banks of gravel at depths of between 60 and 70 fathoms on the floor of the sea off the mouth of the Bristol Channel. They included limpets, winkles, mussels, and cockles—all molluscs of the littoral zone—and although we have no means of equating them with the activities of man in our area, they indicate substantial submergence in geologically recent times. [3]

The earliest picture of a coastline that we can associate with the human era is afforded by a study of the fossil remains of the animals of pre-glacial times. This shows that the land animals of Britain and Ireland were similar to those on the adjacent parts of the continent—as, indeed, would be expected, since there were times when our area was part of the continental mass.

The rigorous conditions which obtained in the glaciated regions during the Ice Age resulted in the destruction of much of this fauna, and when the climate changed at the end of the glaciation many of the species which had so far survived became extinct or migrated and were, in time, replaced by others from Central Europe. Some of the latter entered Britain and became the ancestors of our present fauna, and that they came at all shows that the land connexion with the continent existed after the close of the Glacial Period. But the connexion did not last for long because, as the ice melted, the rise in the level of the sea resulted in the isolation of the island mass when only part of the continental flora and fauna had reached Britain.

This is shown by the much smaller number of species of purely terrestrial animals (mammals, reptiles, and amphibia) in Britain than there are on the adjacent parts of the Continent. Great Britain has only about half as many indigenous mammals as Germany, and Ireland less than a third. In the case of the reptiles and amphibia, which have smaller powers of dispersal, the disparity is even greater. Belgium for example has 22 species, Britain 13 and Ireland only 4. These are the figures given by A. R. Wallace in *Island Life* (3rd Ed., 1911), and although the actual number of recognized species may now be different as a result of refinements in classification, the significance of the proportions given remains unchanged.

That the terrestrial animals reached Ireland at all shows that there were land connexions between that island and Britain in post-glacial times, but the meagreness of the fauna that got there shows that Ireland was separated from Britain before the latter was separated from the Continent. This is because the gap between Ireland and Wales is deeper than the North Sea and the English Channel, so that when the sea-level began to rise a continuous sea would have been established between Ireland and Wales earlier than between Britain and the Continent.

The submarine contours between Ireland and Wales are shown in Fig. 14, from which it will be seen that for a land bridge to be re-established it would be necessary for there to be an uplift of the land or a lowering of the sea to the extent of nearly 300 feet. There would then be a comparatively narrow land connection at about the latitude of Barmouth with another opposite Liverpool Bay.

An uplift of only 240 feet would leave a sea channel nearly 20 miles wide where narrowest, and this would be as effective a barrier to the passage of land vertebrates as the present sea that separates the two regions : there has, it is clear, been considerable submergence since Ireland was completely separated from Britain.

It is not necessary for our purpose to try to determine exactly when the sea broke through and completed the separation of Ireland from Britain. It is certain that it had done so long

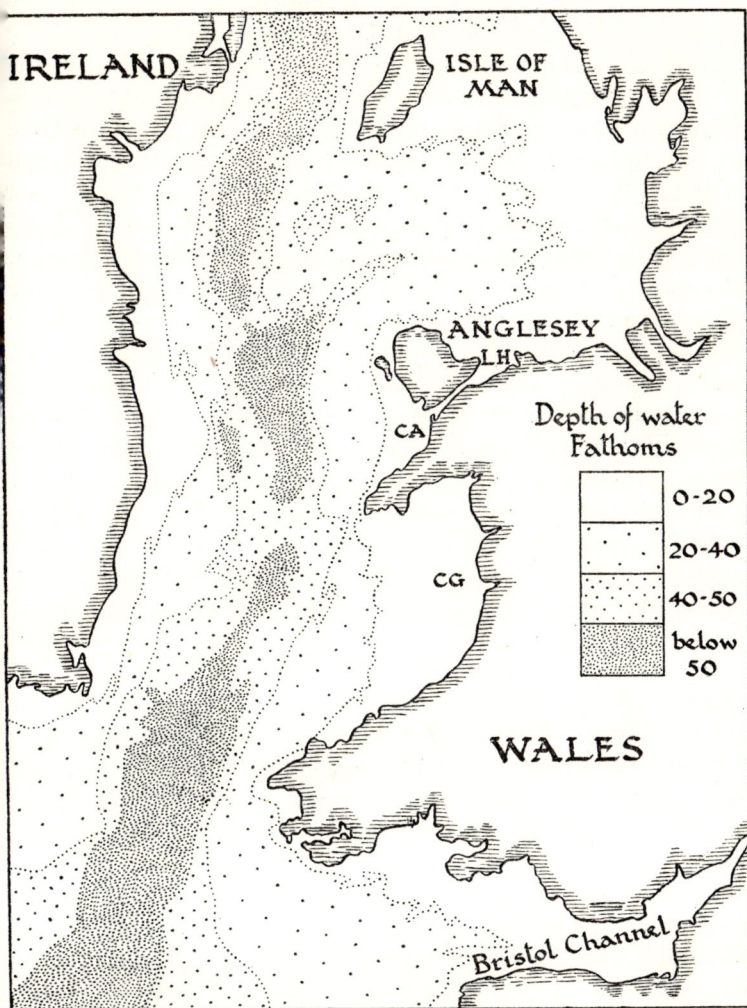

Fig. 14.   The relation between Wales and Ireland

The sea-floor contours, indicating the position of the deepest channel separating the two countries and the extent of the relatively shallow water covering Cardigan Bay.   LH, Llys Helig ; CA, Caer Aranrhod ; CG, Cantre'r Gwaelod.

before early Neolithic time, but we want to know, if possible, just how far had it by that time extended.

The early part of the Neolithic period is also known as the Megalithic age because it was then that the builders of the great chambered tombs and stone circles (megalithic monuments), that are so numerous in parts of Wales, began to arrive by sea from the Atlantic coast of Europe. The distribution of megalithic monuments shows that the people who erected them were able to land on the shores of Ireland and of Wales and to proceed up the west coast of Scotland. The distribution of chambered tombs in Wales is especially significant in our present enquiry for they are very numerous in Pembrokeshire and in the north-western counties (Merioneth, Caernarvon, and Anglesey), but are absent from the region between. Conditions favourable to landing on the extremities of Pembrokeshire, the Lleyn Peninsula, and Anglesey, would have been established when the submergence had proceeded sufficiently far for the coastline to approximate to the present 20-fathom submarine contour. (Fig. 8).

In such circumstances, however, what is now Cardigan Bay would have been an extensive low-lying and gently undulating region with no rocky promontories and no good natural anchorages—conditions quite sufficient to account for the absence of chambered tombs from mid-Wales. The rock-bound coasts at the extremities of the bay, with coves for landing and extensive wind-swept treeless areas of hinterland, would have been more inviting than the low-lying forest-clad region between them, and even if the visitors had landed on the latter they are not likely to have remained there; stones suitable for the erection of the massive monuments they favoured would not have been available, whereas they were to be obtained in abundance in the other regions. This confirms the opinion expressed by W. F. Grimes, who, in his discussion of the distribution of megalithic monuments, remarked ' I can only wonder whether the former presence of a belt of low lying land in front of the present coast [of Cardigan Bay] may have hindered settlement here while allowing it elsewhere.' [56]

Even when the subsidence had progressed sufficiently for the coast to approximate to the present 10-fathom submarine contour the desirable land-falls would still have been confined to Caernarvonshire and Pembrokeshire. All the available evidence, then, goes to show that there was a time, well within the human era, when the Cardigan Bay we know had not been fully developed. This confirms the conclusion, arrived at on other grounds, that people living in the region could have been affected by the encroachment of the sea to which the bay owes its origin.

Our case seems to be so well established that supporting evidence might be regarded as unnecessary, but since the evidence relates to matters that are often cited in discussions of this nature it will be convenient to draw attention to it. One line of inquiry relates to the rate at which subsidence is now taking place in regions where it is still in progress, and the rate at which it is known to have occurred in areas where observations have been made over a sufficiently long period.

Extensive areas in Holland have been inundated during the last thousand years and nearly a quarter of the country would be beneath the sea were it not for the active and efficient steps that are taken to prevent such a state of affairs from materializing. Records kept between the 16th and 19th centuries indicate that the average amount of the depression was about one third of an inch in a year. In Finland, which is, on the other hand, gradually rising from the sea, the movement is at the rate of a little less than half an inch per year along the northern coast of the Gulf of Bothnia and about half that amount in the south-west near Hangö. The mean of these two is also about one third of an inch.

We have seen that the Welsh coastline of early Megalithic times could have approximated, taking an extreme figure, to the present 20-fathom submarine contour—and movement to the extent of 120 feet at the rate of one third of an inch a year would take rather more than 4,000 years. Bearing in mind that the subsidence had all but ceased before the beginning of the Christian Era, 4,000 or so years takes us well back into the Mesolithic age if we assume that the subsidence took place at a uniform rate. But what we know of such movements in general shows that more often than not they take place more rapidly in the initial stages, and evidence afforded by the submerged peat beds in the Swansea area throws light upon the local application of that general principle. [44-5]

Borings in the lower part of the Tawe Valley have shown that layers of peat occur at intervals down to 54 feet below sea level, in association with silt and other deposits of estuarine origin that fill a buried channel about 200 feet deep. For such a channel to have been formed the sea-level must have been considerably lower (or the land considerably higher) than at present.

A large part of the subsidence indicated by the peat beds in this area must have taken place before and during Mesolithic times because the assemblage of pollen grains in the deposits at about 54 feet below O.D. shows that they accumulated towards the end of that age, whilst those at lesser depths (five feet or so below O.D.) are indicative of late Neolithic Age. [49] The characters of the successive peats and the varying thickness of the strata between them carry us a little farther, because they show that the subsidence was taking place more quickly towards the end of the Mesolithic Age than after its close.

The pollen-bearing peat at 54 feet below O.D. implies a former land surface high enough to be out of reach of the sea, and if we put that level at about 20 feet above O.D., the peat would indicate subsidence to the extent of 74 feet, which is near enough to 10 fathoms to suggest that the coast line towards the end of Mesolithic times, i.e., at the beginning of Neolithic times, approximated to the present 10-fathom submarine contour—which again confirms the belief that Neolithic man was affected by the later stages of the inundations.

It will be of interest to note, before we leave this aspect of our subject, that a coast-line approximating to the 20-fathom submarine contour, moving gradually to the 10-fathom line and subsequently to its present position, makes intelligible the presence of the large quantities of mammalian bones in the limestone caves of Pembrokeshire and Gower. The variety and numerical strength of the animals which they indicate imply a much greater amount of suitable living room and food supplies than are now available in the district where the caves occur.

At the present time many of the caves have their entrances in cliffs washed by the sea, and, like Paviland Cave in Gower, are difficult of access, but some of them were undoubtedly occupied by early man and mammals that were contemporary with him. The bones discovered in them include those of mammoth, rhinoceros, hyaena, wolf, and bear, and one cave (Bosco's Den) yielded about 1,100 antlers of reindeer. [119]

We cannot associate such animals, in such numbers, with the terrain as we know it today, but no difficulty arises if we envisage the caves as looking out over an extensive and more or less hospitable plain, in part wooded, and extending for a considerable distance from hills out of which the present cliffs have been carved. Similarly, the bones found in a cave on Caldy Island indicate a far bigger animal population than so small a tract of land could have supported, but no difficulty arises if we think of Caldy as a low hill in a wooded plain.

(c) The causes of sudden coastal flooding

A common feature of the coastal legends is the suddenness of the inundations, and we now have to ask whether and in what circumstances sudden flooding could have taken place on a sufficiently large scale to have left a deep impression upon the memories of those affected by it : we have not, as our inquiries up to now have clearly shown, to think in terms of territories as extensive as those associated with Helig ap Glannog and Gwyddno Garanhir.

On a low-lying coast tidal action may in certain circumstances build up an embankment consisting of pebbles or silt (according to the nature of the available material) that may eventually become high enough and massive enough to prevent the sea from reaching as far inland as it would if the natural barriers were not there. The long pebble beaches at Newgale in Pembrokeshire and between Barry and Porthkerry in Glamorgan are examples. The growth of sand-dunes may have a similar effect, as they have along parts of the coast of Holland, and, nearer home, at Aberavon, where an extensive area of alluvial deposits—Aberavon Moors—has accumulated behind sand dunes. [115e] If heightened and reinforced by man such natural barriers would still further inhibit encroachment by the sea. A combination of exceptionally high tides and strong winds might cause the water to over-ride such banks, giving rise to destructive floods like those which affected the counties bordering the Severn Estuary in 1607 and those which devastated so many regions in the east of England in 1953.

Rivers flowing over relatively level ground like that we have in mind also tend to build natural barriers which temporarily protect the adjacent land from floods. Whenever the stream overflows its banks some of its burden of sediment is deposited near the edge of the channel. In the course of time this results in the building up of a low embankment or levee on each side of the river. The confined channel then tends to get silted up with material that would normally be spread over the adjacent plain, so that both the bed of the stream and the levees are raised until the river flows (as the Thames does, near its mouth) well above the level of the adjacent land. In such a case, exceptional tide and weather conditions may cause the river to overflow or to burst its raised banks, and flooding ensues ; but, for the most part, floods caused by the breaking of natural dams would be temporary, for in time the water would drain away from most if not from all of the affected area—and our legends demand permanent flooding.

This could take place if, whilst the barriers were being raised, the land had been slowly sinking (or the sea-level rising). In these circumstances the land immediately behind the barrier may well have been brought to such a low level that the flooding would be permanent, and a noteworthy inundation of a limited area could take place without any sudden change in the relative levels of land and sea.

The ' submerged forest ' seen from time to time near Llanaber, north of Barmouth, seems to preserve a record of a sequence of events like this. When well-exposed in 1911 and studied by T. G. B. Osborn it was seen to include layers of clay, peat, and sandy clay with gravel, the nature and order of deposition of which suggested the following history : What is now the ' submerged forest ' appears to have originated as a marshy tract, with reeds, that developed behind a storm-beach. It gradually silted up and birch scrub established itself. Later on a sudden and considerable incursion by the sea killed off the birch and allowed reeds to re-establish themselves amongst and on the stumps of the dead trees. Another rather sudden inundation caused the whole to be overspread with sandy clay and finally with gravel. [124]

There is, however, a limit to the depth to which land could be flooded as a result of the sea finding its way over naturally formed barriers, and that limit is far less than the 60 feet or so that is indicated by the submerged land surfaces near our present coasts. Although natural barriers may keep out the sea, the natural drainage of the land must be prevented from accumulating behind the barriers and covering, with fresh water, land from which the sea has been excluded. This is only possible so long as the land remains above normal high tide level.

Man could, it is true, reinforce and increase the height of the bank and so postpone the flooding in a subsiding area, but to do this it would be necessary to take steps (e.g., by the erection of sluice gates) to prevent sea water from invading the land as the tide came in, and to allow land-water to drain away as the tide went out. If the land had sunk below low-tide level its water could not drain away naturally at any time, and it would be necessary to provide ditches or reens to collect it and windmills or pumps to lift it over the dams.

Sluice gates are, indeed, referred to in the modern versions of the Lowland Hundred legend, but, as we have already had occasion no note, one has only to think of the magnitude of the work and the engineering skill involved in maintaining the low-lying regions of Holland as dry land to realize that the early inhabitants of the coastal regions of Wales could not have undertaken a task involving even greater areas and depths than the Dutch engineers have to contend with,—the low-lying regions of Holland are only from 2 to 16 feet below sea level. It is certain that such protective works did not exist in our area and it is most likely that they were, as already suggested, introduced into the local story when news of what was being done to combat flooding in Holland was brought to this country.

*　　　*　　　*

Even when we have shown that subsidence to the extent required by the legend could not have occurred, and have eliminated the artificial embankments and the sluice gates, we are still left with the fact that sudden flooding on a limited scale, both as to area and depth, could have taken place here and there along the shores of a Cardigan Bay known to human beings.

There is, therefore, nothing improbable in the view that stories originating in a period of slow and intermittent submergence may have been handed down during the centuries— that stories of the destruction of a few homesteads gradually grew into a legend telling of the sudden loss of a region comparable in size with a Cantref. Such legends might easily have incorporated allusions to springs (often popularly called wells) which broke out on the shores and mingled their water with that of the sea.

The stories could, of course, have been part of the traditional lore of people who migrated into the area, and, they could, during subsequent generations, have become associated with events of a similar nature that affected the lives of the people in their new homes; but in the case of the Lowland Hundred it is not necessary to think in terms of an imported legend to provide the *foundation* for the story : it is the embellishments that are not indigenous.

The Llys Helig story, on the other hand, has less claim to be regarded as originating in the locality with which it is associated because, although the evidence of flooding is as obvious in that region as in Cardigan Bay, the earliest references to Helig do not associate him with it. Indeed, the difficulty of giving Helig an indubitable location would lend colour to the suggestion made by Rhŷs that ' we seem to have the other selves of Gwyddno and his son Elphin in Glannog and his son Helig ' [143e], were it not for the fact that the Exeter Triad (not known to Rhŷs, or, at least, not mentioned by him) is so explicit in its location of Helig's land in Cardigan Bay. Might we not reverse the suggestion, and see in Gwyddno a popular hero supplanting Helig and leaving to story-tellers the task of

Pl. 13A. Boulders on the beach at Degannwy *Photo : F.J.N.*

General view at low tide. The stones remaining after the removal of the clay
with which they were associated give rise to conditions similar to those seen in the
central part of Llys Helig.

Pl. 13B. The 'black rocks' at Penmaen-bach *Photo : F.J.N.*

Stones remaining after the denudation of boulder clay. A few large stones
appear as if they might be part of a circle and illustrate some of the interpretations
of Caer Aranrhod.

finding the latter a domicile in some other region where
submerged lands were in evidence ?

*   *   *

Having shown that the rise in sea level which led to the
submergence of the coastal areas of Wales was in progress for a
very long time and that people living in the affected areas
would have had to shift their dwellings from time to time, it is
interesting to note that we are not altogether without a hint as
to the periods when local inundations are likely to have occurred on such a scale as to become a topic of conversation among
the descendants of the people affected by them.

Studies in *Climatic Variations in Historic and Prehistoric Times*
[133] were made some forty years ago by O. Pettersson in
Sweden.   They were based upon astronomical calculations
relating to periodic variations in the forces responsible for the
generation of tides and led to the conclusion that those forces
varied from a minimum at about 1200 B.C. to a maximum at
about 350 B.C.

Increased tidal range is followed by greater movement of
oceanic waters and more interchange between the colder
waters of arctic regions and the warmer ones of farther south.
This, in turn, results in a more southerly distribution of colder
water and floating ice from the north, and wider place-to-place
variations in the temperature of the surface of the sea and the
conditions of the atmosphere above it.

Such conditions favour the development of cyclonic storms,
so that, following a relatively calm period about 1200 B.C.,
that is, about the middle of the Bronze Age in Britain, increas-
ingly unfavourable weather conditions accompanied by high
tides are likely to have been experienced during the next few
centuries, reaching a maximum by about 350 B.C., not long
after the beginning of the Iron Age.

From whichever way we approach our problem the answer
is the same, and we realize that whilst our critical examination
of the stories relating to the coasts of Wales shows that they are
not acceptable as statements of fact in their modern forms, or
even in the forms they had assumed when they first began to be
committed to writing, we have not torn gaps in the early

o

literature of Wales but have given the coastal inundation stories a more honourable place by showing that their application to the regions with which they are now associated is likely to have been inspired by events which took place between Neolithic and Iron Age times. That, in passing from generation to generation, recollections of encroachments by the sea should have been clothed in language that relates them to stories of wide distribution is not at all surprising when we remember the extent to which early man travelled in these regions ; nor is it surprising that the simple stories should have been further obscured by masses of superimposed detail since the days when they were discovered by the seventeenth century romantics.

(d) The Bristol Channel : a drowned estuary without legends

A matter of more than passing interest in relation to the legends of submerged lands around the Welsh coast is their absence from the region of the Bristol Channel where the indications of subsidence during the early part of the human era are as abundant and obvious as elsewhere. Its geological history, discussed in a publication recently issued by the National Museum of Wales [115], and its present submarine contours (Fig. 15), show that the channel is a river valley drowned as a result of a rise in the relative level of the sea.

Submerged land surfaces, mostly indicated by beds of peat, occur at a number of places from St. Brides Bay to Cardiff, and also on the southern side of the channel. The plants represented in the peat as well as the abundance of mammalian bones (e.g., mammoth, rhinoceros, wolf, hyaena, bear and reindeer) in the caves of Gower and Caldy Island indicate that much of the region now covered by the sea was, in comparatively recent geological times, a richly wooded valley. The presence in the coastal peat of articles of human manufacture shows that here, as around other parts of Wales, man saw at least the closing stages of the encroachment that showly drowned the land and came to an end at about the beginning of the Christian era.

In these circumstances it is not unreasonable to ask why no ' ancient legends ' have been associated with the region. There is, it is true, a tradition that the Tusker Rock opposite the

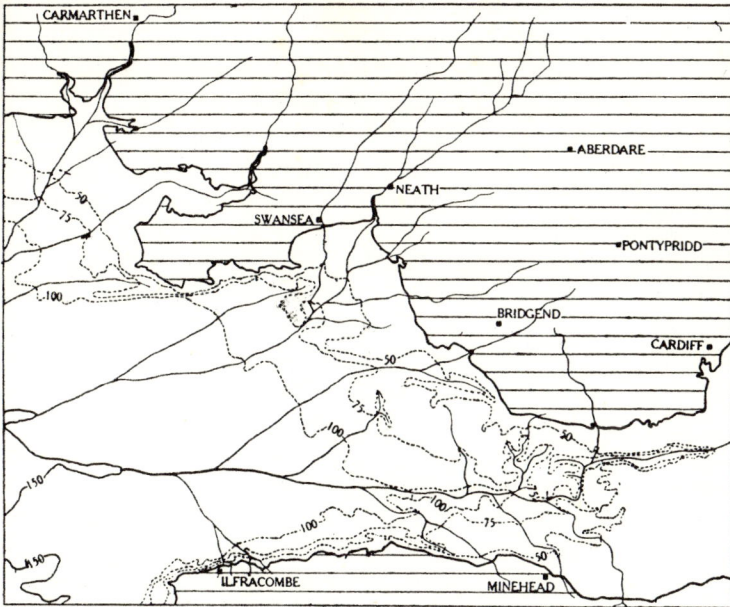

Fig. 15. Map of the Bristol Channel with submarine contours
indicating that the channel is a drowned river valley.

mouth of the Ogmore River, now deeply covered at every tide,
was a sheep pasture within the memory of living man [115c];
but that is quite a different matter, and in any case it cannot
be a statement of fact.   The rock may have been covered with
turf in a remote past, but certainly not within the memory of
any person living in the twentieth century.

A whetstone and some fragments of iron ore found in submerged peat beds in Swansea Bay [44] suggest that Early Iron
Age man was living in the region before it was finally overwhelmed, and there are said to be traditions about a forest
called Silverwood [109] that once occupied part of the bay.
They probably originated in a desire to explain the tree stumps
and peat beds associated with the clays of the foreshore but
they never seem to have acquired the status of folk stories, and
there are no stories associated with the submerged land surfaces
off the Pembrokeshire coast or those at Barry and Cardiff.

A likely reason for the absence of legends is that when the sea began to encroach upon the land after the end of the Ice Age, what is now the Bristol Channel was a valley and not an open bay like that between Pembrokeshire and the Lleyn Peninsula. Because the sides of the valley sloped more steeply than the floor of the bay the land between what are now the 10-fathom and 5-fathom submarine contours was narrower in the former than in the northern part of the latter, i.e., the region to which the legends relate.

In the circumstances the encroachment of the sea over the lands bordering the Bristol Channel would have been more rapid than over the region represented by the Cantre'r Gwaelod of the legend, and such inhabitants as there may have been are not likely to have settled in any one area sufficiently long for them to have been affected by local floodings sudden and severe enough to have left impressions so vivid as to have become embodied in traditions. Had there been such traditions in an early period their failure to survive may be accounted for by the more complete dilution or replacement (by immigrants from the south and east) here than in the regions bordering Cardigan Bay.

With the picture we are now able to envisage of the geographical conditions of past ages it will be interesting to see what happens when we consider stories like those preserved in the Mabinogion, in relation to conditions that are likely to have obtained when they were first put together and when they were first committed to writing, rather than in terms of the maps of to-day ; and since our purpose is to introduce the subject, not to exhaust it, it will be sufficient to take two examples that illustrate the kind of result that is obtained. The stories chosen are those of *Math, the son of Mathonwy*, and *Branwen, the daughter of Llŷr*. The former shows how this mode of approach throws light upon the identity of places mentioned in the stories, and the latter shows how it enables us to recognize what, in the stories, is likely to be really old.

XI

CAER ARANRHOD

Caer Aranrhod figures in the Mabinogi of Math the son of Mathonwy, but the name does not appear to have been associated with the submerged reef now so-called until Humphrey Llwyd included it in a map of Wales published in 1573.

An examination of the story in the light of past and present geography suggests that it is an old one (not, however, relating to an inundation) superimposed upon local geography.

Although variously interpreted by visitors as a Druids' Circle, a Roman fort, or a Roman port, the accumulation of stones called Caer Aranrhod is of natural origin, having resulted from the denudation of stone-laden Boulder Clay, transported during and deposited at the close of the Ice Age.

(a) A sunken ' city ' in Caernarvon Bay

CONWAY Bay has its story of submerged Llys Helig and Cardigan Bay its story of submerged Cantre'r Gwaelod : between them, in the angle enclosed by Anglesey and the Lleyn peninsula, lies Caernarvon Bay with its story of submerged Caer Aranrhod. A reef of stones about half a mile from the shore between Dinas Dinlle and the mouth of Afon Llyfni, and some three miles north of Clynnog Fawr, is traditionally regarded as the site of the Caer. Dinas Dinlle is the name of an earthwork or ancient fort on the top of a mound, about 100 feet high, which rises from the low-lying land that fringes the coast hereabouts. It is being slowly destroyed by erosion (not subsidence) and an appreciable part has already been washed away.

There were, as we have seen, vague connexions between the stories relating to the two other regions we have considered, but tradition says nothing that would associate Caer Aranrhod with either of them, and the problems created by the site so named are peculiar to it.

Although much older than those associated with the regions we have already considered (for Aranrhod and her castle figure prominently in the Mabinogi of Math, the son of Mathonwy) the fully elaborated story contains no reference to the loss of land due to an inrush of the sea.

The name first appears as Aranrot (hence Aranrhod in the edition of the Mabinogion recently published by Gwyn Jones and Thomas Jones), but it is often spelt Arianrhod, as in an unpublished 15th century poem, by Lewis Môn, who mentioned *Yng Nghaer Arianrhod*.

The supposed site of the Caer was indicated and named on printed maps before the Llys Helig and Cantre'r Gwaelod stories had begun to assume their present forms, but this does not necessarily indicate that the site now so-called was, indeed, the place referred to in the story.

The name *Caer Ierjenrhod*, with the symbol for a village actually in the sea, occurs on the first printed map of Wales—Humphrey Llwyd's *Cambriae Typus*. This was completed in manuscript in 1568, but was not printed until 1573 when it was included in the first Supplement to the Atlas (*Theatrum*) of maps which had been published by Abraham Ortelius of Antwerp in 1570.

The peculiar form of the name—derived from the then-current Arianrhod—is probably due to the fact that the map was engraved in the Low Countries by men who knew nothing of Welsh place-names and were unfamiliar with Llwyd's hand-writing. Because of this, Llwyd's map of *England and Wales*, prepared at the same time and published in the same Supplement, has a symbol indicating a village in the sea in the same position as the Caer Ierjenrhod of his map of Wales, but the name against it is *L. Tefrydank* and it is quite certain that the reef was never known by that name. (Fig. 16).

This strange mistake illustrates the way in which inaccuracies crept into the maps of Britain during the period when they were mostly, if not entirely, engraved by foreigners, for *L. Tefrydank* was obviously intended for what is now called *Llan-dyfrydog* in north-eastern Anglesey ; it appears as *Tefri* in its proper place in Llwyd's map of Wales. The circumstances in which the name came to be mis-spelt in two cases and mis-placed in one would seem to be these : (*a*) Llwyd used the abbreviation *L.* for *Llan*, and in several cases the engraver left it out ; (*b*) it is often necessary to break up map-names in order to accommodate them to the space available ; and (*c*) it is always possible for one person to misinterpret another's hand-writing.

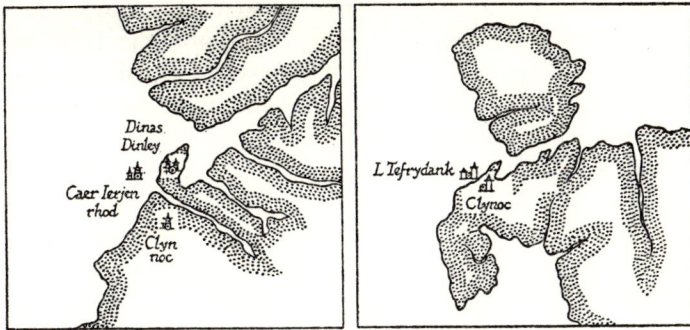

Fig. 16. Caer Aranrhod on Humphrey Llwyd's maps

Copied from (*right*) the map of England and Wales, where it is wrongly named, and (*left*) from the map of Wales (Cambriae Typus). The maps were prepared in 1568 and published in 1573.

Tefri and *Tefrydank* for what we now write as *Tyfrydog* (the initial letter is mutated in Llandyfrydog) are easily understood if we inquire into the sources from which Llwyd derived his information. Writing of Anglesey, Giraldus Cambrensis said : 'There is also a church on this island, the church of Saint Tefredaucus, into which Hugh, Earl of Shrewsbury on a certain night put some dogs, which on the following morning were found mad and himself died within a month.' [46e] Llwyd mentioned the story in a description of Anglesey which Ortelius published in certain of his Atlases, and if, in quoting from Giraldus, he wrote L. Tefredaucus, we can see how, by omitting the *L.*, miscopying the second *e*, and failing to copy the second part of a word that has been broken up into *Tefre* and *daucus* on the manuscript, the map engraver arrived at *Tefri* for the printed map of Wales.

On the manuscript of his map of England and Wales, where Anglesey is quite small and the place-names he wished to include were numerous, the obvious thing for Llwyd to do was to write some of the names in the surrounding sea, perhaps with guide-lines to indicate where they should go ; then, for want of adequate proof-checking (for Llwyd died before the map was engraved) the name of an Anglesey village got associated with a symbol in the sea that, on the map of Wales, was called Caer Ierjenrhod.

It is not possible to say who, Llwyd or the engraver, was responsible for the transformation of Tefredaucus into Tefrydank—Llwyd may have written Tefrydauk but it must have been the engraver who mistook a *u* for an *n* and finally arrived at Tefrydank. By metamorphosis along different lines the name became Llandourodock on a map of Anglesey prepared by J. Cowley in 1744. Once printed, such mistakes tend to become fixed for long periods and Caer Ierjenrhod or some variant of it continued to appear on maps for nearly two centuries.

Llwyd's own map was reprinted and re-engraved at intervals until 1741, when it was included in *A Compleat Body of Ancient Geography*, (a late edition of the *Accuratissima Orbis Antiqui Delineato* of George Horn, first published in 1654), and Caer Aranrhod (as Caer Ierienrode or Caer Ierienrhod) was introduced to a much wider public when it appeared on two of the maps which Christopher Saxton prepared in the fifteen-seventies. This series, which included thirty-five maps of the counties of England and Wales, singly or in groups, and one of the country as a whole soon achieved great popularity. It was the basis of nearly all the county and regional maps of England and Wales that were published during the 17th century by John Speed in England, and by the Houses of Blaeu, Jansson, and Hondius in the Netherlands, as well as of many maps of England and Wales such as those in the *Theatrum* of Ortelius and The *Atlas* of Mercator. On the map of Great Britain and Ireland published by Peter Plancius of Amsterdam in 1592, Caer Ierienrhod is one of eleven names around the Welsh coast between Holyhead and Ramsey Island, ranking with Bardsey, Barmouth, Aberdovey, and Aberystwyth. [95]

On Saxton's map of Anglesey and Caernarvon (1578) we have *Caer Ierienrode*, written in the sea as though it were the name of a cape or some other coastal feature, and on his map of England and Wales (1579) *Caer Ierienrhod*, with the symbol for a town near to the Caernarvonshire coast, is one of nine names in or associated with the county. Saxton travelled and made observations during the preparation of his map, and in order to facilitate his work in Wales instructions were sent from

the Privy Council to all the Mayors and Justices of the Peace
in the Principality instructing them to help him by providing
guides and interpreters. [116] The spellings he adopted for
place-names, however, suggest that he made free use of earlier
maps of England and Wales such as those of Llwyd, as well as
of the writings of John Leland.

The *Caer Ierienrode* on one of the Saxton maps probably arose
because at some time during the preparation of the manuscript
or the engraving of the plate the name was dictated and not
copied.   Place names of strange appearance due to this cause
are by no means uncommon : Leland for example, writing of
the river Glas-ffrwd, a tributary of the Teifi, said ' The water,
as I hard say, is caullid Glesse rode '. [156d]

Saxton's *Caer Ierienrhod* was incorporated into the map of
England and Wales (*Anglia Regnum*) in the Atlas prepared by
Mercator and first published in 1595, but the ' town ' had
become a small island !   In some maps of England and Wales
published by J. Covens and C. Mortier, and by Cornelius
Danckerts in Amsterdam, in the middle of the 17th century,
the name had become Caer Ierceurhod, whilst the map of
Caernarvonshire by J. Cowley, 1744, gives it as Caer Jerienroda.

In due course, John Speed produced the collection of maps
which he called *Theatre of the Empire of Great Britain*.   It was
published in 1611 although many of the maps, including those
of the Welsh counties, were dated 1610. To many people
Speed's maps are the ultimate authority for the 17th century
geography and topography of our country, but they were based
largely upon and in many cases were little more than adapt-
ations of Saxton's, and they continued to be reprinted until
1676, whilst some of Saxton's own plates with additions made
by later publishers, were still being used at least until 1749.

Speed, basing his maps upon Saxton's county maps (not like
some of the other publishers we have considered, upon his map
of England and Wales) adopted the spelling *Caer Ierienrode* ; this
appears also in several 17th century Speed derivatives. He also,
following Saxton's county map, placed the name in the sea
without reference to a town-symbol or an island, as if it were
the name of a cape.

Many people not otherwise interested in geography had their attention drawn to the name when *Caer Ierienrhod* appeared in association with a small island or rock off the Caernarvonshire coast on one of the maps printed on a set of playing cards published by Robert Morden in 1676. Each card bore the map of one of the 52 counties of England and Wales and that allotted to Caernarvonshire was the two of Spades. Only 15 names are given in and around the county, but they include *Dinas Dinnly*, associated with the symbol for a village, as well as *Caer Ierienrhod*.

From the foregoing notes it will appear that the reference to Caer Aranrhod in early maps is in no way proof that the site was so-called in antiquity. Humphrey Llwyd was the first to use the name on a map, and the site is not mentioned in topographical works which appeared before his time. It is not marked on the map of the British Isles published by Mercator in 1564, nor is it on the manuscript map of England and Wales prepared by Lawrence Nowell, also about 1564. Nowell was sometime Dean of Lichfield, and his map, prepared under the patronage of William Cecil, afterwards Lord Treasurer Burleigh, was intended to have historical as well as geographical significance. [116a] Earlier manuscript maps were on too small a scale to have included the name of a site like this.

Leland does not seem to have heard the story during the course of his journeys in the fifteen-thirties. He says nothing about Caer Aranrhod although he mentions matters such as an ancient overflowing of the sea between *Abredewy* (Aberdovey) and *Towen Merioneth* ; this may have been an allusion to the Cantre'r Gwaelod story, or, in view of the small area involved, it may have been an inference based upon an exposure of one of the submerged forests. That Leland was not unmindful of antiquarian information is indicated by his record that in parts of North Wales, there were certain ' stony hillokkes ', in some of which had been found ' yerthen pottes with the mouthes turned douneward, conteyning burnt bones.' [156b] These were burial places and urns of Bronze Age people.

There is no mystery attached to Llwyd's inclusion of Caer

Ierjenrhod in his map.   He was interested in early books and documents relating to Wales and, writing to Abraham Ortelius in 1568 he said : ' I hope before very long to send you a description . . . of our Wales illustrated both with the auntient names of rivers, townes, people and places mentioned by the modern English whereby they are knowen at this day of that Nation.' [117b]

Its frequent reproduction on printed maps from 1573 to the middle of the 18th century cannot be taken as an indication of popular interest either in the name Caer Aranrhod or in the site.   With few exceptions the maps were prepared and published for purely commercial ends ; few of the men by whom they were engraved had any knowledge of the countries they were delineating, and the Caer continued to be included, not because of any special interest in it but because a name written out in the sea is less likely to have been omitted, as a result of changes in the scale of the map or the style of the lettering, than those on the land areas where the space available might vary from one edition to another according to the scale and purpose of the map.

After the middle of the 18th century, when the maps derived from Saxton by way of Speed lost their popularity and began to be replaced by others involving new surveys and inquiries, e.g., those published from about 1750 onwards in the *Large English Atlas* of Emanuel Bowen and Thomas Kitchin, Caer Aranrhod ceased to be a feature of the maps of Wales or of its separate regions, although the *Accurate Map of North Wales*, in the Bowen and Kitchin Atlas gives Llys Elis ap Clynnog, showing the influence of Lewis Morris, and marks Dinas Dinlle as an ' Old British Camp.'

None of those who wrote of their Tours in Wales in the closing years of the 18th century or early in the 19th had anything to say about Caer Aranrhod although some of them mentioned Dinas Dinlle. W. Hutton, for example, in his *Remarks upon North Wales* (1803) describes Dinas Dinlle as ' generally supposed to have been a Roman fort.'

Caer Aranrhod as a topic of interest seems to have been rediscovered by William Owen Pughe early in the 19th century. In a letter to T. C. Croker, author of the *Fairy Legends of the South of Ireland* (1828) and published in that work, Pughe wrote :

'The other instance of fidelity of tradition [i.e., in *The Mabinogion*] relates to the discovery of the fortress of Arianrhod, mentioned in the tale of Math. Its situation was thus found . . . A late friend of mine (from Anglesey) said that there was a remarkable ruin in the sea nearly midway between Llandwyn Point and the Church of Clynog in Caernarvonshire, which sailors in passing over can see in the water, and which is dangerous to vessels and called by them Caer Arianrhod. Thus, by mere accident, I found what I had vainly enquired for. I thought that it was to be found somewhere on the coast of Arvon, and not about two miles from it in the sea.' [16]

It is not likely that Pughe made a personal visit to the site or he would have discovered that it was much nearer to Clynnog than to Llanddwyn and only half a mile from the shore. His remark that he thought it would have been somewhere on the coast and not out in the sea, is, as we shall see, significant.

In due course, *Caer Arianrhod*, as the name of the submerged stones, again became a recognized map feature when the one-inch Ordnance Survey map of Caernarvonshire was published in 1841,—but it was not engraved in the style of lettering used to designate sites of antiquarian importance—and it became still more widely known after the publication of Lady Charlotte Guest's translation of the collection of early Welsh tales now commonly referred to as *The Mabinogion* although only four of them are properly so called.

By the beginning of the present century, and in the region to which it relates, the idea that the so-called Caer marked the site of a drowned habitation had acquired a definiteness born of uncritical interest. In 1907, when the *Royal Commission on Coast Erosion and the Reclamation of Tidal Lands* received evidence on behalf of the 'Carnarvon Harbour Trust,' the story received 'Blue Book' authority in the following words :

' When the Romans occupied Britain they had on the coast of Carnarvon Bay a town called now Caer Arianrhod, which had a paved road, still existing, leading direct to their great Roman station, Segontium, now Carnarvon. The said town of Caer Arianrhod, visible at low water spring tides, is now one mile from the existing sea beach, showing the rate of erosion since Roman times '   [153]

Except in its reference to visibility at low spring tides, everything in that statement is either manifestly inaccurate, or wholly unsupported by evidence.

(b)   Aranrhod, her ' Castle ' and her contemporaries

Sir John Rhŷs summarized what was known of Aranrhod's place in literature by saying that she was the daughter of Dôn, the Welsh equivalent of the Irish Donu or Danu, who was the mother of several Celtic gods [144], but the Mabinogi of *Math, son of Mathonwy* is the authority for connecting her with Caer Aranrhod.

As we are concerned only with a comparatively small part of the story it will be sufficient to say that it belongs to the 'King with the prophesied death' type, and has an Irish counterpart.   Very briefly its essentials are as follows :

Aranrhod was the mother of Llew Llaw Gyffes, and she laid a destiny on him that he should never marry a woman of any race on earth at the time.   His uncles Gwydion (who in the original form of the legend was the father of Llew) and Math made a wife (Blodeuwedd) for him out of flowers and leaves—a variant of the fairy wife theme so grossly misused by the creator of the modern story of Llynclys.

Blodeuwedd entered into a plot to kill her husband, but at the critical moment he changed his form into that of an eagle and flew away.   After many adventures Gwydion found him, restored him to his own form, and set out to punish Blodeuwedd [74].   The allusions to Caer Aranrhod come in that part of the story which relates to Llew as a boy and we have to consider them in the light of their implication concerning the situation of the site.

Some apparent inconsistencies in the story enable us to

picture the geographical conditions which obtained at the time when the events in the story were enacted—or were imagined as being enacted, according to whether we regard the story as the creation of an imaginative mind or as based upon a fragment of history that has survived from a remote past—but in order fully to appreciate those inconsistencies it is necessary to quote the relevant parts of the story.   They are taken from the recent translation by Gwyn Jones and Thomas Jones. [74] The boy had been reared by Gwydion at Dinas Dinlle (Dinlleu), and,

' One day he followed after Gwydion to go out a-walking. He made for Caer Aranrhod and the boy with him.   After he had come to the court, Aranrhod arose to meet him, to make him welcome and give him greeting.'

On the next occasion,

' He took the boy with him and went to walk along the sea shore.   And where he saw some dulse and sea-girdle he made a ship by magic, and out of seaweed and dulse they made cordwain, much of it . . . And he fitted a sail to the ship and came, he and the boy in the ship, to the entrance of the gate of Caer Aranrhod.   And then they began to fashion shoes and to stitch them . . . "What are those men in the ship ?" asked Aranrhod . . . '

Having achieved their object, ' the work [the shoes they were making] vanished into dulse and seaweed . . . Then they went towards Dinas Dinlleu.   And there Lleu Llaw Gyffes was reared.'

In order to defeat the destiny which had been laid upon the boy :

' They took their way along the sea shore . . . and at the top of Cefn Clun Tyno they made ready on horseback and came towards Caer Aranrhod . . . and made towards the gate in the guise of two youths . . At early cockcrow Gwydion arose.   And then he summoned to him his magic and his power . . . When day was coming [Aranrhod said] "We cannot see the colour of the deep for the ships thronging together, and they are making for the land with all the speed they can ".'

In their series of adventures Gwydion and the boy *walked* to the castle, they *rode to it* and *entered it* on horseback, and they *went to it by boat*, whilst Aranrhod saw vessels approaching *from the sea*. These are not necessarily contradictory statements, for there is nothing in the story to suggest that the castle was situated *out in the sea*. The requirements of the story would be met by a site on the shore similar to that occupied by Dinas Dinlle at the present time. Wm. Owen Pughe, as we have already seen, realized that.

The Caer Aranrhod of modern maps is covered by more than 20 feet of water at spring tides. It has certainly not been submerged to that extent since the days when the Mabinogion were reduced to writing, but during Bronze age times the site might well have been on the mainland close to the sea shore. In that case the geographical conditions would be satisfied if we consider the story as relating to a habitation then situated at the sea-side but now destroyed by erosion and subsidence, and as having originated amongst the people who lived in the days before the present relations of land and sea had been established. The story is not, as the Royal Commission's informant believed, a measure of the extent of the encroachment of the sea since Roman times.

We can at least be sure that since Lleu, the Gaulish Lugus, the Llew of the Mabinogion, is a well-known figure in Celtic mythology, the association of the legend with [Dinas] Din-lleu is of pre-Christian origin, but there is nothing to show that, to those who reduced the story of Math to writing, Caer Aranrhod meant the submerged reef to which the name is now given.

Humphrey Llwyd appears to have been the first to associate the submerged stones and the name, probably in an attempt to adapt the story to the geographical details of the locality— we cannot tell, because no mention is made of the Caer in his *Commentarioli* or its English translation, and the notes he sent to Ortelius with his map do not seem to have survived. Of those notes he wrote, ' I send unto you my Wales not beutifully set forth in all poynctes, yet truly depeinted, so be that certeyn notes be observed, which I gathered even when I was ready to die . . . Besides certein fragments which, notwithstandynge that they be written foorth in a rude hande and seeme to be imperfect, . . . be well grounded by proofes and authorities of auntient writers.' [117b]

The nature of the notes we can surmise from the introductory remarks in the *Breviary* (fol. 2) in which he explained that, amongst other things, he wished to correct errors that had arisen in respect of the names of places, ' for ignorance of the British tongue ' had ' driven many notable men to soche shiftes that endeuorynge to winde themselves out of one they have fallen into many more, and these more grosser errours.' [167]

It will have been noticed that although the story of Math the son of Mathonwy relates to a site accessible from the sea, it says nothing about an inundating catastrophe. In this respect it differs fundamentally from the stories of Llys Helig and Cantre'r Gwaelod, which, in their earliest forms, were no more than allusions to inundations and only in their later development acquired circumstantial details of what happened before and after the catastrophe occurred.

It was not until towards the end of the nineteenth century, when the stories of Llys Helig, Cantre'r Gwaelod and Llyn Syfaddon and all the rest had become widely known, that Rhŷs was able to record a local legend to the effect that while some women had come to fetch food and water the place was swallowed by the sea because of the evil lives of the dwellers. [145s] According to one of his informants three women were involved. ' They were named Gwen, or Gwennan, Maelan, and Elen ' and, he added, ' all appear, like Arianrhod, to have belonged to the class of goddesses associated with the dawn.' [144a]

An inquiry into the origin of these embellishments leads to conclusions similar to those arrived at after studying the development of the Llys Helig story and shows how such stories tend to grow with telling ; it also illustrates the necessity for giving careful consideration to the relative value of the component parts of the stories.

Rhŷs records in *Celtic Folklore* that in 1882 he spent a good deal of time in Caernarvonshire, where he ' made notes of a great many scraps of legends,' adding, ' I will now string some of them together as I found them.' [145t] In August he ' went to see Dinas Dinlle and to ascertain what traditions still existed there respecting Caer Arianrhod and other names that figure in the *Mabinogi* of Math mab Mathonwy.'

Hugh Evans, the clerk of Llandwrog, told him that ' he had often heard people talk of some women once on a time having come from Tregar Anthreg to Cae'r Loda, a place near the shore, to fetch food and water, and that when they looked back they beheld the town overflowed by the sea : the walls can still be seen at low water. Gwennan was the name of one of the women, and she was buried at the place called Bedd Gwennan.'

Tregar Anthreg (of which a local variant collected by Rhŷs was Tregan Anthrod) appears to have been a corruption of Caer Aranrhod—as if it had first become Caranthreg and had had Tre' (= Tref, meaning a settlement or homestead) added to it by people who did not realize that the first syllable was a corruption of Caer. Cae'r Loda has been explained [145w] as Cae'r Aelodau, but the story relating to it does not seem to have been recorded. Another possibility, having regard to the changes involved in arriving at Tregar Anthreg, is that it may have been a much dimmed recollection of the Caer Ierienroda of some 18th century maps.

'Tregar Anthreg,' wrote Rhŷs, ' is to be seen at low water from Dinas Dinlle as a rock not far from the shore, . . . Tregar Anthrod (another local form) is undoubtedly Caer Arianrhod or the "fortress of Arianrhod" in the *Mabinogi* ; it is duly marked as such in a map of Speede's at the spot where it should be.'

This, however, does not seem to be sound argument ; our inquiry into the circumstances in which it came to be engraved on Speed's map shows that the name was given to some rocks, half a mile or so from the shore, because Humphrey Llwyd, in the 16th century, supposed them to represent the site referred to in the ancient tale. It is going far beyond the evidence to say that the rocks are undoubtedly the Caer Aranrhod or

P

fortress of Aranrhod in the Mabinogi. The same kind of
unsatisfactory argument was used by Pennant. ' I find,' he
wrote, ' on the old maps, both of Saxton and Speed, the name
Caer Ierienrode ; and by the addition of the word Caer it
must have been a fortified place.' [131c]

(c)   The submerged reef called Caer Aranrhod

There are very few records of visits to ' Caer Aranrhod ' and
the one of which we have the most detailed account was made
by a party that set out in the belief that the site had been
correctly named : in the circumstances it is not surprising
to find that what the visitors saw fully confirmed their belief.
The expedition, led by William Ashton in 1909, is described
in his *Evolution of a Coastline* to which we have frequently had
occasion to refer [4p].   The party

' found, about 200 yards west of a huge stone about
9 x 6 x 6 feet in size, standing amidst a cluster of smaller
ones, a semi-circle of flat topped stones, about 25 yards
from point to point.   The tops of these stones of which 15
were counted, were oblong square in shape, and about
15 x 11 inches in size.   At one point a short straight line
of stones was also noticed.   All these were seen about a foot
below the surface of the sea.   The form of the semi-circle
seemed to be quite regular, as also the distance separating
each stone.'

[Had it been possible to row or wade farther] ' presumably
we should have found a full circle . . . The arrangement of
the stones was such as to leave little room for doubt that
this is an ancient British or Brythonic circle such as it has
been customary to call a Druid's Circle.   It is now generally
agreed that they [the so-called Druids circles] are of Neolithic
or Bronze Age date.'

Ashton's illustration of the site, copied in Fig. 17. is described as ' Site of Caer Arianrhod, a Roman Fort or Port down
to its submergence in the 6th century.   From a photo. taken
at Ebb tide . . . Crescent of stones (inset) was seen just below
the surface of the water.'   In the text it is suggested that ' Caer
Arianrhod was used by the Romans as a port or landing place

when access to Caernarvon (Segontium) from the sea was much more difficult even than it is today.' This, of course, merely repeats what was given as evidence before the Royal Commission two years before.

These suppositions need not long detain us, but they are of interest because they afford an excellent illustration of the credulity which is often displayed by those whose interest in matters of which they know sufficient to see resemblances is not extensive enough to prevent them from drawing wrong conclusions. This applies not only to features like the sub-merged region we are now considering, but also to individual specimens. Stones which, from natural causes, have acquired a superficial resemblance to ' prehistoric axes ' are often brought to museums because their finders have not noticed that the fabric is too soft or too brittle to have been used as tools or weapons, or to have been thought suitable for such by Stone Age man, whose appreciation of what we should now call technological matters was surprisingly keen.

Is it likely, we may ask, that a comparatively limited cluster of stones could represent the Caer Aranrhod to which Gwydion took the infant Lleu, could also be the debris of a Roman fort or port, and at the same time display, almost undisturbed, the elements of a prehistoric stone-circle ? Even the ' stone-circle ' is suspect, for neither the illustration not the description will stand up to critical examination.

It is true that the diameter of the ' circle ' is well within the average limits of the stone-circles typical of Wales, i.e., between 50 and 80 feet, although the stones themselves are smaller than is usually the case. The inset plan in Fig. 17 is misleading because, by greatly increasing the relative size of the stones, it gives the impression that we are looking at part of a well-defined and roughly circular enclosure, which might suggest the margin of a destroyed burial mound rather than a ' stone circle ' : actually, however, since the stones are said to be about 15 inches long they should be separated in the diagram by spaces equal to about 6 times their long axes, not by spaces about equal to those axes.

Stone circles in Wales are characteristic of upland regions—

one of the best known being the 'Druids' circle on Penmaen-
mawr (Pl. 2)—whereas the Caer Aranrhod of the Mabinogi
was so sited that boats could be moored alongside ! The
stones of a circle, as now found, have usually been displaced or
overturned, as in the case of one on Mynydd Epynt in
Brecknockshire described a few years ago by G. C. Dunning
whose photographs are convenient for comparison with the
sketches of Caer Aranrhod. The original diameter of the
Mynydd Epynt circle was about 56 feet and the stones varied
in shape and in size ; they ranged from roughly rectangular
columns about three feet in greatest dimension to broad slabby
masses as much as seven feet by four—more than twenty
times as large as those described by Ashton as occurring at
Caer Aranrhod. The appearance of the circle on Mynydd
Epynt when the fallen stones had been exposed by the removal
of the soil is illustrated in Pl. 10B. [25]

Finally, it may be asked if it is conceivable that a stone
circle would have been erected in a site so universally stony
as the present Caer Aranrhod ; it cannot be argued that the
other stones have been brought thither by the waves whilst
those of the circle remained undisturbed, or that the latter
have been exposed by waves, which removed the soil and at the
same time so gently treated the stones of the circle as not to
upset their original arrangement.

Similar objections apply if we try to regard the stones as
representing a burial cairn of Neolithic or early Bronze Age.
Such mounds were built of earth or small stones, either with or
without a complete or partial kerb of larger stones, and they
would not retain their indentity in the face of an encroaching
sea.

Pl. 10A illustrates a cairn near the circle on Mynydd Epynt,
after the earthen mound had been cleared away. There
were, around the central burial place, a broad ring of stones,
a single circular line of stones, and a kerb of stones that had
formed the margin of the mound. It will be apparent that a
site like this could never have been regarded as a castle or
fortress by anyone who had seen it, nor could such a structure,
if overwhelmed by the sea, have given rise to the reef called

Caer Aranrhod ; nor would it be recognizable had it been erected upon soil that once covered such a reef, and its stones left behind after the soil had been washed away.

As with Llys Helig, the patch of stones on the sea floor near Clynnog Fawr has impressed different visitors differently In 1912 the Hon. F. G. Wynn, [182] found the sea all around ' the reef of stones known as Caer Arianrod the Roman town on the sea-coast when Segontium and Conovium were occupied ' to be very shallow at low water. The bottom seemed to be ' covered with boulders and fine gravel, thickly coated with seaweed.' He ' found the Caer Arianrod itself to consist of boulder stones,' and said that ' no part ever really dries, except a circular patch about 40 feet in diameter,' which ' has a few stones [and] large boulders around it which give the idea of a circle.'

'About 40 yards from the circle' he wrote, ' I noticed some large boulders of great size which formed a clearly defined square [sic] of about 20 yard by 10 yards. The lines seemed too regular to be natural, the stones, especially the largest, being equally distant apart. The longer sides really looked like the foundations of a regular building. On the north-west end of the reef, which covers perhaps two acres in extent, stands up . . . a very curious and perfect pillar of stone with a conical top, 8 feet in total height and 3 feet across, and of three sided form.'

He expressed surprise that the pillar could stand up and ' resist the terrible buffetting that this Caer Arianrod sustains by stormy seas.'

The description was accompanied by a sketch (see Fig. 17) giving ' a rough idea how the reef is at low water,' but the two fail to agree in all essential respects. Re-drawn in accordance with the dimensions given, the reef, with its circular and rectangular enclosure would appear as indicated in Fig. 17, and the plan does not then suggest either a prehistoric structure, or a Roman fort or port, even assuming that any remains of such would have retained their relative positions after centuries of exposure to ' terrible buffetting by stormy seas.'

This impression of the site differs materially from that

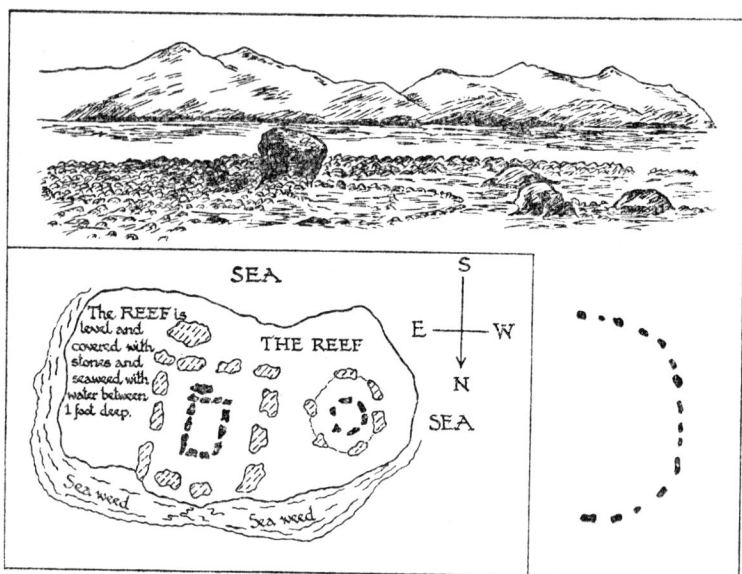

Fig. 17. Impressions of Caer Aranrhod

(*a*) ' Caer Arianrhod, a Roman Fort down to its submergence in the 6th Century '
as sketched by W. Ashton in 1909 [4], with his diagram illustrating the 'crescent of
stones seen just below the surface of the water.'

(*b*) Plan of ' Caer Arianrod ' drawn by F. C. Wynn [182] with the addition
(in solid black) of the rectangular and circular enclosures redrawn according
to the dimensions given.

brought back by Ashton, who saw, not a circle 40 feet in
diameter outlined by a few large stones, but a semi-circle outlined by 15 widely spaced small stones, assumed to be the
exposed half of a circle 75 feet in diameter. He saw also a
short straight line of stones, but not a ' square ' enclosure 20
yards by 10.

It would seem that, as in the case of the descriptions of Llys
Helig, those of the castle or fortress of Caer Aranrhod also
vary because they are attempts to read some kind of regularity,
regarded as indicative of human design, into an adventitious
accumulation of stones. In such circumstances it is most
unlikely that various observers who set out to see, in the Caer
Aranrhod of the maps, the site of buildings or structures made
by man, would be similarly impressed by what they saw or

would agree in their interpretation of it. It is by no means certain that all the descriptions relate to the same group of stones. Ashton described it as being three miles west of Clynnog Fawr, but the Caer Aranrhod of the maps is three miles north of that village.

The photograph, Pl. 13B, illustrates what Caer Aranrhod is likely to have been when the encroachment of the sea had progressed only far enough for the spot to have been near high water mark, and shows how easy it is for an imaginative observer with a preconceived notion to see human design where actually there is none. It depicts part of the stone-strewn beach near Penmaen-bach, about a mile and a half NE of Penmaen-mawr ; from the chosen viewpoint it is quite easy to visualize part of a ring of more or less equally spaced large stones, but seen either at closer quarters or from farther away it is apparent that such an interpretation is not correct.

Having no personal knowledge of the site (for conditions during the last few years have not favoured such expeditions) I should not have ventured thus to discuss the interpretation of what is to be seen at Caer Aranrhod, had not the experience gained during the investigation of Llys Helig made it clear that the ' plans ' to be seen on sites of this character are, like pictures in the fire and forms in the clouds, dependent upon the imagination and predilections of the observer. Even what is actually seen is liable to change, not so rapidly perhaps as cloud and flame forms but none the less surely, because the disposition of the surrounding sand and gravel may be affected by storms, and the number of stones that can be seen on any one occasion will be determined by the extent of the fall of the tide.

There can be little doubt but that the reef called Caer Aranrhod is one of a number of accumulations of glacially transported stones like those seen at Llys Helig, Degannwy, and Penmaen-bach. The stones are relics of the Boulder Clay that once spread over the region as an extension of tracts that still remain to conceal the foundation rocks of much of the Lleyn peninsula ; they are exposed because, owing to the level at which they occur, waves from time to time break over them and prevent the accumulation of sand and gravel.

The fact that, during an early part of the human era, there may have been land where Caer Aranrhod now stands does not justify the claim that the submerged reef represents the Caer Aranrhod of the legend. If the story told in the Mabinogi is indeed a survival, in Dark Age or Medieval garb, of an allusion to events of some prehistoric age, it was quite understandably superimposed upon the topographical features with which the writers were familiar. Their Caer Aranrhod, the home of the daughter of Dôn, was on the sea coast, and if what we now call Caer Aranrhod was not already a submerged reef it can only have been no more than a low island from which the soil has since been washed away. It was, as far as can be ascertained, a 16th century scholar, and not the medieval writers, who thought of associating the legend with the reef. It is true that, since the present relation between land and sea has come about after a long period of submergence and erosion, the spot where Caer Aranrhod now stands must once have been actually on the coast, but that does not allow us to suppose that we have in the reef the ruins of buildings that might have figured in the Mabinogi : any such buildings would have been destroyed, not merely submerged.

Eddystone Lighthouse stands out in the sea and is not destroyed, but that is because its massive well-shaped stones are cemented to a rock especially chosen for its strength and stability ; if there really had been buildings in the area now covered by the sea off the Caernarvonshire coast between Anglesey and Clynnog they would have been built upon glacial deposits which, wherever they are exposed in the cliffs, are seen to be weak, incoherent, and easily eroded.

It transpires then that the story of Aranrhod is an old one (or collection of old ones) elaborated and made to fit the geographical and social conditions of the medieval time when it was committed to writing. From this it follows that a feature called Caer Aranrhod which then existed on or near the shore has since been so completely destroyed by erosion that no recognizable trace of it can be found.

Identification with the Caer Aranrhod of the maps would imply that since the 13th century there has been subsidence and erosion to such an extent that what was then a stronghold on the coast is now covered by more than 20 feet of water at high tide. There is no evidence that such a subsidence has taken place, but a great deal to show that it has not.

There have, from time to time, been reports of pottery picked up at Caer Aranrhod but no one has yet been found who can either produce the pottery or, having seen it, can say what it was like.

If the conclusions here put forward are correct, one would not expect to find pottery on the site, unless it were modern crockery dropped from a passing boat, but if these pages come to the notice of any one who possesses or has seen the pottery or anything else of human manufacture from Caer Aranrhod, many others besides the writer would be glad to hear of it. It is by no means unlikely that an explanation for the ' pottery ' is to be found in a remark made by Ashton in the account of his visit in 1909 [4p]. He reported that, amongst other things, his skipper had seen ' with the aid of a little imagination —crockery ! (really a cream-coloured, cup-shaped seaweed).' As a well-known parlour game shows, a statement has only to be repeated a few times for it to take on a character that its originator can hardly recognize !

XII
BRÂN, BRANWEN, AND IRELAND

OF the geographical allusions in the Mabinogi of Branwen, the daughter of Llŷr, some may have been based on dim recollections of lands that had been lost beneath the sea, whilst others relate to conditions which obtained when the stories were taking the forms in which they have survived but which do not obtain now.

THE popular story of Llys Helig has been built up in comparatively recent times upon a simple foundation statement (that can be traced back to the 13th century) to the effect that the lands of a certain man were overwhelmed by the sea : the story of Cantre'r Gwaelod is a modern expansion of a similar statement also of 13th century origin, supported by an earlier story that mentions an inundation but attributes it to a cause entirely different from that given in the modern versions. Caer Aranrhod, on the other hand, introduces us to a story that was fully elaborated long before it was first committed to writing in the 13th or 14th century.

Although documentary evidence fails, our inquiries into the nature and extent of coastal changes during the human era have shown that we are not altogether without material which might throw light upon the history and significance of Caer Aranrhod, and the same applies to some geographical details in the last of the stories with which we shall concern ourselves—that of Branwen, the daughter of Llŷr.

Briefly, the part of the story which is relevant to our purpose is as follows : one day, when Brân (Bendigeidfran, or Brân the Blessed, described as King of Britain) was sitting on the rock of Harlech (Harddlech) with his courtiers, he saw ships sailing towards him from the south of Ireland. He sent some of his men down to meet them and learnt that it was the fleet of Matholwch, King of Ireland, with messengers who had come to ask for his (Brân's) sister, Branwen, as his wife.

Brân, still seated on the rock, talked to the visitors and asked them to land. In due course they went by land to Aberffraw, where the wedding took place, and, after some unpleasant

experiences with which we are not here concerned, Matholwch
went back to Ireland with Branwen.

Some years later, owing to court intrigues, but from no fault
of her own, Branwen was disgraced and banished to the
kitchen. After a time she managed, by means of a bird, to
send a message to Brân, who set out for Ireland to rescue her
and to punish those who had illtreated her. [Can the recollections of this Mabinogi be the origin of the references to
the bird who gave warning messages in several of the stories we
have discussed ?]

Instead of sailing, Brân waded through the intervening
water because no ship had been built that was large enough
to hold him. From fear of what they could see coming
Matholwch and his people hastened to a place where a river
separated them from the invader, but Brân laid himself across
the stream and his men passed over hurdles placed upon his
body.

The Irish placated him by building a house large enough
for him, but as a result of a quarrel all but seven of Brân's men
were killed. Although able to rescue his sister, Brân was
mortally wounded and ordered the seven survivors to cut off
his head and to take it with them to their own country. In
accordance with the detailed instructions he gave them, they
took it first to Harlech where they lived for seven years, and
then went to Gwales in Penfro [Pembrokeshire], where they
stayed for 80 years.

We are not here concerned with, nor am I in the slightest
degree competent to discuss, the ultimate origin of this story
and its components or to add to what has already been written
by the late W. J. Gruffydd. [59, 60] That the Mabinogi is
indeed founded upon a series of originally unrelated stories is
suggested by its final paragraph, which is as follows :

'And that is how this branch of the Mabinogi ends, concerning the blow to Branwen which was one of the Three
Unhappy Blows in this Island ; and concerning the Assembly
of Brân, when the hosts of sevenscore districts and fourteen
went over to Ireland to avenge the blow to Branwen ; and
concerning the feasting in Harddlech seven years ; and the

singing of the birds of Rhiannon, and the Assembly of the Head for fourscore years.'

It is sufficient for the moment to note that there are affinities with old Irish tales like that of the voyage of Brân to the land of the living, in which, for example, there is a Manannan son of Ler, to correspond with Mananwydan son of Llŷr who figures in the Branwen story and whose adventures in Britain are told in the Mabinogi which bears his name.

The oldest copy of the Irish Saga—an incomplete one—is a manuscript believed to be of about 1100 A.D., perhaps a little earlier than the first writing of the Mabinogion. The other surviving copies are of the 14th and 15th centuries, that is, later than the earliest extant copies of the Welsh stories. [97] These dates show how likely it is that the contemporary stories of Ireland and of Wales should have influenced one another ; they show how interesting and intricate are the problems concerning their individual contributions, and the extent to which we have survivals in each area, of fragments of earlier tales once current in both. We have, in previous chapters, noted Irish associations with the legends connected with Cardigan Bay and some of the lakes.

For our immediate purpose we are only concerned with the significance of certain details that, from the narrative point of view, might appear to be of no importance ; in the order in which they are mentioned, they are as follows :

1. Brân was sitting on the rock of Harlech overlooking the sea, and, when he saw ships coming from Ireland and sent some of his people down to learn the reason for the visit, he ' could hear them from the place where he was, upon the rock above their heads.'

2. Matholwch and his host went to Aberffraw by boat, whilst Brân and his people went by land.

3. Whilst at Aberffraw Brân gave Matholwch a cauldron which had life-restoring properties, and, asked by Matholwch whence he got it, replied, ' I had it of a man who had been in thy land,' i.e., the cauldron came from Ireland.

4. After leaving Aberffraw they went ' from Aber Menai with 13 ships and came to Ireland.'

5. When Brân went to punish the Irish for their ill-treatment of his sister, ' it was not far across the sea, and he came to shoal water. There were but two rivers : Lli and Archan they were called ' The Guest translation adds ' and the nations covered the sea,' but that is considered to be a bad rendering, and ' since then the sea multiplied his realms,' ' after that the ocean separated the Kingdoms ' or (in the new Everyman's translation), ' but thereafter the deep water grew wider when the deep overflowed the Kingdom ' [74b], have been given as alternatives. However worded, the passage suggests recognition of a time when the Irish Sea was less extensive than it is now and on that account is one of the most significant we have encountered in this part of our inquiry.

The references to ships coming from Ireland towards Harlech, to Matholwch's journeys to Aberffraw and Abermenai, and to a place ' in Penfro ' overlooking the sea, suggest geographical conditions generally similar to those which now obtain, but the picture created by the description of Brân's journey to Ireland does not. If that has any meaning at all it must relate to the conditions of an earlier period, to a time when the sea had less fully occupied the region that it now commands between Britain and Ireland. The statement that Brân went from Harlech to Aberffraw by land does not introduce a difficulty by implying that Anglesey was not at that time an island, since, in relation to these two places, ' by land ' as distinct from ' by sea ' most likely means by land to a ferry on Menai and thence by land to Aberffraw, instead of, as would have been possible, all the way by sea.

These apparent geographical inconsistencies, instead of making nonsense, provide additional evidence that some parts of the Mabinogion are very ancient—that they may, indeed, be relics of prehistoric records that survived sufficiently long for them to have been incorporated into the written literature of medieval days.

We have already seen that the Irish Sea has ' extended its bounds ' and was doing so during the Bronze Age : this being the case it is not a matter for surprise if the effects of the encroachment loomed so largely in the experience of the people of those days that they were incorporated into their oral history.

It is not of course suggested that the stories originated in the experience of men who actually crossed to Ireland without boats, for the isolation of the island took place much too early for that, but, on the thesis here developed, they could have originated in the recollections of persons affected by the encroachment of the sea. The realization that the sea between Wales and Ireland was gradually becoming wider would quite naturally have suggested a time when it was narrower still or even non-existent. Although, as we have seen, the channel separating Ireland from Wales may at one time have been no more than a river and its estuary, the river in the story was one arrived at by inference and not one recorded out of experience.

A passage in the old Irish story of the voyage of Brân reminds us of the obscure poetical references to Gwyddno's lost lands, and seems to have more meaning if we consider it as referring to a phenomenon of which the writer had but a hazy notion, but which was, in fact, an inundation. When Brân was at sea he saw a man in a chariot coming towards him over the sea. He was told that it was Manannan son of Ler, and the narrator says :

> Brân deems it a marvellous beauty
> In his coracle across the clear sea ;
> While to me in my chariot, from afar,
> It is a flowery plain on which he rides about . . .

> Along the top of a wood has swum
> Thy coracle across ridges,
> There is a wood of beautiful fruit
> Under the prow of thy little skiff [97].

The reference to them by Giraldus Cambrensis shows that the existence of the submerged forests around our coats had been recognized at the time the tales were being committed to writing.

The story of the cauldron which Brân gave to Matholwch also suggests connexions with Ireland. Some of the most interesting and spectacular of the Bronze Age relics found in Wales are cauldrons. Two of them were, as we have mentioned, found in the peat of Llyn Fawr, a mountain tarn in the northern part of Glamorgan, in association with a hoard of bronze and iron weapons and implements that appear to have been thrown into the lake—or the swampy bog by which it was then represented—somewhere about 500 B.C. ; that is, at approximately the end of the Bronze Age.

Both cauldrons were built up of bronze plates rivetted together, and were provided with well designed rims and handles. They were between 13 and 14 inches high and 22 inches in diameter where widest. Such objects must have been highly cherished by the few families that were fortunate enough to possess them, and were, no doubt, objects of envy amongst those who did not. The workmanship of these and similar cauldrons found in other parts of Wales and England shows that they came from Ireland and are indications of trade relations between the two countries.

The distribution of known finds of cauldrons and related vessels in England and Wales suggests that those who brought them from Ireland came by way of the Bristol Channel, and unless some new discovery indicates otherwise, we may assume that the objects never actually found their way into Central and North Wales where they became known by repute rather than by experience. The cauldron of Ceridwen, it will be remembered, was a magic vessel, not a culinary utensil.

Before leaving cauldrons we may note that when Brân and Matholwch were discussing the one which had come from Ireland, Matholwch said that he had seen a big man with yellow hair coming from a lake with a cauldron on his back. May we not see in this man the prototype of the ' gigantic man ' who came out of Llyn Cwm Llwch ? The latter had no cauldron, it is true, but that was not necessary to his particular story.

The account of the arrival of the men from Ireland, with Brân viewing the ships from the rock of Harlech, is based upon the geography of the time when the story as we now have it was put together, not on that of an earlier time when there

were narrower waters to cross, and the information that he
conversed with the men in the boats whilst sitting upon the
rock confirms the view that local geographical details were used
by the story tellers when it suited their convenience to do so.
To carry on such a conversation at the present time would
require super-stentorian voices for the rock of Harlech is
nearly a mile from the sea ; but instead of being an objection
to the view that old stories were adapted to the geographical
conditions of a later age, it is confirmation, because present
day conditions are of comparatively modern origin.

The apparent anomaly shows that the story does, indeed,
reflect the conditions which obtained when it was being
committed to writing, because at that time the rock on which
Brân is supposed to have sat *was* close to the sea.   This condition obtained when the castle was built in the 13th century,
and there are several references in 14th century manuscripts in
the Public Record Office to Harlech as a port.   On April 15,
1325, for example, instructions were given to the bailiffs and
community of the port of Hardelowe (Harlech) forbidding
anyone damaging or annoying the men of Flanders using the
port.   Harlech was also included in the ports to which other
instructions were given over the next few years [158].   As long
as the castle had military significance a harbour or wharf
would have been of vital importance, for the sea would have
provided the easiest and sometimes the only means of communication with supply bases.

For how long these conditions obtained is uncertain.   There
is no further mention of Harlech as a port after the 15th
century, but a manuscript of about 1600 [183] refers to the
Castle as having havens, creeks, and landing places on either
side, whilst a plan on Speed's map of Merionethshire (1610)
shows a creek extending to the base of the rock on which the
castle stands (Pl. 8B) : since then the drift of material along
the coast and the accumulating sand has built up a tract of
level land (the southern extremity of Morfa Harlech) isolating
the castle from the sea.

XIII

CONCLUSION

WHATEVER through the whole history is written well let no man envy ; what slips there are (through ignorance) those with more knowledge are very welcome to amend.

Diodorus Siculus—1st Century B.C.

WE have travelled a long way through both space and time ; but to what purpose? Have we merely succeeded, with the expenditure of a great deal of energy and ink, in disproving what no serious reader ever believed to be true ? That was not the idea at all. The stories of sunken cities and palaces were not examined only with a view to deciding whether or not the incidents described in them actually took place, but mainly in order to discover how and when simple thirteenth century statements about the sea encroaching upon the land originated, and how they grew into modern legends like those of Llys Helig, Cantre'r Gwaelod, and Llyn Syfaddon.

With the passage of time, and especially since the beginning of the 19th century, the stories became thoroughly mixed and embellished with a great deal of irrelevant detail, but the fundamental facts remain—the sea has encroached upon the land, and lakes have changed their limits during the ages that have elapsed since man found his way into our country. In the fertile imagination of story-tellers the traditions and super-stitions of one age grew out of the historical facts of another, just as plants grow from seed. The analogy is not, of course, complete, but it is apt. The plant is much more complex and usually much more interesting to look at than the seed, and although the seed eventually disappears there is a period during which we can find out what it was like by examining the remains that cling to the roots ; and have we not found that by trying to trace the stories back to their origins we sometimes discover traces of the ' seed ' out of which they grew ? This enables us to reduce an apparently confused mass of tales into some kind of order.

One series of stories relates to encroachment by the sea.

Q

The most important in this group is that about Cantre'r
Gwaelod in which the effects of a number of inundations
appear to have been amalgamated and attributed to one
catastrophe of greater severity and wider extent than any that
actually took place.   This story seems to have inspired the one
told about Llys Helig, and its association with Conway Bay
was probably due to a desire to explain obvious indications of
inundation there, although very dim recollections of a once-
current story of which the details had been completely forgotten, may have been a contributory factor.   The coastal
inundation stories include those told of the Scilly Isles and
Brittany and probably originated amongst the people who
brought the Megalithic culture to Wales during the Neolithic
period.

The stories in another series, dealing with lakes, had mixed
origins and appear for the most part to be representatives of
widely-spread ancient tales, superimposed upon the lakes and
pools to which they now relate.   Some of their details appear to
have been inspired by Biblical history, and whilst in a few
instances (e.g., Llyn Syfaddon) their present attribution
may have been suggested by changes that actually took place
in the region, in others (e.g., Llynclys) they either replace very
simple stories that were current before the 16th century or
(e.g., Kenfig), have no roots at all in a distant past.   Through
a variant relating to wells, the lake stories contributed to the
earliest known form of the Cantre'r Gwaelod tale, and they
also played a part in the synthesis of other coastal legends,
especially after they began to attract popular attention.

Changes in the relation between land and sea are implied in
some of the Mabinogion.   The tales are of Irish origin, and in
their Welsh forms are more highly elaborated than the more
primitive tales from which they were derived.

Since our inquiries have confirmed, and in some directions
amplified, the conclusions of those who have studied the
Mabinogion as literature rather than as evidence in a scientific
investigation, a brief summary of those conclusions, restated in
the light of our geological-geographical approach, may not
be regarded as superfluous by readers as yet unfamiliar with

this part of the ancient literature of Wales.

In the Mabinogion and associated stories we have a collection of ancient tales that were being told in Wales between the 11th and the 14th centuries. They were skilfully pieced together and relate mainly to the coastal regions between Pembrokeshire and Anglesey. Their foundations were laid many hundreds of years before they were committed to writing, but with re-telling and amplification some of them were made to conform to the geographical and social background of the period of their crystallization in manuscript. At that time they mostly related to rulers and powerful personages, to castles rather than to cottages ; they were stories of and for the upper classes rather than the peasantry.

In due course they were studied by students of ancient literature whose writings made them more generally known, but it is doubtful whether they caught the imagination of ordinary folk to any great extent until well into the 19th century, when they were printed in books and magazines written for the general public rather than for what used to be called ' the curious reader.'

These are not new conclusions ; they have been stated before—and more learnedly. The principal contribution made by the present study is the demonstration that the Mabinogion include recollections of stories that had survived from a time when present-day geographical conditions had not been fully established, and that, as they assumed the forms in which they have come down to us, they were adapted to the familiar features of a more recent age. In these circumstances their inconsistencies appear in a new guise. Instead of being meaningless interpolations they take their place amongst the more significant elements which the stories contain, because they help to distinguish between the original (or at least the old) details and those which have been subsequently added. Woven into the series of tales that make the Mabinogi of Brân and Branwen, for example, we have dim memories of a time when the sea between Wales and Ireland was extending its bounds, whilst the story of Aranrhod reveals itself as an ancient tale that was adapted to the local geography of medieval times and only acquired ' sunken city ' status in the nineteenth century.

Committed to writing in full at an early date, The Mabinogion have retained their identities in spite of the passage of time, but other contemporary stories of which hints only had survived were furnished with details and, starting in one locality, have spread from place to place, growing as they went, and often, as with the Mabinogion in their oral stages, tending to mix.

During the 19th century professional writers supplied legends for places that lacked them, and amplified well-established ones by compounding the stories of all ages, all kinds, and all origins—and it is not always remembered that the products were not genuine old tales which had caught the popular fancy. As a result, the tales as now told often have much in common with palimpsests. Just as many an ancient manuscript is of greater interest by reason of an earlier record that has been largely obliterated, but not so completely that, with effort, part or the whole of it may be deciphered, so the study of folk-tales has much to offer to those who try to see, beyond the modern versions, the almost forgotten records of ages past and hints concerning physical conditions that no longer obtain.

When indicating the purpose of this book, comparison was made with stripping the ivy from an old ruin in order to reveal the material which the builders used, and to discover what it was they built. In subsequent pages the metaphor has been varied to suit the point it was desired to emphasize, and in taking leave of the subject yet another comparison may not be inapt. The review of ancient legends has much in common with the process of cleaning an old picture. It sometimes happens that the removal of the cracked and age-stained varnish, in the hope of restoring the picture to its former brilliance, reveals traces of retouching and perhaps of extensive alteration and addition by hands other than those of the original artist, and calls for careful removal of all the added paint. This done, another picture reveals itself, better perhaps, or more important than the one by which it had been concealed.

Removing the superimposed coats of literary varnish, so to speak—the details acquired during centuries of retelling—does not destroy, as legends, the stories of sunken cities, or prevent us from enjoying, as literary efforts, the tales into which they have grown. On the contrary, it adds to their interest by showing how they acquired their present forms and revealing them, in their origins, as amongst the oldest records of human experience in Wales.

BIBLIOGRAPHY

This list does not include publications or references that can be readily identified from the allusions in the text.

Abbreviations used :

Arch. Camb.	Archaeologia Cambrensis.
B. B. Celtic Studies.	Bulletin of the Board of Celtic Studies.
Journ. Roy. Anthr. Inst.	Journal of the Royal Anthropological Institute.
Cymm. Rec. Ser.	Cymmrodorion Record Series.
Mem. Geol. Surv.	Memoirs of the Geological Survey.
Proc. Geol. Assn.	Proceedings of the Geologists' Association.
Proc. Prehist. Soc.	Proceedings of the Prehistoric Society.
Q.J.G.S.	Quarterly Journal Geological Society.
Trans. Cardiff Nat. Soc.	Transactions of the Cardiff Naturalists' Society.
Trans. Hon. Soc. Cymm.	Transactions of the Honourable Society of Cymmrodorion.

1. ADMIRALTY, Hydrographic Dept., *West Coast of England Pilot*, 8th Ed., London, 1933, p. 247 ; (a) p. 254.
2. ANON., *Tales from Welsh Legends and History*, London and Edinburgh, n.d., p. 7.
3. AUSTEN, R. A. C. GODWIN, ' On the Valley of the English Channel', *Q.J.G.S.*, Vol. 6, 1850, pp. 69-97, map opp. p. 96.
4. ASHTON, W., *The Evolution of a Coast Line ; Barrow to Aberystwyth, with notes on Lost Towns, Submarine Discoveries, etc.*, London, 1920, p. 196 ; (a) p. 210 ; (b) p. 197 ; (d) p. 152 ; (e) pp. 179-193 ; (f) p. 199 ; (g) p. 198 ; (h) Fig. 37b ; (j) p. 261 ; (k) p. 257 ; (l) pp. 274-5 ; (m) p. 239 ; (n) p. 268 ; (p) p. 225 ; (q) p. 188.
5. BELL, H. I., and D., *Dafydd ap Gwilym, fifty poems . . .*, London, 1942, p. 126.
6. BORROW, GEORGE, *Wild Wales*, Everyman Edition, London, 1906, p. 415.
7. BURNE, C. S., *The Handbook of Folklore* (Folklore Society), 2nd Ed., London, 1914, p. 306.
8. BURNE, C. S., *Shropshire Folklore ; A Sheaf of Gleanings from the collection of Georgina F. Jackson*, London, 1883.
9. BURTON, ROBERT, *The Anatomy of Melancholy*, 1621, quoted from Everyman Edition, London, 1936, Vol. 1, p. 192.
10. CAMDEN, WILLIAM, *Britannia ; Camden's Britannia newly translated into English . . . published by Edmund Gibson*, London, 1695, Col. 672 ; (a) Col. 590 ; (b) Col. 592 ; (c) Col. 658 ; (d) Col. 631 ; (e) Col. 632.
11. CANTRILL, T. C., ' Shell mounds on Laugharne Burrows, Carmarthenshire', *Arch. Camb.*, Vol. 9, 6th Series, 1909, pp. 433-72.
12. CLARK, C. T., *Cartae et Alia Munimenta quae ad Dominium de Glamorgan pertinent*, Dowlais, Vol. 2, 1890, p. 45 ; (a) Vol. 2, p. 139, CXXXIX ; (b) Vol. 3, p. 787, DCCXXI.
13. CLARK, J. G. D., ' The Separation of Britain from the Continent', *Proc. Prehist. Soc.*, N.S., Vol. 2, 1936, p. 239.
14. CRAWFORD, O. G. S., and WHEELER, R. E. M., ' The Llynfawr and other Hoards of the Bronze Age', *Archaeologia*, Vol. 71, 1921, pp. 33-140.
15. CRAWFORD, O. G. S., ' Lyonesse', *Antiquity*, Vol. 1, 1927, pp. 5-14.
16. CROKER, T. C., *Fairy Legends of the South of Ireland*, London, 1828, Vol. 2, p. 175.
17. DAFYDD, WMFFRE, ' Traeth yr Oerlefain', *Cymru Fu*, Wrexham, 1862, pp. 244-7.
18. DAVIES, D. J., ' Cantref y Gwaelod', *Trans. Card. Antiq. Soc.*, Vol. 5, 1927, pp. 21-33 ; (a) p. 24.
19. DAVIES, MARGARET, ' The diffusion and distribution pattern of the Megalithic Monuments of the Irish Sea and North Channel Coastlands', *Antiq. Journ.*, Vol. 26, 1946, pp. 38-60.

20. DAVIES, WALTER, *General View of the Agricultural and Domestic Economy of North Wales*, London, 1810, p. 28.

21. DOBSON, D. P., ' A Beaker from Somerset', *Antiq. Journ.*, Vol. 18, 1938, p. 172.

22. D[ODD], A. H., ' Floods at Abergele', *Trans. Denbighshire Historical Society*, Vol. 2, 1953, pp. 154-5.

23. DOVASTON, JOHN F. M., *Fitz-Gwarine : A ballad of the Welsh Border, in three cantos, with other Poems, legendary, incidental, and humorous*, Shrewsbury, 1812. Citations from 2nd Ed., London, 1816, p. 128 ; (a) p. 127 ; (b) p. 139.

24. DUMBLETON, E. N., ' On a Crannoge, or stockaded island in Llangorse Lake, near Brecon', *Arch Camb.*, 4th Series, Vol. 1, 1870, pp. 192-8.

25. DUNNING, G. C., ' A stone circle and cairn on Mynydd Epynt, Brecknock-shire', *Arch. Camb.*, Vol. 97, 1943, pp. 169-194.

26. EDWARDS, GRIFFITH, ' Cantre'r Gwaelod ; or the Lowland Hundred', *Arch. Camb.*, Vol. 4, 1849, pp. 153-160 ; (a) p. 155.

27. EDWARDS, GRIFFITH, ' The Inundation of Cantre'r Gwaelod : or, the Lowland Hundred. Reprinted from *The Archaeologia Cambrensis*', Tenby, 1849, p. 16.

28. EDWARDS, OWEN M., *Clych Adgof*, Caernarvon, 1906, p. 92.

29. EVANS, EVAN, ' Old Aberystwyth', *Trans. Card. Antiq. Soc.*, Vol. 5, 1927, pp. 57-68.

30. ELLIS, ROBERT (CYNDDELW), ' Chwedlau y Llynoedd', *Y Brython*, Cyf. 5, 1862-3. Tremadog, 1863, pp. 338.

31. EVANS, J. GWENOGVRYN, *Facsimile edition of The Black Book of Carmarthen*, Oxford, 1888.

32. EVANS, J. GWENOGVRYN, *The Black Book of Carmarthen*. Reproduced and edited by J.G.E., Pwllheli, 1906.

33. FARRINGTON, A., ' The Level of the Ocean in Glacial and late-glacial times'. *Proc. Royal Irish Academy*, Vol. 50, Section B, 1945, pp. 237-243.

34. FFOULKES, W. WYNNE, ' Castra Clwydiana, No. 1, Moel Fenlli', *Arch. Camb.*, Vol. 1, 2nd Series, 1850, pp. 81-89.

35. FISHER, JOHN, *Tours in Wales (1804-1813), by Richard Fenton*, London, 1917, pp. 279-306 ; (a) p. 307 ; (b) p. 302.

36. FLEURE, H. J., and JAMES, T. C., ' Geographical Distribution of Anthropo-logical Types in Wales', *Journ. Roy. Anthrop. Inst.*, Vol. 8, 1921, pp. 309-312.

37. FOX, [Sir] CYRIL, ' A "Dug-out" Canoe from South Wales', *Antiq. Journ.*, Vol. 6, 1926, pp. 121-151 ; (a) p. 126.

38. FOX, [Sir] CYRIL, ' A Settlement of the Early Iron Age . . . on Merthyr Mawr Warren, Glamorgan', *Arch. Camb.*, Vol. 82, 1927, pp. 44-66.

39. FOX, Sir CYRIL, and HYDE, H. A., ' A Second Cauldron . . . from the Llyn Fawr Hoard, Rhigos, Glamorganshire', *Antiq. Journ.*, Vol. 19, 1939, pp. 369-404.

40. FOX, Sir CYRIL, *The Personality of Britain*, 4th Ed., Cardiff, 1943, p. 9 ; (a) p. 20.

41. FOX, Sir CYRIL, ' A Bronze Age Barrow in Llandow Parish, Glamorgan-shire', *Archaeologia*, Vol. 89, 1943, pp. 89-126 ; see p. 90.

42. GARDNER, WILLOUGHBY, ' Ancient Hill-fort on Moel Fenlli, Denbighshire', *Arch. Camb.*, Vol. 76, 1921, pp. 237-252.

43. GARDNER, WILLOUGHBY, ' The Native Hill-forts in North Wales and their defences', *Arch. Camb.*, Vol. 81, 1926, pp. 221-282 ; see p. 252.

44. GEORGE, T. NEVILLE, ' The Submerged Forests in Gower', *Proc. Swansea Scientific and Field Nat. Soc.*, Vol. 1, 1930, pp. 100-108.

45. GEORGE, T. N., and GRIFFITHS, J. C., ' The Superficial Deposits at the Mouth of the River Tawe', *Proc. Swansea Scientific and Field Nat. Soc.*, Vol. 2, 1938, pp. 63-71.

46. GIRALDUS CAMBRENSIS, *The Itinerary of Archbishop Baldwin through Wales, and Description of Wales*, Everyman Edition, London, 1944, p. 162-3 ; (a) p. 53 ; (b) pp. 32-3 ; (c) pp. 91-2 ; (d) p. 115 ; (e) p. 121 ; (f) p. 159.

47. GLENN, T. A., 'Distribution of the Graig-Lwyd Axe and its associated cultures,' *Arch. Camb.*, Vol. 90, 1935, pp. 189-218.
48. GODWIN, H. and NEWTON, L., ' The Submerged forest at Borth and Ynyslas, Cardiganshire', *New Phytologist*, Vol. 37, 1938, pp. 333-344.
49. GODWIN, H., ' A boreal transgression of the sea in Swansea Bay', *New Phytologist*, Vol. 39, 1940, pp. 308-21.
50. GOMME, G. L., *The Handbook of Folklore* (Folklore Society), London, 1890, p. 5.
51. GOULD, S. BARING, and FISHER, J., *The Lives of the British Saints*, London, Vol. 4, 1913, pp. 177-180 ; (a) Vol. 4, p. 178 ; (b) Vol. 3, pp. 52-60 ; (c) Vol. 3, pp. 185-196 ; (d) Vol. 3, pp. 60-79.
52. GOULD, S. BARING, *Curious Myths of the Middle Ages*, London, 1894, pp. 471-523.
53. GRAY, THOMAS, *Buried City of Kenfig*, London, 1909, p. 146 ; (a) pp. 21-3 ; (b) p. 32 ; (c) p. 110 ; (d) p. 181 ; (e) p. 29 ; (f) p. 182.
54. GRIMES, W. F., ' Stone Axe from Kenfig', *Arch. Camb.*, Vol. 84, 1929, pp. 149-150.
55. GRIMES, W. F., *The Prehistory of Wales*, National Museum of Wales, Cardiff, 1951, p. xiv ; (a) pp. 18-19.
56. GRIMES, W. F., ' The Megalithic Monuments of Wales', *Proc. Prehist. Soc.*, Vol. 2, 1936, pp. 106-139 ; see esp. p. 112.
57. GRISCOM, A., *The Historiae Regnum Britanniae of Geoffrey of Monmouth*, London, 1928, pp. 338-343.
58. GROSVENOR, Earl of, ' Description of a torque found at Eskeiviog, Flintshire', (in 1816), *Archaeologia*, Vol. 18, 1817, p. 448.
59. GRUFFYDD, W. J., ' The Mabinogion', *Trans. Hon. Soc. Cymm.*, 1912-3, London, 1914, pp. 14-80 ; (a) p. 64.
60. GRUFFYDD, W. J., *Math vab Mathonwy*, Cardiff, 1928.
61. GUEST, LADY CHARLOTTE, *The Mabinogion, from the Llyfr Coch o Hergest*, London, 1838-49 ; (a) pp. 482-3.
62. HACKET, JOHN, *A Memorial . . . of John Williams, D.D., Ld. Keeper of the Great Seal of England, Ld. Bishop of Lincoln, and Ld. Archbishop of York*, London, 1693, p. 6.
63. HALL, C. R., ' Some conjectural hints towards determining the ancient coast line of North Wales, between the River Dee and the Island of Anglesey', *Proc. Liverpool Geol. Soc.*, 1864-5, 1865, pp. 7-20.
64. HALLIWELL, JAMES O., *An Ancient Survey of Pen Maen Mawr, North Wales, from the original manuscript of the time of Charles I*, London, 1859.
65. HICKLIN, JOHN, *The Handbook to Llandudno and its vicinity*, 2nd Ed., London, 1858, pp. 83-86.
66. HIGGINS, L. S., 'An Investigation into the problem of the sand dune areas on the South Wales Coast', *Arch. Camb.*, Vol. 88, 1933, pp. 26-67 ; (a) p. 35 ; (b) p. 34.
67. HOWARD, F. T., ' Observations on the Lakes and Tarns of South Wales', *Trans. Cardiff Nat. Soc.*, Vol. 32, 1901, pp. 29-43 ; (a) p. 33.
68. HOWELLS, W., *Cambrian Superstitions*, Tipton, 1831, p. 100 ; (a) p. 91.
69. HUGHES, HAROLD, ' Prehistoric remains on Penmaenmawr, known as Braich-y-Dinas', *Arch. Camb.*, Vol. 78, 1923, pp. 243-268.
70. HYDE, H. A., ' On a Peat bed at the East Moors, Cardiff', *Trans. Cardiff Nat. Soc.*, Vol. 69, 1936, pp. 39-48.
71. HUGHES, I. C., ' The Legend of Savaddon Lake', *Folklore*, Vol. 19, 1908, pp. 459-63.
72. JAMES, R., ' Iter Lancastrense, a poem written A.D. 1636, . . . from the MS in the Bodleian Library, Oxford', Ed. T. Corser, *Chetham Soc. Publications*, Vol. 7, 1845.
73. JONES, EIRWEN, *Folk Tales of Wales*, London, 1947 ; (a) pp. 77-86.
74. JONES, GWYN, and THOMAS JONES, *The Mabinogion. A new translation from the White Book of Rhydderch and the Red Book of Hergest*, London, 1948, also Everyman's Library, London, 1949 ; (a) p. 102 ; (b) p. 33.

75. JONES, OWEN, and others, *The Myvyrian Archaiology of Wales*, originally published London, 1801-7, in 3 volumes. Citations from the one-volume ed., Denbigh, 1870 ; (a) p. 429 ; (b) p. 404 ; (c) p. 389 ; (d) p. 231 ; (e) p. 25.

76. JONES, O. T., ' The Origin of the Welsh Legends', *Welsh Outlook*, Vol. 8, 1921, pp. 309-12.

77. JONES, O. T., ' Some Observations on Recent Geological Movements of the British Coastline', *Antiquity*, Vol. 8, 1934, pp. 303-309.

78. JONES, THEOPHILUS, *History of the County of Brecknock*, 1805, Vol. 1, p. 6 ; (a) Vol. 2 ; p. 356, (b) Vol. 1, p. 100 ; (c) Vol. 1, p. 110 ; (d) Vol. 1, p. 38.

79. JONES, T. LOMAS, ' Triawd Lladin ar y Gorlifiadau', *B. B. Celtic Studies*, Vol. 12, 1948, pp. 79-83.

80. JONES, THOMAS, ' Cronica de Wallia, and other documents from Exeter Cathedral Library MS 3514', *B. B. Celtic Studies*, Vol. 12, 1946, pp. 27-44.

81. JONES, T. GWYNN, *Welsh Folklore and Folk-customs*, London, 1930, pp. 98-9 ; (a) p. 98 ; (b) p. 97 ; (c) p. 16.

82. JUKES-BROWN, A. J., *The Building of the British Isles*, London, 1922.

83. JUVENAL, Satire XIV, in *Juvenal and Persius, with an English translation by G. G. Ramsay*, London, 1918, p. 279.

84. LEACH, A. L., ' Stone implements from Soil-Drifts and Chipping-Floors, etc., in South Pembroke', *Arch. Camb.*, 6th Series, Vol. 13, 1913, pp. 391-432.

85. LEACH, A. L. ' Flint working sites on the submerged land (submerged forests) bordering the Pembrokeshire coast', *Proc. Geol. Assn.*, Vol. 29, 1918, pp. 46-7.

86. LEES, H., ' The Palace under the Sea', *The Field*, Oct. 4, 1913, No. 3171, p. 725.

87. LLEWELLYN, R. W., ' The Borough of Kenfig', *Arch. Camb.*, 5th Series, Vol. 15, 1898, pp. 132-153.

88. LLOYD, [Sir] J. E., ' *The Welsh Chronicles*', Sir J. Rhŷs Memorial Lecture, (British Academy), London, 1928.

89. LLOYD, Sir J. E. (ed.) *A History of Carmarthenshire*, Vol. 2, Cardiff, 1939, p. 410.

90. LLOYD, [Sir] J. E., ' Oed Llyfr du Caerfyrddin', *B. B. Celtic Studies*, Vol. 7, 1934, pp. 95-6.

91. LLOYD, Sir J. E., *A History of Wales*, 3rd Ed., London, 1939 [Reprinted 1948], Vol. 1, p. 5 ; (a) Vol. 1, p. 179 ; (b) Vol. 1, p. 160 ; (c) Vol 2, p. 433 ; (d) Vol. 1, pp. 25-6 ; (e) Vol. 1, p. 97.

92. LLWYD, ANGHARAD, ' The History of Helig ap Glannog', *The Cambrian Quarterly Magazine, and Celtic Repertory*, London, 1831, Vol. 3.

93. ' Llyn Safaddan', *Y Brython*, Vol. 5, 1862-3, Tremadog, 1863, pp. 114-5.

94. LOWE, W. BEZANT, *An Ancient Survey of Pen Maen Mawr, by Sir John Gwynn of Gwedyr*, Llanfairfechan, 1906.

95. MANLEY, G., ' The Plancius Map of England, Wales, and Ireland, 1592', *Geog. Journ.*, Vol. 84, 1934, pp. 252-3.

96. MAP, WALTER, ' De Nugis Curialium', trans. by M. R. James ; ed. by E. S. Hartland, *Cymm. Rec. Ser.*, Vol. 9, London, 1923, p. 82.

97. MEYER, K., *Voyage of Bran to the land of the living. An Old Irish saga*, London, 1895, Vol. 1, p. 16.

98. MEYRICK, S. R., *History and Antiquities of the county of Cardigan*, 1st Edn., 1808 ; 2nd edn., Brecon, 1907, p. 159 ; (a) p. 156.

MANUSCRIPTS

99. Hafod MS. 16, c. 1400 ; now in Central Library, Cardiff.

100. Llanstephan MS. 28 ; now in Central Library, Cardiff : see also *Arch. Camb.*, Vol. 86, 1931, p. 161.

101. Mostyn MS. 144, 17th cent :

102. Peniarth MS. 12 : (formerly Hengwrt MS. 202) ; now in National Library of Wales. Printed by E. Phillimore, *A fragment from Hengwrt MS. No. 202. Y Cymmrodor* Vol. 7, 1886, pp. 89-134.

103. Peniarth MS. 16 (formerly Hengwrt MS. 54) ; now in the National Library of Wales. Printed by S. Baring Gould and J. Fisher. *Lives of the British Saints*, London, Vol. 4, 1913, pp. 369-371.

104. Peniarth MS. 45 (formerly Hengwrt MS. 536), late 13th century : now in National Library of Wales.

105. Peniarth MS. 77, 16th century ; now in National Library of Wales.

106. Peniarth MS. 127, 16th century, pt. 1 (formerly Hengwrt MS. 194) : now in National Library of Wales.

107. Peniarth MS. 139, pt. II ; now in National Library of Wales.

108. Peniarth MS. 182 (formerly Hengwrt MS. 357) : now in National Library of Wales.

109. MOGGRIDGE, M., ' On the Sections exposed in the excavation of Swansea Dock', *Q.J.G.S.*, Vol. 12, 1856, pp. 169-70.

110. MORRIS, LEWIS, ' Celtic Remains', ed. D. Silvan Evans, London, *Arch. Camb.*, 1878, p. 284 ; (a) p. 73 ; (b) p. 233.

111. NEAVERSON, E., ' Coastal Changes around Liverpool Bay since the Ice Age', *Proc. Liverpool Geol. Soc.*, Vol. 19, 1947, pp. 184-209.

112. NEAVERSON, E., *Mediaeval Castles in North Wales*, Liverpool, 1947, pp. 45-8.

113. ' Newes out of Summersetshire, 1607. A true report of certain wonderful overflowings of Waters now lately in Summersetshire, etc.' Reprint, edited by E. E. Baker, Weston-Super-Mare, 1884.

114. NICHOLSON, GEORGE, *The Cambrian Travellers Guide*, 2nd Ed., London, 1813, Col. 1306 ; (a) Col. 184.

115. NORTH, F. J., *The Evolution of the Bristol Channel*, Nat. Mus. Wales, Cardiff, 1955, pp. 58-64 ; (a) p. 42 ; (b) pp. 87-8 ; (c) p. 81 ; (d) p. 68 ; (e) pp. 78-9.

116. NORTH, F. J., ' The map of Wales before 1600 A.D.', *Arch. Camb.*, Vol. 90, 1935, pp. 1-68, esp. p. 61 ; (a) p. 65.

117. NORTH, F. J., ' Humphrey Lhuyd's Maps of England and Wales', *Arch. Camb.*, Vol. 92, 1937 ; (a) Plate 1 ; (b) p. 10.

118. NORTH, F. J., ' The Legend of Llys Helig, its origin and its significance, with an appendix on the archaeological aspect by W. F. Grimes', Llandudno, *Colwyn Bay and District Field Club*. A supplement to the Proceedings, Llandudno, 1940.

119. NORTH, F. J., ' Paviland Cave, "The Red Lady," the Deluge, and William Buckland', *Annals of Science*, Vol. 5, 1942, pp. 91-128.

120. NORTH, F. J., and others, *Snowdonia*, London, 1949.

121. NOWELL, LAURENCE, MS. Sectional maps of England and Wales, c. 1563, British Museum, Cotton Coll., Dom. XVIII.

122. O'GRADY, S. H., *Silva Gadelica, a collection of tales in Irish*, London, 1892, Vol. 1, pp. 223-7, Vol. 2, pp. 265-9.

123. ORDNANCE SURVEY, ' The Subsidence of London', *Professional Papers*, New Series, No. 4, London, 1932.

124. OSBORN, T. G. B., ' A note on the Submerged Forest at Llanaber, Barmouth', *Manchester Memoirs*, 56, 1912, pp. 1-10.

125. OWEN, EDWARD, *Catalogue of MSS. relating to Wales in the British Museum*, London, pt. 2, pp. 479-490.

126. OWEN, GEORGE, ' Description of Pembrokeshire', Ed. H. Owen, *Cymm. Rec. Ser.*, No. 1, Pt. 1, p. 146.

127. OWEN, WILLIAM, *The Cambrian Biography*, London, 1803, p. 332 ; (a) p. 314.

128. PALMER, W., *The Verge of Wales*, London, 1942, p. 16.

129. PARK, THOMAS (ed.), *Harleian Miscellany*, Vol. 3, London, 1809, pp. 379-384.

130. PARRY, C., ' Mynydd Llandudno', *Y Brython*, Vol. V, 1862-3, Tremadog, 1863, pp. 393-4.

131. PENNANT, THOMAS, *Tours in Wales*, London, 1810, Vol. 3, p. 116 ; (a) Vol. 3, p. 38 ; (b) Vol. 3, pp. 155-6 ; (c) Vol. 2, p. 402 ; (d) Vol. 2, p. 274.

132. PETERSEN, W., ' Tacitus, Dialogus ; Agricola, Germania', *Loebe Classical Library*, London, 1932, pp. 201-2.

133. PETTERSSON, O., ' Climatic Variations in Historic and Prehistoric Time', *Svenska Hydrog.-Biol. Komm. Skrifter*, Heft. 5, Goteborg, 1914.

134. PRICE, [Sir] JOHN, *A Description of Cambria now called Wales*, see D. Powel's *Historie of Cambria*, ed. 1811, p. XV.

135. PUBLIC RECORD OFFICE, ' Ancient Correspondence, lviii, No. 35, 1930-32. Register of Edward the Black Prince, London', Pt. 1, 1930, 1346-1348, Pt. 3, 1932, 1351-1365.

136. PUGHE, JOHN, ' Gwragedd Annwn—The dames of Elfin Land. A legend of Llyn Barfog', *Arch. Camb.*, New Series, Vol. 4, 1855, pp. 201-5.

137. PUGHE, W. OWEN, ' Description of a torque found on Cader Idris', (in 1823) *Archaeologia*, Vol. 21, 1827, pp. 557-9.

138. PUGHE, W. OWEN, ' The Mabinogi of Taliesin', *The Cambrian and Caledonian Quarterly Magazine & Celtic Repertory*, Vol. 5, London, 1833, pp. 198-214, 366-381.

139. READE, T. MELLARD, ' The Moraine of Llyn Cwm Llŵch on the Beacons of Brecon', *Proc. Liverpool Geol. Soc.*, Vol. 7, 1895, pp. 270-276.

140. READE, T. MELLARD, ' The Date of the last change of Level in Lancashire', *Q.J.G.S.*, Vol. 37, 1881, pp. 436-9.

141. RHŶS, [Sir] J., ' Sacred Wells in Wales', *Trans. Hon. Soc. Cymm.*, 1892-3, London, 1893, pp. 1-28. See pp. 14-16.

142. RHŶS, [Sir] J., ' Welsh Fairy Tales', *Y Cymmrodor*, Vol. 6, 1883, pp. 155-221, see p. 171.

143. RHŶS, [Sir] J., *Studies on the Arthurian Legend*, Oxford, 1891, pp. 312-4 ; (a) p. 263 ; (b) p. 270 ; (c) p. 388 ; (d) p. 10 ; (e) p. 326.

144. RHŶS, [Sir] J., ' Lectures on the origin and Growth of Religion as illustrated by Celtic Heathendom', *The Hibbert Lectures*, 1886, 3rd Ed., London, 1898, pp. 89-90 ; (a) p. 161.

145. RHŶS, [Sir] J., *Celtic Folklore, Welsh and Manx*, 2 Vols., Oxford, 1901, see pp. 558-9 ; (a) pp. 401-2 ; (b) p. 577 ; (c) pp. 402-4 ; (d) p. 408 ; (e) p. 413 ; (f) p. 417 ; (g) p. 256 ; (h) p. 74 ; (k) pp. 576-7 ; (m) p. 61 ; (n) p. 18 ; (o) p. 410 ; (p) p. 379 ; (q) pp. 141-6 ; (r) p. 416 ; (s) pp. 207-10 ; (t) pp. 197-8 ; (u) p. 21 ; (w) p. 207.

146. RHŶS, [Sir] J., *Celtic Britain*, 3rd. Ed., London, 1904.

147. RICHARD, A. J., ' Kenfig Castle', *Arch. Camb.*, Vol. 82, 1927, pp. 161-182. (See especially pp. 163-167).

148. ROBERTS, ASKEW, *The History of the Gwydir Family, by Sir J. Wynne*, Oswestry, 1878 ; (a) pp. 7-8.

149. ROBERTS, ASKEW, ' Where did King Oswald Die ? ', p. 4 in ' Contributions to Oswestry History . . . reprinted from the *Trans. Shrops. Arch. and Nat. Hist. Soc.*', Oswestry, 1881.

150. ROBERTS, H. A. E., *Legends and Folklore of South Wales*, London, 1931, pp. 12-16.

151. ROBERTS, H. A. E., *Legends and Folklore of North Wales*, London, 1931, pp. 19-20.

152. ROYAL COMMISSION ON Ancient Monuments. *An Inventory of the Ancient Monuments in Wales and Monmouthshire, II, County of Radnor*, London, 1913, p. 118.

153. ROYAL COMMISSION ON Coast Erosion and the Reclamation of Tidal Lands, Vol. 1, pt. II, 1907, app. xxiii, p. 300 ; (a) p. 301 ; (b) p. 142.

154. SKENE, W. F., *The Four Ancient Books of Wales*, 2 vols., Edinburgh, 1868, Vol. 1, p. 315, Vol. 2, p. 32 ; (a) Vol. 2, p. 10, Vol. 2, p. 10 ; (b) Vol. 2, pp. 456-7 ; (c) Vol. 2, pp. 458-9 ; (d) Vol. 1, pp. 166-9.

155. SMITH, B., and GEORGE, T. NEVILLE, ' British Regional Geology of North Wales', *Geol. Surv. and Mus.*, London, 1935, Fig. 27 (also new ed., 1951).

156. SMITH, L. T., *The Itinerary in Wales of John Leland in and about the years 1536-1539*, London, 1906, p. 134 ; (a) p. 88 ; (b) p. 90 ; (c) pp. 106-7 ; (d) p. 56.

157. STEERS, J. A., 'Sand and Shingle formations in Cardigan Bay', *Geog. Journ.*, Vol. 94, 1939, pp. 209-227.

158. STEERS, J. A., *The Coastline of England and Wales*, Cambridge, 1948, pp. 135-6.

159. STRAHAN, A., with notes by R. H. TIDDEMAN, 'The Geology of the Coasts adjoining Rhyl, Abergele, and Colwyn', *Mem. Geol. Surv.*, London, 1885, pp. 42-43.

160. STRAHAN, A., 'Geology of the Neighbourhoods of Flint and Mold and Ruthin', *Mem. Geol. Surv.*, London, 1890, pp. 151-158.

161. STRAHAN, A., 'On submerged land surfaces at Barry, Glamorganshire', *Q.J.G.S.*, Vol. 52, 1896, pp. 474-489.

162. STRAHAN, A., and others, 'The Country around Swansea', *Mem. Geol. Surv.*, London, 1907, pp. 122-7.

163. THOMAS, W. JENKYN, *The Welsh Fairy Book*, Cardiff, 1952, pp. 71-5 ; (a) pp. 114-6 ; (b) pp. 195-200 ; (c) pp. 269-71 ; (d) pp. 27-41.

164. THORNTON, J. C. and M. J., *Ovid ; Selected Works ; Metamorphoses*, (Trans. Arthur Golding, 1567), London, 1939, p. 114.

165. TOUT, T. F., 'The Welsh Shires', *Y Cymmrodor*, Vol. 9, 1888, pp. 201-226.

166. TREVELYAN, MARIE, *Folklore and Folk-stories of Wales*, London, 1909, pp. 10-11 ; (a) pp. 11-12 ; (b) p. 10.

167. TWYNE, T., *The Breviary of Britayne* . . . by Humphrey Lhuyd of Denbigh . . . Englished by Thomas Twyne, 1573 ; (a) Fol. 69 ; (b) Fol. 1.

168. URBAN, Mr., 'Tracts of Land swallowed by the sea', *The Gentleman's Magazine and Historical Chronicle*, Vol. 21, 1751, p. 60.

169. WADE-EVANS, A. W., '*Nennius's "History of the Britons"*', London, 1938 ; (a) pp. 55-7.

170. WARREN, S. HAZZELDENE, 'Excavation at the Stone Axe factory of Graig-Lwyd, Penmaenmawr', *Journ. Roy. Anthr. Inst.*, Vol. 51, 1921, pp. 165-199.

171. WATERS, W. H. W., 'Account of the Sheriff of Caernarvon for 1303-4', *B. B. Celtic Studies*, Vol. 7, 1935, pp. 143-153, (see p. 146).

172. WELLS, A. K., *Outline of Historical Geology*, London, 1937.

173. WILLIAMS ab ITHEL, JOHN (ed.), *Annales Cambriae*, Rolls Edition, London, 1860, p. 11 ; (a) p. 6.

174. WILLIAMS ab ITHEL, J., (ed.), *Brut y Tywysogion*, London, 1860, p. 12.

175. WILLIAMS, DAVID, 'John Evans's Strange Journey', *Trans. Hon. Soc. Cymm.*, 1948, London, 1949, pp. 105-146, see p. 110 ; (a) p. 108.

176. WILLIAMS, G. J., *Iolo Morganwg, a Chywyddau'r Ychwanegiad*, London, 1926.

177. WILLIAMS, H., 'Gildas, De Excidio Brittaniae', *Cymm. Rec. Ser.*, 3, London, 1899-1901.

178. WILLIAMS, [Sir] IFOR, *Pedeir Keinc y Mabinogi*, Cardiff, 1930, pp. 269-70, 272-3.

179. WILLIAMS, T., *Iolo Manuscripts. A Selection of Ancient Welsh Manuscripts*, London, 1848, pp. 124, 524 ; (b) p. 417 ; (c) pp. 125 & 526 ; (d) pp. 113 & 513 ; (e) pp. 106 & 504 ; (f) pp. 40 & 417 ; (g) pp. 194 & 607 ; (h) p. 337.

180. WOOD, ANTHONY, *Athenae Oxonienses*, Oxford, 1691-2.

181. WYNN, *Calendar of Wynn (of Gwydir) Papers in the National Library of Wales*, Aberystwyth, 1926, No. 2352, p. 371 ; (a) No. 1091, p. 175 ; (b) No. 1377, p. 221.

182. WYNN, FREDERICK G., 'Caer Arianrod', *Arch. Camb.*, Vol. 13, 6th Scr., 1913, pp. 199-200.

183. WYNNE, W. W. E., 'Documents relating to the town and castle of Harlech ; VIII, Consideracions for the Keeping of the Sessions, etc., at Harlech', *Arch. Camb.*, Vol. 1, 1846, pp. 246-267, see p. 256.

184. YATES, JAMES, 'A Notice of a Submarine Forest in Cardigan Bay', *Proc. Geol. Soc.*, London, 1832-3, No. 28, p. 407.

185. ZEUNER, F. E., 'Archaeology and Geology', *South Eastern Naturalist and Antiquary*, Vol. 55, 1950, pp. 9-10.

INDEX